About Pearson

Pearson is the world's learning company, with presence across 70 countries worldwide. Our unique insights and world-class expertise comes from a long history of working closely with renowned teachers, authors and thought leaders, as a result of which, we have emerged as the preferred choice for millions of teachers and learners across the world.

We believe learning opens up opportunities, creates fulfilling careers and hence better lives. We hence collaborate with the best of minds to deliver you class-leading products, spread across the Higher Education and Test Preparation spectrum.

Superior learning experience and improved outcomes are at the heart of everything we do. This product is the result of one such effort.

Your feedback plays a critical role in the evolution of our products and you can contact us - reachus@pearson.com. *We look forward to it.*

CLASS

7

Trishna's

PEARSON IIT FOUNDATION

Chemistry

Twelfth Edition

2025

Pearson

Photo Credits

Chapter 1 Opener: Pix One / Shutterstock
Chapter 2 Opener: Sebastian Duda / Shutterstock
Chapter 3 Opener: Shawn Hempel / Shutterstock
Chapter 4 Opener: Roland Barat / 123RF
Chapter 5 Opener: Yuriy Kulik / Shutterstock
Chapter 6 Opener: mrkob / Shutterstock

ISBN 978-93-6159-271-3

First Impression

Published by Pearson India Education Services Pvt. Ltd, CIN: U72200TN2005PTC057128.

Head Office: 1st Floor, Berger Tower, Plot No. C-001A/2, Sector 16B, Noida - 201 301, Uttar Pradesh, India.

Registered Office: Featherlite, 'The Address' 5th Floor, Survey No 203/10B, 200 Ft MMRD Road, Zamin Pallavaram, Chennai - 600044

Phone: 044-66540100

Website: in.pearson.com, Email: companysecretary.india@pearson.com

Compositor: Saksham Printographics, Delhi
Printed in India at MP Printers (A Unit of D B Corp Ltd), Noida 201305

Brief Contents

Contents

Preface

"If you have a great ambition, take as big a step as possible in the direction of fulfilling it. The step may only be a tiny one, but trust that it may be the largest one possible for now.".

Mildred McAfee

The *Pearson IIT Foundation* Series has been created keeping in mind the learner's ambition to excel in a competitive examination like IIT-JEE. The series can be used in addition to the books being studied in school to attain that extra edge required to strengthen the concepts and prepare well for future endeavours.

Why Start Early with Pearson IIT Foundation

Classes VI to X are the base years of a learner's academic life. In these years learner explore their interests and determine the goals they wish to attain. *Pearson IIT Foundation* series is filled with interactive learning that not only nurtures a learner's interest in science and mathematics but also strengthens their concepts.

The series uses real-life examples and application-based problems to teach theoretical concepts. The objective of this series is to help learners cultivate an analytical mind.

Most of the lessons to be learnt are introduced to the learners in the books for class VI. As they get promoted to higher classes, new topics are added to these lessons. This additive method helps the learners' span their learning over four standards, from VI-X. Thus, learners are not overwhelmed by the introduction of completely new lessons every time they are promoted to a new class.

While their learning is being spanned across five years, so is their ability to resolve doubts for further conceptual clarity. For instance, they can use concepts learnt in class VI to solve questions in class VII. If, in case, they get stuck while answering a question, the learners can infer for themselves that they might be lacking in conceptual clarity. They can then approach their teachers, requesting them to explain the concept once again. This helps the learner to clarify their concepts while revising the lessons previously learnt.

Since classes VI-X are deemed to be a student's formative years, we, at Pearson, aim to provide a foundation level course which serves more than just a standard curriculum.

Here is how it makes a difference to a learner's overall learning...

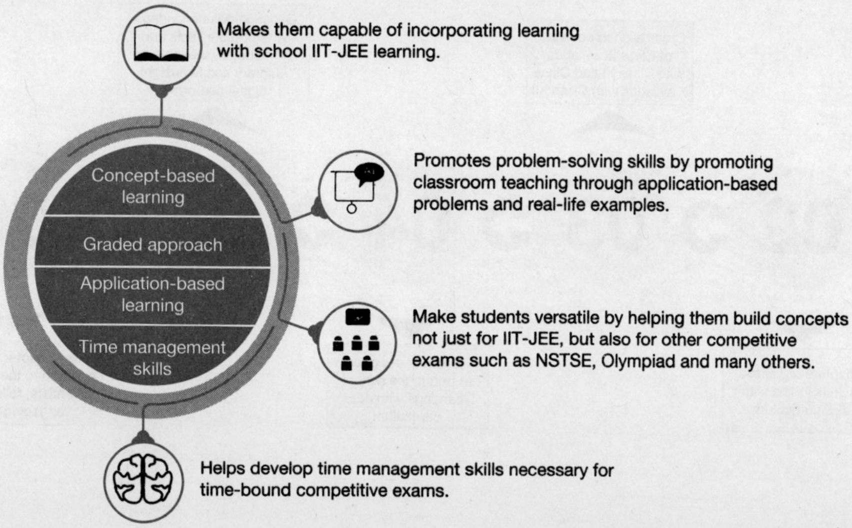

Other Uses of the Series

Instead of limiting themselves to IIT-JEE, a learner can also use this series to prepare for several other competitive examinations such as NSTSE, National and International Olympiads, NEET, BITSAT, etc. This series offers a level of concept learning that empowers learners to handle the challenging nature of questions posed in these examinations. Moreover, this will also allow the learners to have an early insight into their key strengths as well as improvement areas and help them work on themselves.

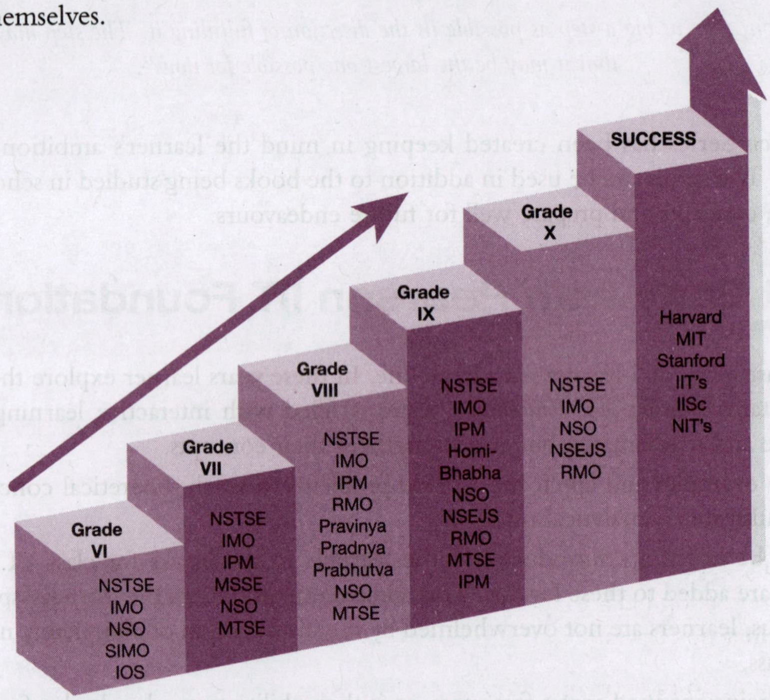

[IMO: International Mathematics Olympiad; NSO: National Science Olympiad, IOS: International Olympiad of Science, NSTSE: National Level Science Talent Search Examination, MTSE: Maharashtra Talent Search Examination, RMO: Regional Mathematical Olympiad, PPP: Pravinya Pradnya Prabhutva, NSEJS: National Standard Examination in Junior Science, IIT: Indian Institute of Technology, IISc: Indian Institute of Science, NIT: National Institute of Technology.]

Highlights of the Series

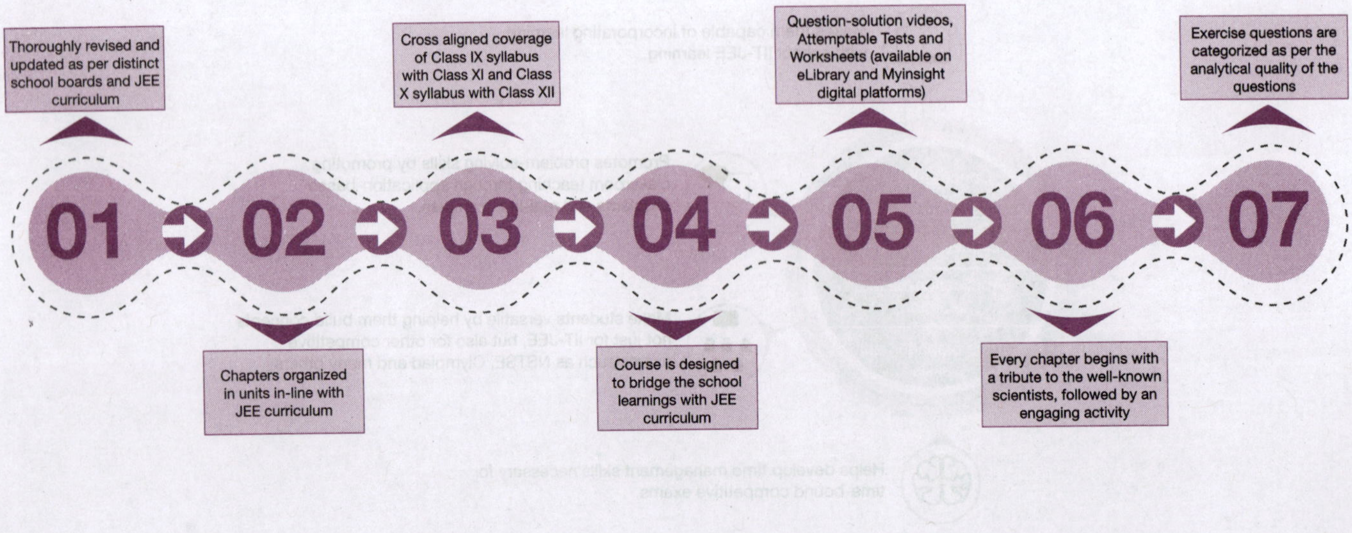

Pearson IIT Foundation series provides a perfect blend of learning through theory and practice questions with a fusion of school and JEE curriculum. It is imperative to note that this series would be as profound as you want it to be. Therefore, to get maximum benefit from this book, we recommend following the given study plan.

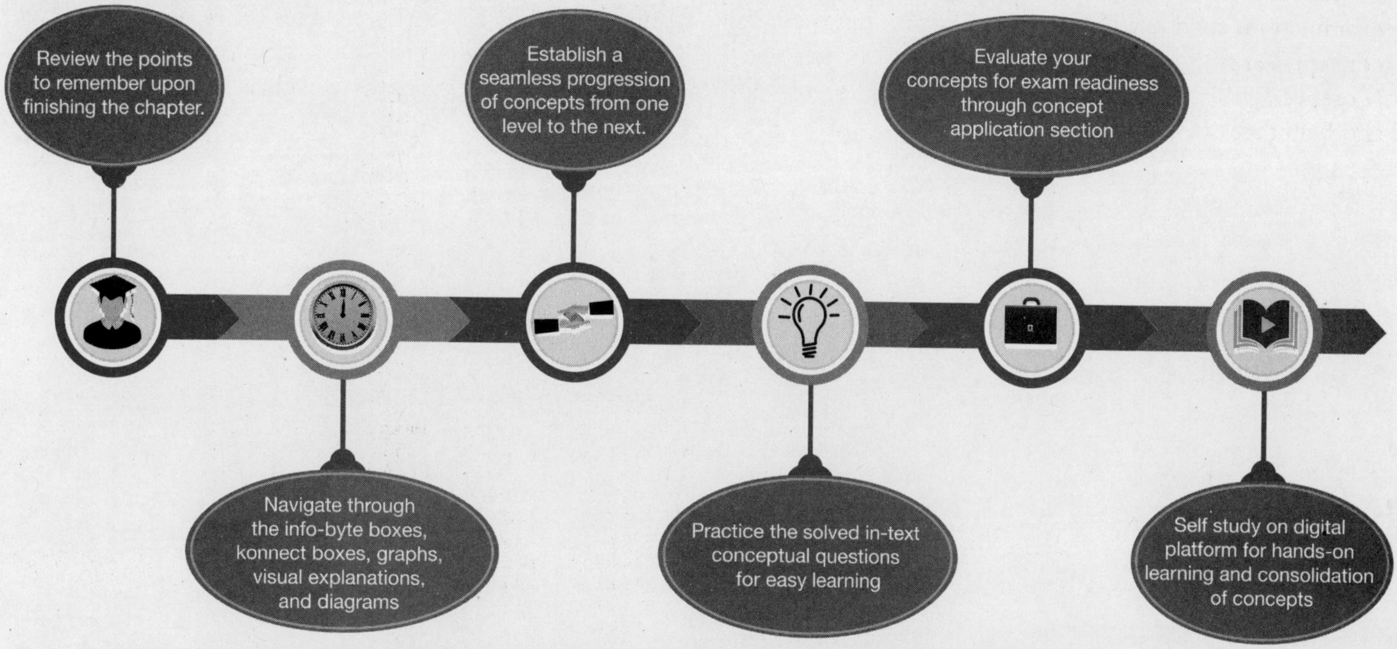

To provide a graded learning approach, the exercise part of each chapter is categorized by using four icons for question tagging. The question categorization helps the learners assess their own problem-solving and analytical skills and motivates them to improve to reach their objectives.

The following icons are used to categorize the questions with specific meanings:

Real-life Situations Questions: 

Analytical Questions: 

Conceptual Questions: 

Value-based Questions: 

With this refined and well-tuned course from Pearson, students will become more confident when they enter the competitive world for actual IIT-JEE preparation. The effort put in today will transform into a valuable asset, contributing to success in future competitive examinations.

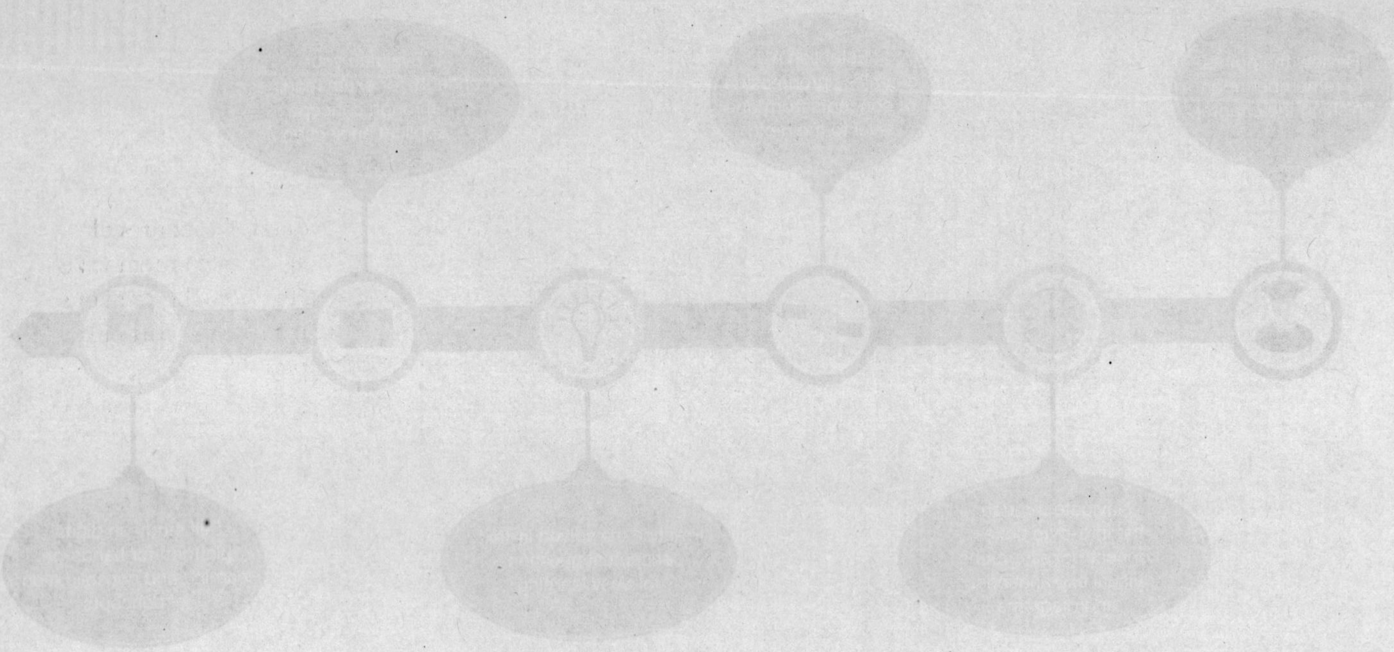

Analytical Questions

Conceptual Questions

Chapter Insights

Remember

Before beginning this chapter, you should be able to:

- understand the concept of matter and atoms.
- review the classification of matter and their

Remember section will help them to memorize and review the previous learning on a particular topic

Key Ideas

After completing this chapter, you should be able to:

- understand the kinetic molecular theory and inter-relationship among various measurable properties of gases.
- understand mole as the chemical counting

Key points will help the students to identify the essential points in a chapter

Scientific Crypt

A tribute to Amedeo Avogadro (1776–1856)

Avogadro is the name familiar among chemists as the name associated with Avogadro number. Though, Avogadro was not the person responsible for the origin of the concept of Avogadro number, in recognition of his earlier contribution to chemistry, the name Avogadro number had been given at the time of introduction of concept of mole which was a major milestone in the advancement of chemistry.

Amedeo Avogadro was an Italian scientist born in Turin, Italy on 9th August 1776. As a son of distinguished lawyer, he had an established legal career. His interest in mathematics and sciences led him to spend most of his career as chair of Mathematical Physics at the University of Turin.

Avogadro's contribution to the field of chemistry should be understood in the context of the ideas prevailing at those times. Avogadro had the distinction of being the first scientist to bring out a clear distinction between atom and molecule. Though Avogadro had many publications in the field of chemistry his major contribution to the field was building on the work of chemist Joseph Louis Gay–Lussac which resulted in Avogadro's hypothesis. The studies made by Avogadro remained dormant during his lifetime. Later, it was after the work of Cannizaro to introduce atomic weights based on Avogadro's work, that his hypothesis was brought into light and became Avogadro's law. As a person who laid the foundation and opened new vistas to quantitative chemistry, he is very well remembered, even after his demise as early as in July 1856.

FUN TIME

CROSSWORD

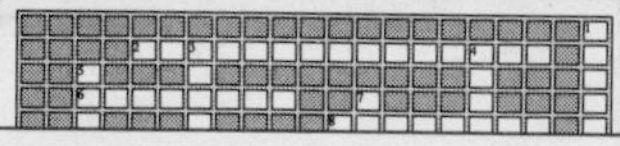

Scientific Crypt provides information about well-known scientists related to the chapter. The engaging activity is also given in the form of a crossword to keep the learners interested.

INTRODUCTION

The study of matter in different perceptions is dealt by a branch of science named Chemistry. Matter can be classified on the basis of molecular composition as elements, compounds, and mixtures. Various elements are given names and symbols, and the names and formulae of various compounds have been derived based on certain rules. The study of naming these compounds and derivation of formulae for these are the prerequisites for representing chemical reactions in the form of chemical equations. Therefore, the language of chemistry,

Introduction section helps to lay the foundation of the following chapter and leads the way for further learning

Symbols and Formulae

All elements are represented by means of their symbols. A symbol represents the atom of an element, which may consist of a single letter or a combination of letters derived either from its English name or its Latin name.

A **symbol** is the shorthand notation that represents a single atom of an element.

Examples:

Element	Symbol
Hydrogen	H
Mercury (formerly known as hydrargyrum)	Hg

Concepts are explained in a well-structured and lucid manner

Konnect boxes are some add-on information of related topic

Konnect

A common example of neutralization is our body's response to heartburn. Antacids are bases that neutralize the excess stomach acid.

Info bytes are interesting trivia and facts that engage young minds and keep the grey cells ticking!

Info Bytes!

The kinetic theory of gases is based on the assumption that gases are composed of a large number of tiny particles (atoms or molecules) that are in constant, random motion. This movement is what gives rise to pressure and temperature.

Examples are given in the form of in-text exercises to reinforce the concepts learnt

Illustrative examples solved in a logical and step-wise manner

EXAMPLE 1.5 Gas laws are universally applicable for all gases whereas such universal laws could established for solids and liquids. Comment on this statement.

SOLUTION

Gases differ from solids and liquids in the extent of intermolecular forces of attraction. Since gases are characteriz negligible forces of attraction, the molecules behave independent of the neighboring molecules. Due to large intermo spaces, the coefficient of volume expansion is same for all gases. Moreover, in case of gases, the molecules are cons as point masses and hence, the volume occupied by the molecules is negligible in comparison to the total volume. The the physical behavior of all gases being similar, certain laws could be established which are universally applicable. In c liquids and solids, the molecules are considered as rigid spheres and the coefficient of volume expansion is not uniform substances, such universal laws cannot be established.

EXAMPLE 1.6 Boyle's law says that pressure and volume are inversely proportional to each other. Ho when a balloon is blown, both volume and pressure increase continuously. Justify.

SOLUTION

When a balloon is blown continuously, more and more air is forced into the balloon that increases the volume as we

Points to remember summarises the concepts and topics presented in each chapter

POINTS TO REMEMBER

- ✔ A symbol is the shorthand notation that represents a single atom of an element.
- ✔ A formula is the shorthand notation which represents a single molecule of an element or compound.
- ✔ The properties of solids and liquids differ widely from substance to substance, but the gases generally obey some common rules known as the gas laws.
- ✔ Boyle's Law states that the volume of a given mass of a gas is inversely proportional to
- ✔ Vapor density (VD) of a gas or vapor is the ratio of the mass of a certain volume of gas or vapor to the mass of the same volume of hydrogen gas when their volumes are measured under similar conditions of temperature and pressure.
- ✔ A mole is defined as the quantity of substance that contains the same number of elementary particles or chemical units as the number of atoms present in 12 g of C-12 isotope.
- ✔ Dalton's law states that 'the total pressure exerted by a mixture of non-reacting gases

PRACTICE QUESTIONS CLASSROOM WING

Very Short Answer Type Questions

Directions for questions from 1 to 5:
Fill in the blanks.

1. The percentage of sulphur in SO_2 is __________ and __________ in SO_3.
2. The vapor density of SO_2 gas is __________ the vapor density of O_2 gas.
3. The molecular formula of a gas with vapor density 15

(A) Reaction between an acid and a base from salt and water
(B) Reaction between zinc and dil. H_2SO_4
(C) Preparation of oxygen from potassium nitrate
(D) Preparation of CO_2 from its constituents

9. What is the molarity of HCl solution containing 0.4 moles in 200 mL of the solution?
10. Calculate the volume occupied by 11 g of CO_2 gas at

Short Answer Type Questions

26. A spherical balloon of volume 253 mL is to be with helium gas at STP from a cylinder containi at 20 atm and 127°C. If the cylinder can hold water, then calculate the number of balloons th be filled up.
27. The composition of a gaseous mixture is N_2 =

Essay Answer Type Questions

41. The density of a mixture of He and O_2 at STP is 1.25 g/L. What is the partial pressure of O_2?
42. A bottle is heated from 27°C to 127°C at constant pressure. What fraction of air gets expelled?
43. An oxide of Cr contains 68.5% of Cr by weight. Find

Different typologies of questions have been included in the *Classroom Wing* which help students to develop the problem-solving skill

Competition Wing at the end of the chapter incorporated for competitive examination inline with JEE syllabus

PRACTICE QUESTIONS COMPETITION WING

Level 1: Apply your Concepts

Direction for questions from 1 to 8:
State whether the following statements are true or false.

1. Doubling the pressure of a gas at constant temperature, doubles the volume occupied by the gas.
2.

16. 'ous' acid of a non-metal 'X' has 2 'O' atoms. Per acid of the same non-metal has the formula _______.
17. The ratio of the gram atomic weight of nitrogen and oxygen is __________.
18. Pressure exerted by water vapor in moist gas is called

Graded as per complexity: Level 1; Level 2; and Level 3

Level 2: Review Your Concepts

51. Out of oxygen, carbon dioxide, sulphur dioxide an nitrogen, which among these gases possesses maximu density at a given temperature and pressure?
52. If the Avogadro number is 9×10^{23}, calculate th weight of 1 mole of CO_2 gas.
53. A gas cylinder is filled with helium at 2000 mm. Du

Level 3: Assess Your Concepts

74. At constant temperature and at 4 atm pressure, the given amount of gas occupies 6 L. If the pressure is increased by 6 atm, calculate the percentage change in the volume of the gas.
75. A gaseous mixture contains 48 g of SO_2 and 33 g of CO_2 at constant temperature and pressure. Calculate the average molecular mass of the gaseous mixture.
76. Calculate the ratio of rates of diffusion of three isotopes of hydrogen protium, deuterium and tritium, respectively, at the same temperature and pressure.

Short Answer Type Questions

63. Arrange the following elements in the decreasing order of the number of electrons in their respective L shells.
(a) Boron (b) Lithium
(c) Helium (d) Oxygen
(e) Calcium
64. Arrange the following negative radicals in the decreasing order of the number of oxygen atoms present in a single radical.
(a) Chromate (b) Silicate
(c) Hydroxyl (d) Nitrite
65. Calculate the number of neutrons in the following:
(a) ${}_{15}X^{31}$ (b) ${}_{92}U^{235}$ (c) ${}_{19}K^{39}$
66. For each of the following reactions identify the products formed and balance the reaction.
(a) $NaCl + AgNO_3 \rightarrow$
(b) $Zn + HCl \rightarrow$

69. In an atom of an element, K and N shells have the same number of electrons. The number of electrons in L and M shells is also the same. Determine the formula of the compound formed by this element and fluorine.
70. Mention different types of combination reactions with example
71. What examp
72. Define examp
73. What the co
74. Disting
75. In the

69. Predict the valencies of the elements with atomic numbers 7, 15, 16, 18, 19 and justify. Also give the formulae of hydrides formed by the above elements if any.
70. In a chemical laboratory, a student took two test tubes A and B. Lead nitrate solution is taken in thest tube "A" and sulphuric acid is taken in the test tube "B". Sodium chloride solution and lithium hydroxide solutions are added to the test tubes "A" and "B" respectively. Predict the products and identify the types of reactions.
71. In an atom, the L and M shells have the same number of electrons. The N shell has one electron less than the

and add thei to h he a the answ
78. Wh whe
79. Giv and (a)

The icons are used for categorisation of the questions in Classroom Wing and Competition Wing

Hints and Explanations

Classroom Wing

Very Short Answer Type Questions

1. 50%, 40%
2. higher than
3. Relation between vapor density and molecular weight. C_2H_6
4. 16/N
5. 40.043%
6. Since the molecular weight of hydrogen is less than

11. $\frac{P_1V_1}{T_1} = \frac{P_2V_2}{T_2}$

$= 5/9$

12. Mole fraction = $\frac{\text{No. of moles of a Substance}}{\text{Total number of moles of all substances in the mixture}}$

Sum of mole fraction in a mixture = 1

$= 0.7$

13. $\frac{r_1}{r_2} = \sqrt{\frac{M_2}{M_1}}$

Hints and Explanation for key questions of classroom wing and competition wing along with highlights on the common mistakes that students usually make in the examinations

Competition Wing

Level 1: Apply your Concepts

20. Calcium bisulphate → $Ca(HSO_4)_2$

Ferric sulphate → $Fe_2(SO_4)_3$

Calcium bisulphite → $Ca(HSO_3)_2$

Ferrous sulphate → $FeSO_4$

(i) → (C); (ii) → (D); (iii) → (B); (iv) → (A)

21. 80 g of SO is equal to 1 mole. 1 mole of any gas at STP occupies 22.4 L.

Hence, the correct option is (a).

22. At low pressure and high temperature, inter-molecular forces of attraction among the gas molecules are negligible. Hence, the gases behave ideally.

Hence, the correct option is (a).

23. (4) HCl + NaOH → NaCl + H_2O → Double displacement

(3) $Cl_2 + H_2$ → HCl → Combination

(2) Mg + H_2SO_4 → $MgSO_4 + H_2$ → Displacement

(C) potassium bicarbonate → $KHCO_3$

% of potassium = $\frac{39}{100} \times 100 = 39\%$

(D) potassium sulphide → K_2S

% of potassium = $\frac{39 \times 2}{110} \times 100 = 70.90\%$

∴ increasing order is (D) > (A) > (B) > (C)

Hence, the correct answer is (d).

38. Let the vapor density of compound be x

Empirical formula weight = $x/2$

Molecular formula weight = $2x$

$$n = \frac{\text{Molecular formula weight}}{\text{Empirical formula weight}} \times \frac{2x}{\left(\frac{x}{2}\right)} = 4$$

Molecular formula = $4 \times A_2B_4 = A_8B_{16}$

Hence, the correct answer is (b).

39. Let the bivalent metal ion be M^{2+}, then the formula of the compound formed will be $M(ClO_4)_2$.

1 mole of compound contains 8 N oxygen atoms.

WORKSHEET

CHAPTER 1: MOLE CONCEPT, STOICHIOMETRY AND BEHAVIOR OF GASES

DW

Direction for questions from 1 to 5:
Select the correct alternative from the following option.

1. A rubber balloon which is permeable to all the isotopes of hydrogen is filled with pure tritium. It is placed in a closed box containing pure hydrogen under similar conditions of temperature and pressure. Identify the correct observation regarding the balloon.
   (a) The balloon first expands and then contracts.
   (b) The balloon first contracts first and then expand.
   (c) The balloon expands.

Directions of questions from 6 to 10:
State whether the following statements are true or false.

6. 80 g of SO_3 corresponds to 1 mole.
7. Real gases behave ideally at high pressure and low temperature.
8. Reaction between an acid and a base form salt and water.
9. Equal volumes of all gases possess unequal number of moles at constant temperature and pressure.

DW: Downloadable worksheets supplementing textual exercises for hand-on learning

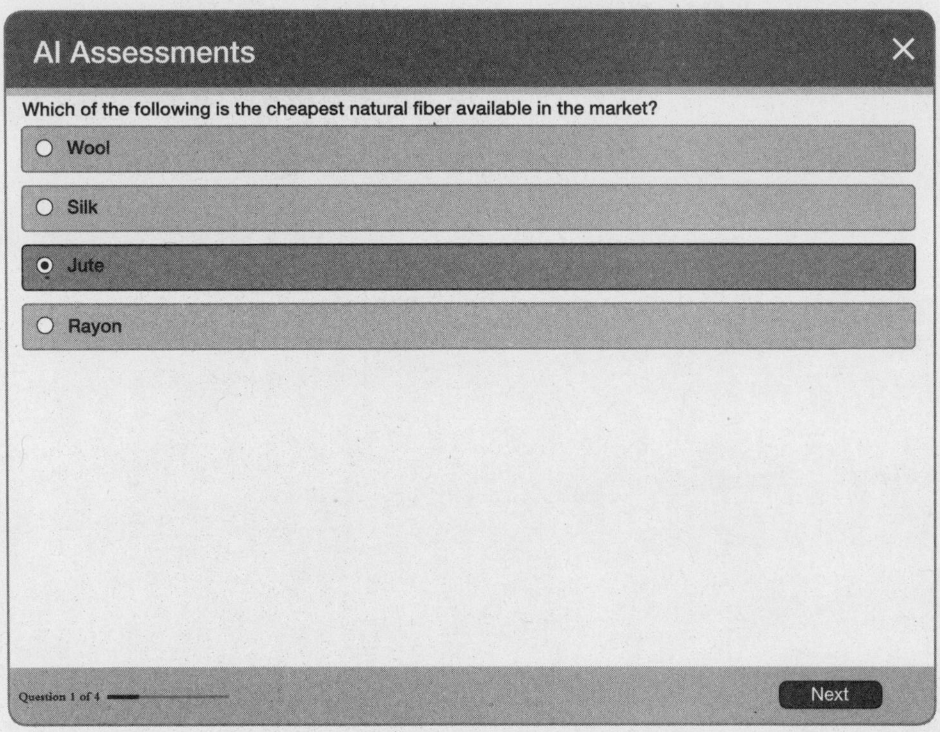

AT

AT: Attemptable Tests for assessing understanding of concepts and getting a clear picture of your exam readiness

51. Na_2CO_3 is dissolved in water at 25°C. Which of the following is/are correct regarding the given statement?

(a) In this solution anionic hydrolysis take place.

(b) The concentration of H^+ ion in the given solution is less than 10^{-7} mole/L

Video icon: Audio and visual learning to difficult questions for effective learning and retention

CHAPTER

1

Classification of Matter

Remember

Before beginning this chapter, you should be able to:

- define substance, mixture, mass, weight, etc.
- know the states of matter—solid, liquid and gas.
- understand basic properties of matter.

Key Ideas

After completing this chapter, you should be able to:

- Understand the classification of materials
- define matter, molecule, atom, etc.
- know the arrangement of molecules in three different states of matter.
- understand the importance of interconversion of matter and correlate it with day-to-day activities.
- learn about different kinds of matter like elements, compounds and mixtures, and also compare metals and non-metals.
- understand the different methods to separate the mixtures.

Scientific Crypt

A Tribute to Democritus (460 BC – 370 BC)

Socrates, Plato, Lucippus, Democritus were some of the renowned thinkers of early Greece who with their achievements, influenced every aspect of chemistry. Many chemical terms have Greek roots as ancient Greeks were pioneers in studying the various aspects of matter. As early as in sixth century B.C, Greek philosophers proposed theories regarding matter that all matter could be categorized into four basic elements namely fire, air, earth and water. Democritus thought further and postulated the existence of ultimate indestructible particles of matter called atoms.

Democritus, an ancient Greek philosopher born in Abdera in the north of Greece, was the most productive and influential of Presocratic philosophers. He was also a student of Leucippus and they together formulated an atomic theory which is regarded as the culmination of early Greek thoughts. This atomic theory had no experimental proof and the ideas were simply hypothetical.

According to this hypothesis, matter is composed of indivisible atoms with different shape and sizes having lot of empty spaces between them and these are always in motion. Their speculations regarding atoms charted the path to the 19th century scientists for the understanding of atomic structure.

Democritus travelled to distant countries to satisfy his thirst for knowledge and worked in various fields such as Maths, Cosmology, Anthropology.

Though his speculative ideas regarding atoms are very primitive and have little significance in modern science, his atomic theory remains as one of the most amazing intellectual accomplishments of the ancient times.

FUN TIME

CROSSWORD

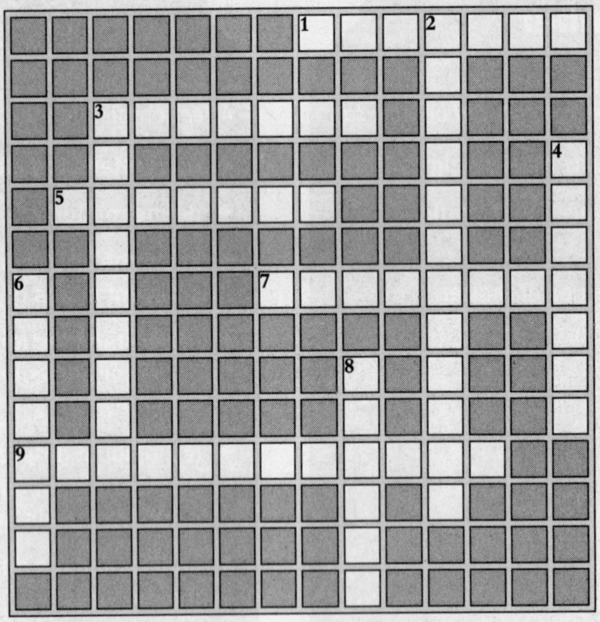

Across

1. Liquid metal at room temperature.
3. Constituents retain the individual properties.
5. Substance made up of only one kind of atoms and cannot be further divided.
7. ______ force of attraction exist between the molecules of same substance.
9. Separation method used for a separating mixture of copper sulphate and water.

Down

2. The process of change of matter from gas to liquid on cooling.
3. Basic building block of the matter.
4. ______ state of matter having maximum inter molecular space.
6. The solid retained on the filter paper during filtration.
8. Any thing that occupies space and has mass.

INTRODUCTION

Our planet Earth is bestowed with a different varieties of various substances like rocks, trees, animals, air, water etc. And this difference in the physical appearance and behaviour of the substances is attributed to the beauty of our planet. However, all these substances, irrespective of their physical appearance and behaviour, have certain things in common, i.e., mass and space they occupy, and are commonly called matter. Hence, **matter** can be defined as anything that occupies space and has mass. The basic building block of matter is known as a **molecule**. The **molecule** is the smallest constituent particle of matter which retains all the properties of the matter and has independent existence. The arrangement of these molecules gives rise to the variation in the physical appearance and behaviour of matter. On the basis of the physical appearance and behaviour of matter, it can be classified into three different states—solid, liquid and gas. Now, a fourth state of matter exists called plasma which is a mixture of electrons and ions. This state is achieved when pressurized gas is heated at a high temperature. In plasma electromagnetic radiations are given out when electrons are released from an atom. which can be seen in the form of light. Thus, plasma has their own light and practical example of this is Tube lights. Bose Einstein condensate is another state of matter which only seen in quantum level. This state consists of boson particles at a temperature which is very near to the temperature near absolute zero. This state is named after the two scientists who discovered it- Satyendra Nath Bose and Albert Einstein.

Arrangement of Molecules in Matter

Molecules are packed in different ways in three different states of matter which leads to the variation in other parameters like intermolecular space, intermolecular force of attraction and the **movement of molecules**.

> **Info Bytes!**
>
> Even though a solid object appears solid, it is actually made up of tiny particles that have space between them. This space allows for the movement of particles in liquids and gases, making them flow.

Particles have Space Between Them

The constituent particles that is molecules are assumed to be hard spherical balls. Whatever be the mode of arrangement of molecules, there will be some spaces left between the molecules. These are called **intermolecular spaces**.

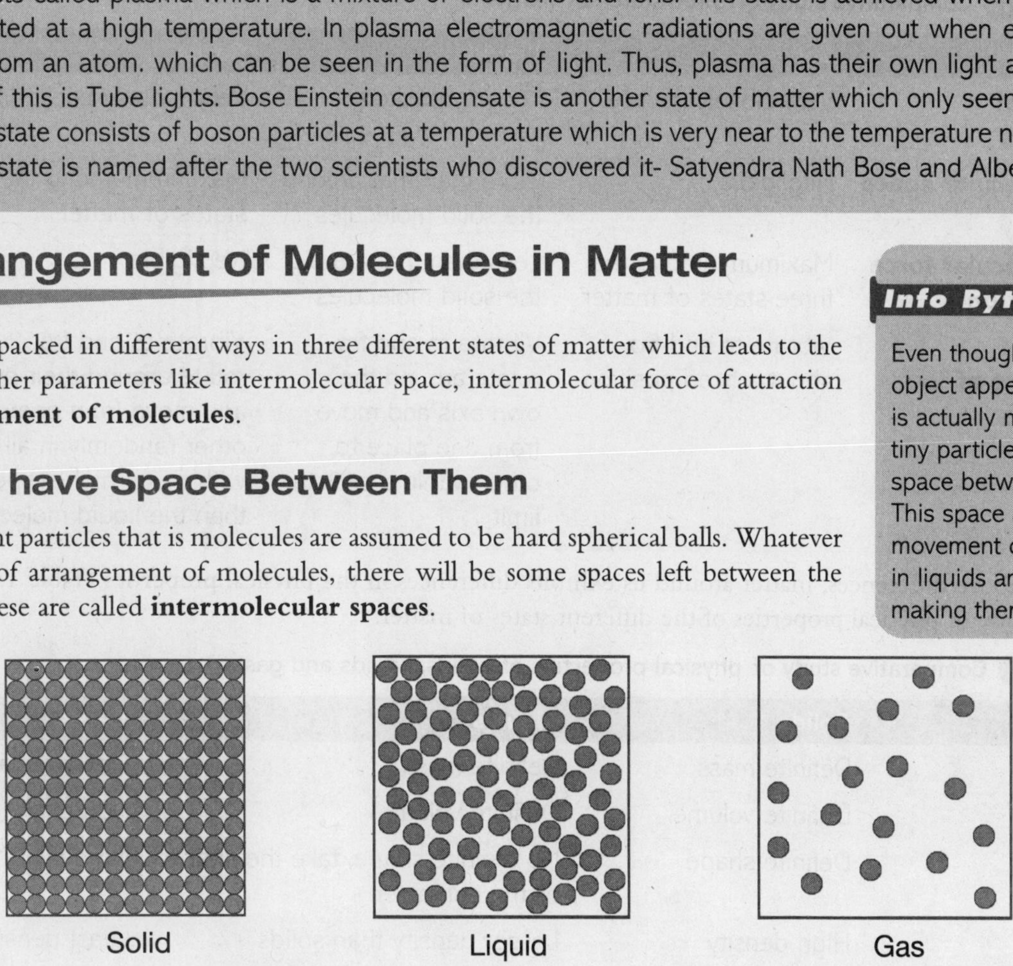

Figure 1.1 Intermolecular spaces in Solid, Liquid and Gas.

In solids, the molecules are closely spaced and the spaces between the molecules are very less. In liquid state, the molecules are loosely packed and hence the intermolecular spaces are larger. In gases, the molecules are far apart from each other. Hence the gaseous state is characterised by huge intermolecular spaces.

Particles are continuously in motion

The particles of matter are continuously in motion and this can be shown with a diffusion experiment. Take two beakers A and B with the same quantity of water but A has hot water and B has cold water. Add a few drops of blue colored dye in both of them at the same time. It is observed that diffusion occurs in both the beakers but it is slower in beaker B than beaker A. This is due to the fact that the particles of dye gain more kinetic energy due to heat and move faster. This shows that the particles are already in motion and application of heat increases their speed.

Particles Attract Each Other

The attractive forces that exist between the adjacent molecules of matter are called **intermolecular forces of attraction**. These forces can be of two types, i.e., cohesive forces and adhesive forces depending on the nature of the participant molecules involved.

Cohesive and Adhesive Forces

The forces of attraction between the molecules of the same substance are known as **cohesive forces**, whereas **adhesive forces** are those which exist between the molecules of two different substances. For example, water molecules stick to the glass rod due to adhesive force.

The comparative study of three different states of matter with respect to the arrangement of molecules and other related parameters is presented in Table 1.1.

Table 1.1 Comparative study of three states of matter

Parameter	Solids	Liquids	Gases
Packing of molecules	Very closely packed	Loosely packed	Very loosely packed
Intermolecular space	Negligible	More than that among the solid molecules	Maximum among the three states of matter
Intermolecular force of attraction	Maximum among the three states of matter	Less than that among the solid molecules	Negligible
Type(s) of movement of molecules	Vibrate to and fro about a fixed position	Vibrate to and fro, rotate around their own axis and move from one place to other within a certain limit	Vibrate to and fro, rotate around their own axis and move from one place to other randomly in all directions with much higher speed than the liquid molecules

Due to the above differences, matter around us exhibits differences in the physical properties. Table 1.2 represents the comparative study of physical properties of the different states of matter.

Table 1.2 Comparative study of physical properties of solids, liquids and gases

Parameter	Solids	Liquids	Gases
Mass	Definite mass	Definite mass	Definite mass
Volume	Definite volume	Definite volume	No definite volume
Shape	Definite shape	No definite shape, take the shape of the container	No definite shape
Density	High density	Lesser density than solids	Least density
Compressibility	Incompressible	Slightly compressible	Highly compressible
Rigidity	Rigid (cannot flow)	Fluid (can flow)	Fluid (can flow)
Free surfaces	Any number of free surfaces	One free surface, i.e., only the upper surface	No free surfaces
Thermal expansion	Very low	Higher than solids	Much greater than both solids and liquids
Diffusion	Do not diffuse	Some liquids can diffuse spontaneously into another (e.g., water and alcohol), but others cannot (e.g., oil and water)	Gases diffuse spontaneously and rapidly

Interconversion of States of Matter

The existence of matter in a particular state depends on two factors, i.e., temperature and pressure. Matter can be transformed from one state to another by altering the temperature and pressure and this phenomenon is called **interconversion of states of matter**. Different types of methods for interconversion of states of matter are given below:

1. **Melting:** The process which involves the change in state of matter from solid to liquid by heating is called **melting or fusion**. The temperature at which a solid changes into a liquid on heating at normal atmospheric pressure is called the **melting point** of that solid.

   Example: Ice changes to water at 0°C under normal atmospheric pressure. Hence, 0°C is the melting point of ice.

2. **Condensation:** The process which involves the change of matter from gas to liquid on cooling is called **condensation**.

   Example: Conversion of water vapour or steam to water.

3. **Solidification:** The process involving the change of matter from liquid to solid on cooling is called **solidification or freezing**. The temperature at which freezing occurs at normal atmospheric pressure is called **freezing point** of that liquid.

   Example: Water changes to ice at 0°C under normal atmospheric pressure. Hence, 0°C is the freezing point of water.

4. **Sublimation:** The process by which some solid substances directly change into the vapour state without passing through the intermediate liquid state is called **sublimation**. The solid obtained on cooling the vapour is called **sublimate** and the gas solid vapour formed is called **sublime**.

   Examples: Camphor, iodine, etc., get converted into their respective vapour states directly under normal atmospheric pressure.

Konnect

Generally, solids expand on melting and liquids contract on freezing (except ice).

5. **Boiling:** The process which involves the change in state of matter from liquid to gas from the bulk of liquid by heating is called **boiling**. The temperature at which a liquid changes into gas from the bulk of the liquid by heating at normal atmospheric pressure is called **boiling point** of that liquid.

   Example: Water changes to water vapour at 100°C under normal atmospheric pressure. Hence, 100°C is the boiling point of water.

6. **Evaporation:** Every liquid exists in its vapour state over its surface at normal temperature and pressure. This is the result of change of state from liquid to vapour, i.e., evaporation. **Evaporation** can be defined as the change of state of liquid to vapour from the surface of liquid at any temperature below its boiling point.

   Factors Affecting the Rate of Evaporation

   Rate of evaporation is affected by three most important factors, i.e., surface area, temperature and humidity. Their effects are listed below.

   - **Surface Area:** The rate of evaporation of a liquid is directly proportional to its surface area.
   - **Temperature:** With the increase of temperature, the rate of evaporation of a liquid increases.
   - **Humidity:** The rate of evaporation of a liquid is inversely proportional to the amount of moisture (humidity) present in the atmosphere.
   - **Wind Speed:** The rate of evaporation is directly proportional to the speed of wind.

Boiling vs Evaporation

Both evaporation and boiling involve the conversion of the same state of matter, but these two phenomena can be differentiated based on the way they take place (Table 1.3).

Table 1.3 Comparative study of evaporation and boiling

Evaporation	Boiling
It is a slow process.	It is a fast process.
It takes place from the surface of a liquid.	It takes place from the bulk of a liquid.
The temperature of the remaining liquid decreases during evaporation.	The temperature of the liquid that is undergoing boiling remains constant.
It can take place at any temperature below the boiling point of the liquid.	Every liquid has a fixed boiling point at a particular pressure.

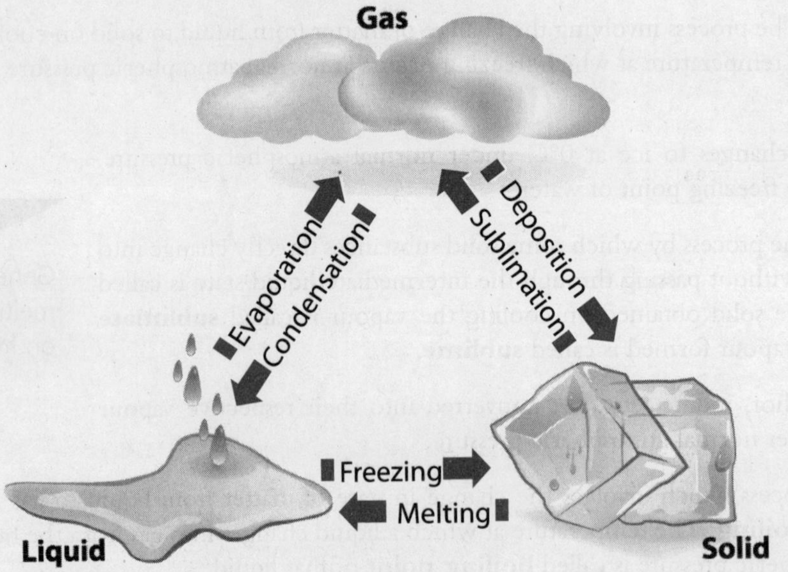

Figure 1.2 Schematic representation of interconversion of matter

EXAMPLE 1.1 Terracotta vessels are commonly used in Jaipur rather than in Kolkata for keeping water cool. Provide a reason.

SOLUTION

The efficiency of cooling in terracotta vessels is directly related to the rate at which water evaporates from their surface. Humidity in the environment plays a pivotal role in this mechanism. Kolkata, being closer to the deltaic region, has a naturally high humidity level. This means the air is quite moisture-laden, which results in a slower rate of evaporation. Conversely, Jaipur, located in the arid region of Rajasthan, experiences drier conditions. Due to the lower humidity, water evaporates more swiftly from the surface of terracotta vessels in Jaipur. As a result, water inside these vessels cools down more effectively in Jaipur than in Kolkata, making them a preferred choice in Jaipur.

EXAMPLE 1.2 People are advised to wear cotton clothes in summer. Give reasons.

SOLUTION

Cotton has the property of absorbing sweat. When this is exposed to atmosphere, sweat undergoes evaporation which causes cooling, and hence, we feel cool by wearing cotton clothes in summer.

Classification of Matter

Matter can be classified based on its composition in the following way irrespective of the state in which it exists.

If the matter is made up of identical molecules, it is called **pure substance**. The matter which is made up of different types of molecules is called **mixture**. Molecules of matter are made up of tiny particles called atoms. **Atoms** are the tiniest particles of matter which may or may not exist independently. There are very few atoms which exist independently. These are the atoms of helium, neon, argon, krypton and xenon. They remain in the gaseous state in the atmosphere and are known as **noble gases**.

Pure substances can further be classified into elements and compounds based on the nature of constituent atoms present in their molecule.

If the molecules of a pure substance contain identical atom(s), then it is called an element. The pure substance in which the molecules are made up of two or more different types of atoms is called compound.

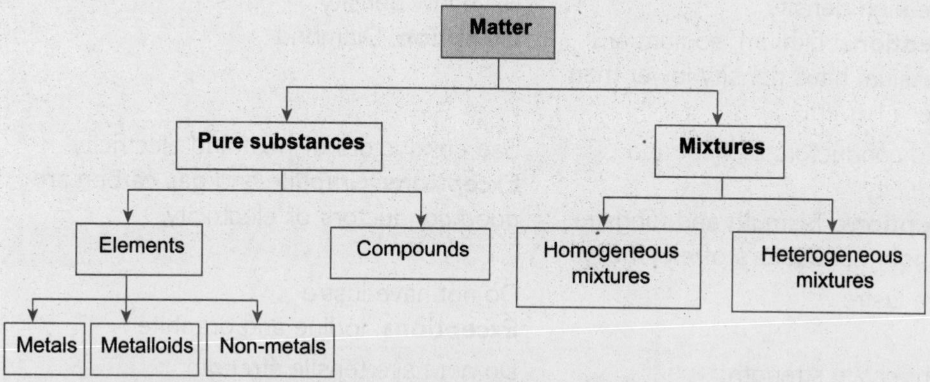

Figure 1.3 Classification of matter based on its composition

Konnect

Everything around us, from the air we breathe to the food we eat, can be classified into elements, compounds, or mixtures.

Element

An **element** is a substance which is constituted of only one kind of atoms and cannot be further divided by any physical or chemical means.

Examples: Hydrogen, oxygen, chlorine, sodium, potassium, etc. Molecules of these substances consist of only one type of atoms. Molecules of different elements may contain different number of atoms.

Metals and Non-metals

An element is made up of identical atoms, but the nature of the atoms is different in different elements which invariably results in differences in their characteristics. Based on the variation in properties, elements are further classified into metals, non-metals and metalloids.

Info Bytes!

India is home to the Kolar Gold Fields, one of the deepest gold mines in the world. This emphasizes the rich abundance of metals in the Indian subcontinent.

Table 1.4 Comparative study of metals and non-metals

Property	Metals	Non-metals
State	Solids at room temperature **Exceptions**: Mercury and gallium are liquids.	Mostly gases **Exceptions**: Some of the solid non-metals are carbon, sulphur, phosphorus, iodine, whereas bromine is a liquid non-metal.
Melting and boiling points	Very high melting and boiling points **Exceptions**: Sodium, potassium and mercury have low melting and boiling points. Gallium has a low melting point but a high boiling point.	Low melting and boiling points **Exceptions**: Carbon, silicon and boron have high melting and boiling points.
Hardness	Generally hard. **Exceptions**: Sodium and potassium are soft.	Solid non-metals are brittle. **Exception**: Diamond is the hardest naturally occurring substance.
Density	Have high density **Exceptions**: Lithium, sodium and potassium have density lower than water (1 g/cm^3).	Have low density **Exception**: Diamond
Conductivity	Good conductors of heat and electricity **Exceptions**: Bismuth and tungsten are poor conductors of electricity.	Bad conductors of heat and electricity **Exceptions**: Graphite and gas carbon are good conductors of electricity.
Lustre	Have lustre	Do not have lustre **Exceptions**: Iodine and graphite
Tensile strength	High tensile strength. **Exception**: Zinc has very less tensile strength.	Do not have tensile strength **Exception**: Carbon fibre, a recently developed allotrope of carbon.
Malleability and ductility	Generally malleable and ductile. **Exception**: Zinc is neither malleable nor ductile	Non-malleable and non-ductile **Exception**: Carbon fibres are ductile
Sonorousness	Sonorous	Non-sonorous
Occurrence	Found in a combined state. **Exception**: Only noble metals are found in the free state. Silver, gold and platinum are called **noble metals**.	Found in a free state as well as in the combined state

Metalloids

Metalloids are elements which show properties of both metals and non-metals.

Examples: Germanium, arsenic, antimony, selenium and tellurium.

Info Bytes!

Silicon, a metalloid, is used in making microchips. Without silicon and its unique properties, our modern world of gadgets and electronics would look very different!

Table 1.5 Properties and uses of some metalloids

Metalloid	Properties	Uses
Boron	• Dark brown powder or Brittle crystalline form • Poor conductor of electricity • High thermal resistance	• Eye drops, antiseptics • Tile glaze (ceramics) • Food preservatives • Washing powders/detergents • Borosilicate glass • Agriculture
Silicon	• Hard, metallic grey solid with lustre • Brittle • Chemical properties similar to metals	• Transistors, computer chips and solar cells • Portland cement • Fire resistant bricks • Alloying in steel
Germanium	• Hardness • Metallic lustre • Brittleness • Formation of oxide [GeO_2] • Poor conductor of heat and electricity	• Semiconductors • Alloying • Infrared spectroscopes • Optical instruments such as lenses
Arsenic	• Metallic lustre • Brittleness • Formation of oxide [As_2O_3] • Poor conductor of heat and electricity	• Semiconductors • Lasers • Insecticides, rat poisons and other poisons
Antimony	• Metallic form • Hardness • Metallic lustre • Non-metallic form • Grey powder • No reaction with acids or alkalis	• Alloying • Semiconductor devices • Safety matches • Fire retardants
Selenium	• Metallic form • Grey crystalline • Good electrical conductivity • Non-metallic form • Red amorphous powder • Chemical properties similar to sulphur	• Photovoltaic cells • Solar panels • Photocopying • Photography • Glass manufacture • Vulcanisation of rubber • Anti-dandruff shampoos
Tellurium	• Metallic form • Grey crystalline with metallic lustre • Non-metallic form • Brown amorphous powder	• Steel manufacture • Alloying • Semiconductor research • Ceramics • Solar panels

Atomicity of Element

The number of atoms that constitute a molecule of an element is called **atomicity** of that element. A molecule of hydrogen is made up of two atoms, and hence, its atomicity is two. Based on the atomicity, elements can be classified as follows:

1. **Monoatomic elements**: The elements in which each molecule contains only one atom.
   Examples: Cu, Ag, He, etc.

2. **Diatomic elements**: The elements in which each molecule contains two atoms.
   Examples: H_2, O_2, N_2, etc.
3. **Polyatomic elements**: The elements in which each molecule contains more than two atoms.
   Examples: O_3, P_4, S_8, etc.

Compounds

A **compound** is a substance which is formed due to the chemical combination of two or more elements in a definite proportion by mass. The constituents of a compound do not retain their properties and they can be separated only by chemical means.

Examples: Water, carbon dioxide, hydrochloric acid, sodium chloride, calcium carbonate, etc. A molecule of carbon dioxide is constituted of one carbon atom and two oxygen atoms. Two atoms of hydrogen and one atom of oxygen combine chemically to form a molecule of water.

Konnect

Table salt, scientifically called sodium chloride, is a compound formed when the metal sodium reacts with the non-metal chlorine. Yet, on their own, sodium is a highly reactive metal, and chlorine is a toxic gas!

Mixtures

A **mixture** is a substance which is formed by mixing two or more substances (elements, compounds or both) physically in any proportion. No chemical reaction takes place during the formation of a mixture and all the constituents of the mixture retain their properties. Constituents of the mixture can easily be separated by physical means.

Examples: A solution of sugar and water is a mixture in which sugar and water both retain their properties and can be separated by a simple physical process, i.e., evaporation. Muddy water is another example of mixture of mud and water which can easily be separated by filtration.

Compounds vs Mixtures

Elements and compounds are the substances in which the composition is uniform throughout the matter, and hence, they are said to be homogeneous. However, the composition of a mixture, i.e., the proportion of its constituents may or may not be uniform throughout. Hence, a mixture may be either homogeneous or heterogeneous.

Examples: A mixture of alcohol and water is an example of a homogeneous mixture because the constituents of this mixture are uniformly distributed. A mixture of sulphur and water is an example of heterogeneous mixture because sulphur remains non-uniformly distributed in water.

Some common examples of mixtures are given below:

1. Milk is a mixture of proteins, fats, vitamins, carbohydrates and mineral salts.
2. Sea water is a mixture of large number of salts and water.
3. Smoke is a mixture of air and carbon particles.
4. Cooking gas is a mixture of gases, like propane and butane.
5. Air is a mixture of nitrogen, oxygen, carbon dioxide and water vapour.

Mixtures of two or more solids are generally heterogeneous while mixtures of two or more gases are always homogeneous. However, a mixture of two or more liquids may be homogeneous or heterogeneous depending on the nature of liquids.

The liquids which completely dissolve in each other are called **miscible liquids**. They always form homogeneous mixtures.

Examples: Water and alcohol.

Konnect

The distinction between mixtures and compounds can sometimes be surprising. For instance, rust, which is a compound of iron and oxygen, has entirely different properties from both iron and oxygen.

The liquids which are insoluble in each other are called **immiscible liquids**. They always form heterogeneous mixtures.

Examples: Coconut oil and water.

Activity

Experiments to Show the Miscibility/Immiscibility of Two Liquids

1. 30 mL of water is taken in a beaker and 15 mL of alcohol is poured into this beaker. The mixture is stirred well with the help of a glass rod. After a few minutes, it is observed that these liquids dissolve in each other forming a homogeneous mixture. Therefore, the two types of liquids are miscible liquids.
2. 30 mL of water is taken in a beaker and 15 mL of oil is poured into it and the mixture is stirred with the help of a glass rod. After a few minutes, it is observed that oil forms the upper layer and water forms the lower layer. Hence, it can be concluded that water and oil are immiscible liquids, and hence, form a heterogeneous mixture.

Table 1.6 Comparative study of compounds and mixtures

Compounds	Mixtures
Constituent atoms of elements combine chemically.	Constituent substances are mixed physically.
Constituent elements do not retain their individual properties in a compound.	The constituents retain their individual properties in a mixture.
Constituents can be separated only by chemical methods.	Constituents can be separated by physical methods.
These are homogeneous.	These can be either homogeneous or heterogeneous.

Separation of a Mixture

Unlike elements, compounds are made up of more than one type of elements and a mixture is composed of more than one type of pure substances. The constituent substances of a mixture may be more than one element or compound or both elements and compounds. However, the basic difference between compound and mixture is that the constituents of the mixture retain their properties, whereas the constituent elements of the compound completely lose their original properties. Hence, constituents of the mixture can be separated easily by means of some physical processes. There are different methods of separation of the mixture based on the physical state and properties of the constituents. Some of the common processes adopted for separation of the mixtures are given below:

Info Bytes!

The process of separating salt from seawater by evaporation is ancient and has been practised in coastal parts of India for centuries. The water evaporates under the sun, leaving behind the salt crystals.

Separation of the Mixture Constituting Two Solids

(a) One constituent is a sublimable substance

Example: Mixture of common salt and ammonium chloride (sublimable substance). This type of mixture can be separated by a simple physical process called **sublimation**.

Sublimation

Process: The mixture of sodium chloride and ammonium chloride is taken in a flat basin and a funnel is inverted over it. The outer surface of the funnel is wrapped with a water-soaked filter paper and the open end of the stem of the funnel is plugged with a piece of paper or cotton to prevent vaporisation. The basin is kept in a sand bath. The sand bath is placed over a wire mesh kept on a tripod stand and then is heated gently with the help of a Bunsen burner.

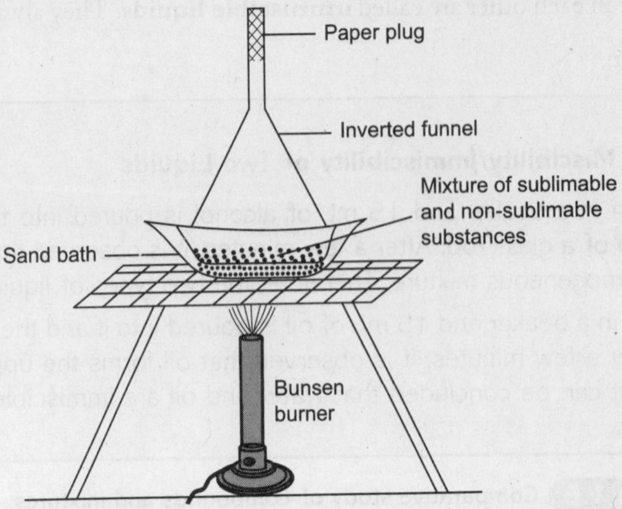

Figure 1.4 Separation of sublimable substance from non-sublimable substance

Observation: A white-coloured fume is observed which condenses as a white powdery substance when it comes in contact with the colder wall of the funnel. The process of heating is continued till the evolution of white vapour is observed.

Conclusion: Since ammonium chloride is a sublimable substance, therefore, it sublimes and then condenses as the white powder. The substance left over on the basin does not sublime. Hence, it is sodium chloride. Ammonium chloride is scrapped off from the wall of the funnel, and thus, the mixture is separated.

(b) One constituent is a magnetic substance

Example: A mixture of iron filings and sand can be separated by a simple physical process called **magnetic separation** as iron is magnetic in nature.

Magnetic Separation

Process: The mixture of iron filings and sand is taken in a flat vessel. A strong bar magnet is brought close to the mixture repeatedly. The iron filings are attracted by the magnet. The iron filings that cling to the magnet can be shaved off from the surface using a piece of cardboard. Thus, iron filings are separated from the sand.

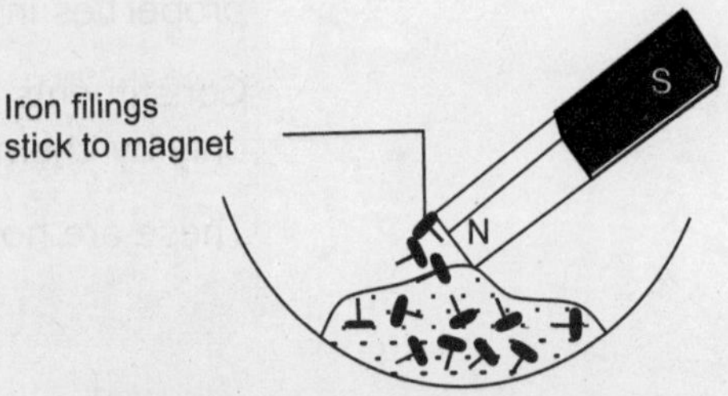

Figure 1.5 Separation of magnetic substance from non-magnetic substance

Separation of a Mixture Constituting One Solid and One Liquid

The mixture of a solid and liquid can be of different types. The solid may be soluble or insoluble in the liquid. In the case of an insoluble solid, it may float on the surface of the liquid or remain suspended in the liquid or settle down. Different methods are adopted for the separation of different types of mixture of the solid and liquid. The processes are described below:

(a) Separation of a mixture of a solid and a liquid in which the solid remains in the dissolved state

Example: Mixture of copper sulphate and water. Copper sulphate is non-volatile (the substance which does not vaporise on heating) in nature and dissolves in water. This type of mixture can be separated by **distillation process.**

Distillation

Process: The solution of copper sulphate is taken in a round-bottomed flask called **distillation flask**. A thermometer and a condenser, known as Liebig condenser, are attached with the round-bottomed flask with the help of adapters. **Liebig condenser** is a long glass tube enclosed in a jacket of glass. Cold water is circulated through the glass jacket continuously. The condenser leads to another flask called **receiver** to collect the liquid that gets separated from the solid during the process of distillation. The distillation flask is placed on a tripod stand and heated with the help of a Bunsen burner.

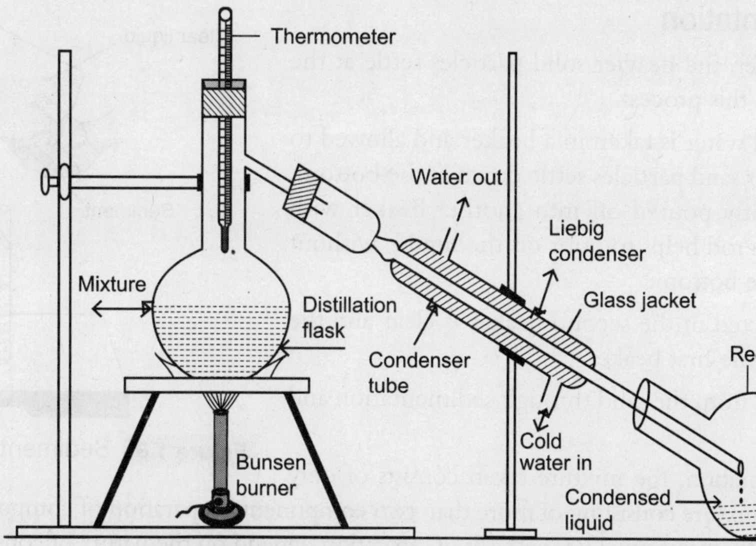

Figure 1.6 Separation of soluble solid from liquid

Observation: The solution starts boiling and water vapour obtained is passed through Liebig condenser where it is converted into water due to condensation and collected in the receiver. A solid residue is observed in the distillation flask.

Conclusion: Water present in the solution is vaporised leaving behind the non-volatile solid that is copper sulphate in the distillation flask, and thus, constituents of the copper sulphate solution are separated.

(b) Separation of a mixture of solid and liquid in which the solid does not dissolve

The insoluble solid may float or remain suspended in the liquid. If the solid particles are heavier, then they settle down.

Example: In a mixture of sawdust and water, the sawdust floats on water, fine sulphur particles remain suspended in a mixture of water and sulphur, and in a mixture of sand and water, sand particles settle down if the container is kept still for some time. There are two different methods of separation, i.e., filtration and sedimentation followed by decantation for the separation of the above mixture.

Konnect

Evaporation is another method of separation of a solid from a solid–liquid mixture. In this method, only the solid can be obtained, but the liquid gets vaporised.

Filtration

All sorts of insoluble solids can be separated from the liquid in this process.

Process: A mixture of sawdust and water is taken in a beaker. A filter paper is folded in the form of a cone and fitted into a funnel by moistening it with a few drops of water. The mixture is poured gently into the filter cone and collected into another beaker.

Observation: The liquid collected is clear and transparent. Sawdust is found over the filter paper.

Conclusion: The mixture of sawdust and water is separated through the filtration process. The clear liquid that is collected in another beaker is called a **filtrate** and the solid retained on the filter paper is known as the **residue**.

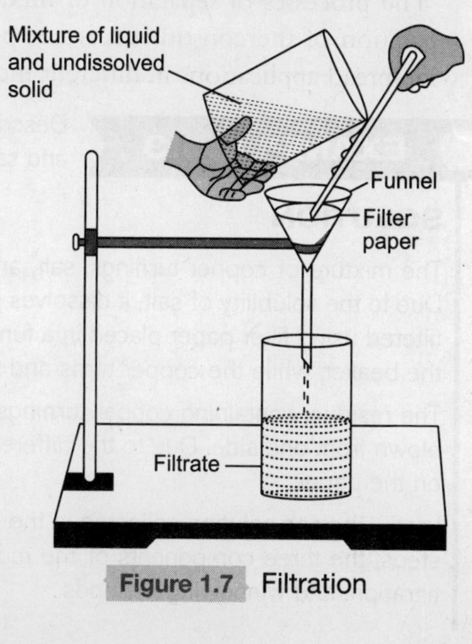

Figure 1.7 Filtration

Sedimentation and Decantation

In the mixture of sand and water, the heavier solid particles settle at the bottom and can be separated by this process.

Process: A mixture of sand and water is taken in a beaker and allowed to stand for some time. The heavier sand particles settle down at the bottom. The clear water above it is gently poured off into another beaker with the help of a glass rod. The glass rod helps to pour off the liquid, without disturbing the solid settled at the bottom.

Observation: The water collected in the second beaker is clear and the sand particles are left behind in the first beaker.

Conclusion: Water is separated from the sand through sedimentation and decantation process.

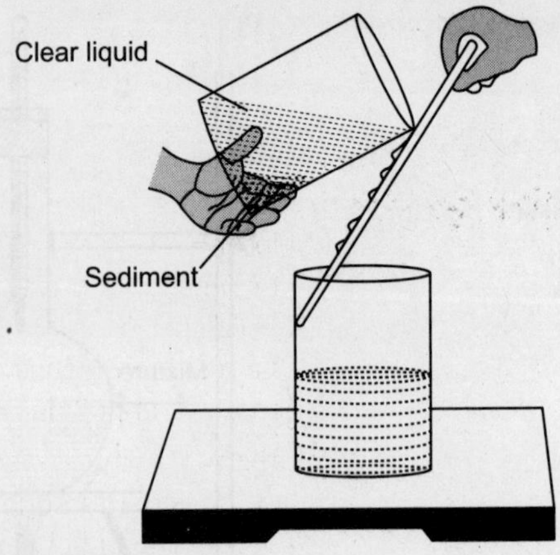

Figure 1.8 Sedimentation and decantation

In the above processes of separation, the mixture taken consists of only two components. In case of the mixture consisting of more than two components, separation of components from the mixture involves more than one method of separation. The methods of separation depend on the nature of constituents in the mixture.

Separation of a Mixture Constituting Coloured Components

Paper Chromatography

Apart from these separation methods, there is another special method called **paper chromatography**. This is mainly used as an identification method rather than a separation method.

Process of Paper Chromatography

A filter paper is suspended in a container with a solvent. The solvent rises on the filter paper. When a mixture containing coloured substances is added to the solvent, these constituents also travel along with the solvent. The various substances have different affinities with the solvent. Hence, they travel different distances with the solvent and form coloured spots at different heights. Based on the heights at which the spots are formed, the constituents can be identified.

Applications of Paper Chromatography

- Separation of pigments in leaves and flowers
- Identification of colours in a dye
- Detection of adulteration in food stuffs
- Conduction of doping tests for sports persons

The processes of separation of mixtures discussed above are simple and convenient to carry out, however, complete separation of the constituents is not possible through these processes. Despite this, these simple physical processes find widespread applications in different industries and chemical laboratories.

EXAMPLE 1.3 Describe the process of separation of the components of a mixture of copper turnings, salt, and sawdust.

SOLUTION

The mixture of copper turnings, salt, and sawdust is spread evenly in a basin. Water is added to the mixture and stirred well. Due to the solubility of salt, it dissolves in water, while the copper turnings and sawdust remain undissolved. The mixture is then filtered using filter paper placed in a funnel over a beaker. The salt solution passes through the filter paper and gets collected in the beaker, while the copper turns and sawdust remains on the filter paper.

The residue, containing copper turnings and sawdust, is then air-dried. After drying, the mixture is taken in a paper and gently blown from one side. Due to the difference in their weight, sawdust gets blown away while the heavier copper turnings remain on the paper.

Lastly, the salt solution collected in the beaker can be subjected to evaporation or crystallization to retrieve solid salt. By these steps, the three components of the mixture—copper turnings, salt, and sawdust—are effectively separated using dissolution, filtration, and winnowing methods.

EXAMPLE 1.4 Describe the process of separation of the components (potassium nitrate [nitre] + carbon + sulphur) of gunpowder.

SOLUTION

Carbon disulphide is added to a beaker containing gunpowder. Sulphur gets dissolved in carbon disulphide. This mixture is then filtered with the help of a filter paper. The filtrate obtained is taken in a flat vessel and exposed to air till carbon disulphide vaporises leaving sulphur behind. The residue obtained contains carbon powder and nitre. It is then transferred to a beaker containing hot water. Nitre dissolves in hot water. The mixture is then filtered with the help of a filter paper. Carbon powder is left on the filter paper as a residue which is collected after drying. The filtrate, on evaporation to dryness by heating, gives solid nitre. Thus, the constituents of gunpowder are separated.

The processes of separation of mixtures discussed above are simple and convenient to carry out, however, complete separation of the constituents is not possible through these processes. Despite this, these simple physical processes find widespread applications in different industries and chemical laboratories.

EXAMPLE 1.5 Establish logically that water is a compound.

SOLUTION

A pure substance is one which is made up of molecules containing same kind of atoms. In water, all the molecules are made up of two hydrogen atoms and one oxygen atom. These constituents are present in a fixed proportion by weight, and hence, water is a compound.

POINTS TO REMEMBER

- ✔ The space between the constituent molecules of matter is called intermolecular space.
- ✔ The attractive forces that exist between the adjacent molecules of matter are called intermolecular forces of attraction.
- ✔ The forces of attraction between the molecules of the same substance are known as cohesive forces, whereas adhesive forces are those which exist between the molecules of two different substances.
- ✔ Matter can be transformed from one state to another by altering the temperature and pressure and this phenomenon is called interconversion of states of matter. The methods for interconversion of states of matter are melting, condensation, solidification, sublimation, boiling, and evaporation.
- ✔ If the matter is made up of identical molecules, it is called pure substance. The matter which is made up of differenttypes of molecules is called mixture.
- ✔ Atoms are the tiniest particles of matter which may or may not exist independently.
- ✔ If the molecules of a pure substance contain identical atom(s), then it is called an element. The pure substance in which the molecules are made up of two or more different types of atoms is called compound.
- ✔ Elements can be classified into metals, non-metals, and metalloids.
- ✔ The number of atoms that constitute a molecule of an element is called atomicity of that element.
- ✔ The liquids which completely dissolve in each other are called miscible liquids.The liquids which are insoluble in each other are called immiscible liquids.
- ✔ Constituents of the mixture can be separated easily by means of some physical processes.

PRACTICE QUESTIONS CLASSROOM WING

Very Short Answer Type Questions

Directions for questions from 1 to 5:
Fill in the blanks.

1. The molecules of LPG are _______ packed.
2. With an increase in the surface area of a liquid, the rate of evaporation_______.
3. The conversion of a liquid to its solid state on cooling is called _______.
4. During freezing, heat is _______.
5. Atomicity of ozone is _______.

Directions for questions from 6 to 34:
For each of the questions, four choices have been provided. Select the correct alternative.

6. Generally metals:
   (a) are solids
   (b) are good conductors of heat
   (c) have high tensile strength
   (d) all the above
7. A mixture of chalk powder and ammonium chloride can be separated by _______.
   (a) distillation (b) evaporation
   (c) filtration (d) sublimation
8. Identify the soft metal among the following.
   (a) Iron (b) Aluminium
   (c) Magnesium (d) Potassium
9. Which among the following is a bad conductor of electricity?
   (a) Zinc (b) Copper
   (c) Aluminium (d) Phosphorus
10. The smallest particle of an element which may or may not have independent existence is called a/an:
   (a) atom (b) molecule
   (c) compound (d) ion
11. Which among the following is an element?
   (a) Calcium oxide
   (b) Common salt
   (c) Ozone
   (d) Water
12. Evaporation is the process of conversion of:
   (a) a liquid to its gaseous state below the boiling point of the substance.
   (b) a liquid to its gaseous state at the boiling point of the substance.
   (c) a solid to its liquid state at the melting point of the substance.
   (d) a solid to its liquid state below the melting point of the substance.
13. The most convenient way of separating sawdust from water is:
   (a) distillation
   (b) evaporation
   (c) filtration
   (d) sedimentation and decantation
14. Which among the following statements is true?
   (a) Compounds are heterogeneous in nature.
   (b) The proportion of constituent elements in a compound is fixed.
   (c) The constituent elements retain their properties in a compound.
   (d) The formation of a compound is a physical process.
15. Which of the following is a heterogeneous mixture?
   (a) A mixture of water and sugar.
   (b) A mixture of water and common salt.
   (c) A mixture of water and sawdust.
   (d) A mixture of water and glucose.
16. Which among the following is a heterogeneous mixture?
   (a) Soda water
   (b) Liquid ammonia
   (c) Milk
   (d) Sugar water
17. Which among the following is a pure substance?
   (a) Dilute sulphuric acid
   (b) Concentrated sulphuric acid
   (c) Aqueous NaCl
   (d) Molten NaCl

18. Identify the true statement among the following.
(a) Gases are highly compressible and diffuse very easily.
(b) Gases are highly compressible and possess strong forces.
(c) Solid molecules are closely packed and highly compressible.
(d) Solid molecules are loosely packed and possess strong forces.

19. Property exploited in the usage of perfumes is______.
(a) compressibility of gases
(b) diffusion of gases
(c) expansibility of gases
(d) Both (b) and (c)

20. Baking soda ($NaHCO_3$) is a compound because:
(a) the constituents retain their properties.
(b) the constituents can be separated by physical methods.
(c) the constituents are combined chemically.
(d) it is heterogeneous in nature.

21. Which among the following pairs possess low boiling points?
(a) Magnesium, mercury
(b) Mercury, manganese
(c) Sodium, potassium
(d) Calcium, manganese

22. A form of which of the following non-metal is the hardest substance?
(a) Phosphorus (b) Sulphur
(c) Iodine (d) Carbon

23. Preparation of salt from sea water involves:
(a) evaporation
(b) filtration
(c) sedimentation and decantation
(d) sublimation

24. Arrange the following in a proper sequence for the separation of constituents of gunpowder.
(1) Carbon disulphide is added to the mixture.
(2) Carbon powder is separated.
(3) Residue is filtered.
(4) KNO_3 is separated from its aqueous solution by heating it.
(5) Mixture is filtered and hot water is added to the residue.
(a) 1,5,4,2,3
(b) 1,5,3,2,4
(c) 1,2,3,4,5
(d) None of these

25. The steps involved in the separation of camphor and sand from a mixture are given below. Arrange them in a proper sequence.
(1) The wet cloth is placed over the funnel and the stem is closed with a cotton plug.
(2) The mixture of camphor and sand is taken in the china dish and an inverted funnel is kept on it.
(3) The vapours are cooled and condensed to form the same solid and sand left behind in the dish.
(4) The mixture is heated gently where the vapours of camphor is formed.
(a) 2,3,4,1
(b) 4,1,2,3
(c) 2,1,4,3
(d) 3,4,2,1

26. Identify the true statement among the following.
(a) The constituents of both a compound and a mixture can be separated by physical methods only.
(b) The constituents of both a compound and a mixture can be separated by chemical methods only.
(c) The constituents of a compound and a mixture can be separated by chemical and physical methods, respectively.
(d) The constituents of a compound and a mixture can be separated by physical and chemical methods, respectively.

27. Which among the following substances has the strongest intermolecular forces of attraction?
(a) Steam (b) Bromine
(c) Oxygen (d) Hydrogen chloride gas

28. Thermal expansion of solids is the least among the three states of matter due to:
(a) high kinetic energy of molecules of solids.
(b) close packing of molecules in solids.
(c) vibratory and rotatory motions of molecules of solids.
(d) large intermolecular space present in solids.

29. **Assertion (A)**: Dogs stretch out their tongues in summer.
Reason (R): Evaporation leads to cooling.
(a) Both A and R are true and R is the correct explanation for A.
(b) Both A and R are true but R is not the correct explanation for A.
(c) A is true and R is false.
(d) A is false and R is true.

30. Arrange the following examples in the order of matter, compound, element and mixture.
(1) Dilute acid
(2) Argon
(3) Water
(4) Ball
(a) 1, 2, 3, 4 (b) 4, 3, 2, 1
(c) 1, 2, 4, 3 (d) 4, 3, 1, 2

31. Which among the following is a heterogeneous mixture?
(a) Soda water (b) Air
(c) Milk (d) Sugar water

32. For the separation of components of a mixture of camphor, iron filings and sand, arrange the following processes in a sequence.
(1) Magnetic separation
(2) Distillation
(3) Sublimation
(4) Sedimentation and decantation
(a) 1, 2, 3, 4 (b) 2, 1
(c) 2, 4 (d) 1, 3

33. Match the following.

Column A Principle	Column B Procedure
(A) Evaporation	(a) Purification of drinking water which contains suspended matter
(B) Filtration	(b) Earthen pots
(C) Sublimation	(c) Odonil used in a washroom

(a) A → a, B → c, C → b
(b) A → c, B → a, C → b
(c) A → c, B → b, C → a
(d) A → b, B → a, C → c

34. Property responsible for spreading of fragrance of a flower is ______.
(a) compressibility of gas/vapour
(b) diffusion of gas/vapour
(c) expansibility of gas/vapour
(d) Both (b) and (c)

Directions for questions from 35 to 37:
Match the entries given in Column A with the appropriate ones in Column B. More than one suitable content of Column B can also be considered correct for an entry in Column A and some content given in Column B may not be the appropriate one for any entry in Column A.

35. Match the statements of Column A with those of Column B.

Column A	Column B
A. Graphite	a. Possesses high tensile strength
B. Carbon fibre	b. Exists in liquid state
C. Diamond	c. Good conductor of electricity
D. Bromine	d. Possesses high density

36.

Column A	Column B
A. Atom	a. Takes the shape of the container
B. Solid	b. Smallest particle of the matter
C. Liquid	c. Highly compressible
D. Gas	d. Any number of free surfaces
E. Molecule	e. Rigid
	f. Basic building block of the matter

37.

Column A	Column B
A. Boiling	a. Gas to liquid
B. Melting	b. Solid to gas
C. Condensation	c. Liquid to solid
D. Freezing	d. Liquid to gas
	e. Solid to liquid

Directions for questions from 38 to 57:
Answer the following questions.

38. The boiling points of two liquids X and Y are 40°C and 90°C, respectively. Compare the evaporation of X and Y at room temperature.

39. Identify the odd one with respect to atomicity: Hydrogen, Nitrogen, Chlorine, Ozone.

40. Identify the substances which float on water.
(a) Lithium (c) Calcium
(b) Sodium (d) Magnesium

41. Define atomicity.

42. What is the difference between an element and a compound?

43. Give two examples of metals which can exist in liquid state below 35°C.

44. What is a metalloid? Give two examples.

45. What type of metals are found in free state?

46. Distinguish sublimate from sublime.

47. What is sublimation?

48. What is meant by intermolecular space and intermolecular forces of attraction?

49. Mention the factors on which the existence of matter in a particular state depends.

50. Distinguish between melting and boiling.

51. 'All pure substances are homogeneous in nature.' Justify.

52. How can the constituents of compounds and a mixture be separated respectively?

53. Give two examples for sublimable substances.

54. Name any two metals which are poor conductors of electricity.

55. Highlight the difference between a filtrate and a residue.

56. Name two elements which have atomicity more than three.

57. Name two states of matter which are fluid.

Short Answer Type Questions

58. X, Y and Z are three states of matter. X is incompressible, Y possesses selective diffusibility and Z has neither definite volume nor shape. Identify the correct order of thermal expansion of X, Y and Z.

59. Ten litres of petrol is kept in four containers as shown in the figure.

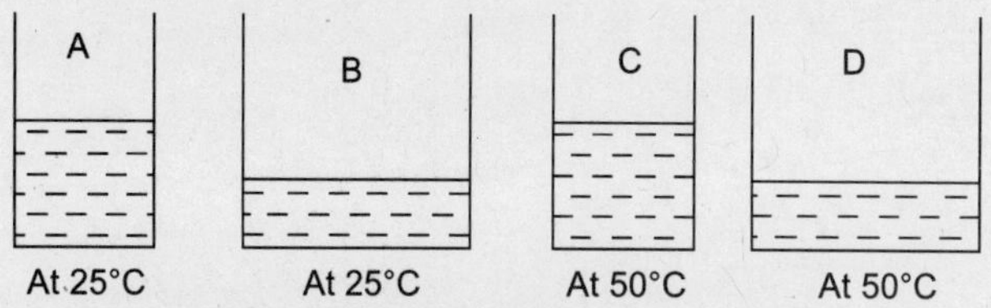

Arrange the containers in the decreasing order of rate of evaporation.

60. Distinguish between compounds and mixtures.

61. Explain the suitable method of separation of ammonium chloride from common salt.

62. Do you consider that distillation can be employed as the method of separation for a mixture containing a volatile substance dissolved in a liquid? If yes, explain the process. If no, suggest a suitable method of separation.

63. Explain the process of sedimentation and decantation.

64. What is a homogeneous and a heterogeneous mixture? Give one example for each.

65. Explain classification of matter based on its molecular composition with suitable examples.

66. Complete the following table.

Matter	Dimension	Molecular movement
	Only one free surface	
Solid		
		Spontaneous and rapid diffusion of molecules

67. Explain the factors affecting the rate of evaporation.

68. Discuss the characteristics of:
(a) an element (b) a mixture
(c) a compound

69. Distinguish between an atom and a molecule. Give example of elements existing as atoms and molecules.

70. Distinguish between malleability and ductility with examples.

71. What is intermolecular force of attraction? Mention two types of intermolecular force of attraction acting between molecules.

72. What is diffusion? Give one application.

73. Give schematic representation of classification of matter based on its composition.

74. Describe the process of separation of mixture of iron filings, camphor and sand.

75. Give reasons for the following:

(a) Doctors advise to put strips of wet cloth on the forehead of a person having high temperatures.

(b) Ice at 0°C is more effective in cooling than water at 0°C.

Essay Answer Type Questions

76. Compare solids, liquids and gases with respect to their physical properties.

77. Compare physical properties of metals and non-metals.

78. Explain the following methods of separation with a suitable example.

(a) Distillation

(b) Filtration

79. Explain different processes of interconversions of states of matter.

80. Describe the process of separation of constituents of gunpowder.

81. Give reasons for the following.

(a) Leaves of plants appear to wilt in summer afternoons.

(b) When a perfume is sprayed on hand, we feel cool.

(c) Leaves of submerged aquatic plants contain wax coating.

(d) Perspiration is greater in coastal areas than in non-coastal areas.

82. Explain sublimation with a suitable example.

83. Compare three different states of matter with respect to the arrangement of molecules and their related parameters.

PRACTICE QUESTIONS COMPETITION WING

Level 1: Apply your Concepts

Directions for questions from 1 to 15:
Fill in the blanks.

1. Saw dust and water can be separated only by ______.
2. A mixture of iodine and sand can be separated by ______.
3. A substance which is formed by the chemical combination of two or more elements is called a ______.
4. Boiling point is the temperature at which ______ is converted into ______ at normal atmospheric pressure.
5. Non-metals usually exist in ______ state.
6. ______ is a surface phenomenon, whereas boiling is a ______.
7. ______ state of matter is incompressible.
8. A pure substance is ______ in nature.
9. ______ is a lustrous non-metal.
10. Generally, the components of a compound are separated by ______.
11. ______ is the non-metal which is a good conductor of electricity.
12. ______ in humidity increases rate of evaporation.
13. A mixture of two solids is generally ______ while a mixture of any number of gases is ______.
14. Mixture of iron filings and sand can be separated by ______.
15. ______ and ______ are the suitable separation methods for mixtures of soluble solids in liquids.

Directions for questions from 16 to 25:
State whether the following statements are true or false.

16. Intermolecular space is maximum in gases.
17. Metals are highly ductile but non-malleable.
18. Evaporation is a surface phenomenon.
19. A pure substance is homogeneous in nature.
20. Tellurium shows the properties of both metals and non-metals.
21. Iodine is a lustrous metal.
22. Sodium floats on water.
23. Ammonium chloride is a sublimable substance.
24. The components of compound are separated by physical processes.
25. Sublimation is the process of the conversion of a solid to its liquid state.

Directions for questions from 26 to 57:
For each of the questions, four choices have been provided. Select the correct alternative.

26. Based on structure of classification, which of the following will be on the top of classification?
    (a) Elements (c) Pure substances
    (b) Metals (d) Monoatomic metal
27. **Assertion (A):** The constituents of a compound can be separated by chemical methods.
    Reason (R): Compounds are homogeneous.
    (a) Both A and R are true and R is the correct explanation of A.
    (b) Both A and R are true, but R is not the correct explanation of A.
    (c) A is true and R is false.
    (d) A is false and R is true.
28. Match the entries given in Column A with the appropriate options in Column B.

Column A	Column B
(A) Sublimation	(a) NaCl + water
(B) Filtration	(b) Iodine + sand
(C) Evaporation	(c) Sawdust + water

(a) A → a B → c C → b
(b) A → c B → a C → b
(c) A → c B → b C → a
(d) A → b B → c C → a

29. **Assertion (A):** A mixture of water and alcohol forms a single layer.
Reason (R): All liquid–liquid mixtures are homogeneous.
(a) Both A and R are true and R is the correct explanation of A.
(b) Both A and R are true, but R is not the correct explanation of A.
(c) A is true and R is false.
(d) A is false and R is true.

30. A drop of water contains ______.
(a) 2 atoms of hydrogen and 1 atom of oxygen.
(b) 1 molecule of hydrogen and 1 atom of oxygen.
(c) millions of molecules of water.
(d) 1 molecule of hydrogen and 1 molecule of oxygen.

31. Germanium is a ______.
(a) gas (b) metal
(c) liquid (d) metalloid

32. The process of separation of components of muddy water is:
(a) decantation (b) sublimation
(c) magnetic separation (d) None of the above

33. Lime water is a ______.
(a) mixture (b) element
(c) compound (d) All the above

34. Water sticks to glass due to ______.
(a) adhesive forces between water and glass
(b) cohesive forces between water and glass
(c) cohesive forces between water molecules
(d) cohesive forces between glass molecules.

35. The temperature at which solid changes to liquid is called ______.
(a) melting point (b) boiling point
(c) evaporation (d) condensation

36. A homogeneous mixture among the following is:
(a) milk (b) muddy water
(c) smoke (d) air

37. The false statement among the following is:
(a) every pure substance is homogeneous in nature.
(b) in compounds the constituents do not retain properties.
(c) the constituents of a mixture can be separated by physical method.
(d) during formation of mixtures, there is a change in the molecular composition.

38. Which among the following has strong forces of attraction?
(a) Hydrogen chloride (b) Bromine
(c) Fluorine (d) Chlorine

39. Gases form homogeneous mixture due to their:
(a) diffusiblity
(b) high compressibility
(c) expansibility
(d) low density

40. Washing soda (Na_2CO_3) is a compound because the constituents combine:
(a) chemically in fixed ratio by weight.
(b) chemically in any ratio by weight.
(c) physically in fixed ratio by weight.
(d) physically in any ratio by weight.

41. Which among the following pairs of substances has strong intermolecular forces of attraction?
(a) Bromine, mercury
(b) Gallium, bromine
(c) Bromine, sodium
(d) Carbon, potassium

42. Among the following which is a pair of soft metals?
(a) Sodium, potassium
(b) Potassium, magnesium
(c) Magnesium, calcium
(d) Calcium, manganese

43. Identify the odd one among the following with respect to tensile strength as well as ductility.
(a) Gas carbon
(b) Diamond
(c) Graphite
(d) Carbon fibre

44. A mixture contains three components namely glucone-D, water and sand. These three can be collected separately by:
(a) filtration and evaporation
(b) filtration and sublimation
(c) filtration and distillation
(d) sedimentation and decantation

45. Identify the false statement among the following.
(a) Evaporation is a surface phenomenon and causes cooling.
(b) Rate of evaporation is directly proportional to temperature.
(c) Rate of evaporation is inversely proportional to surface area of a liquid.

(d) Evaporation causes cooling and depends on humidity.

46. Separation of sawdust from water can be carried out by the following steps given below. Arrange them in a proper sequence.

(1) The mixture is poured gently into the filter cone and collected in another beaker which is called filtrate.

(2) A mixture of sawdust and water is taken in a beaker.

(3) A filter paper is folded in the form of a cone and fitted into a funnel by moistening it with a few drops of water.

(4) Solid retained on the filter paper is called residue.

(a) 3,1,2,4 (b) 1,2,3,4
(c) 3,4,2,1 (d) 2,3,1,4

47. Water shows concave meniscus in a narrow glass tube. This is because:

(a) adhesive force is stronger than cohesive force

(b) adhesive force is weaker than cohesive force

(c) cohesive and adhesive forces are equal

(d) of the absence of adhesive force

48. Iron powder and powder of rust are taken in two containers X and Y, respectively. Dilute sulphuric acid is added to both the containers. Then:

(a) effervescence is observed in both the containers.

(b) effervescence is observed in case of X but not Y.

(c) effervescence is observed in case of Y but not X.

(d) no effervescence is observed in both the cases.

49. X, Y and Z containers are placed at 25°C. Then, decrease in temperature is more in ______.

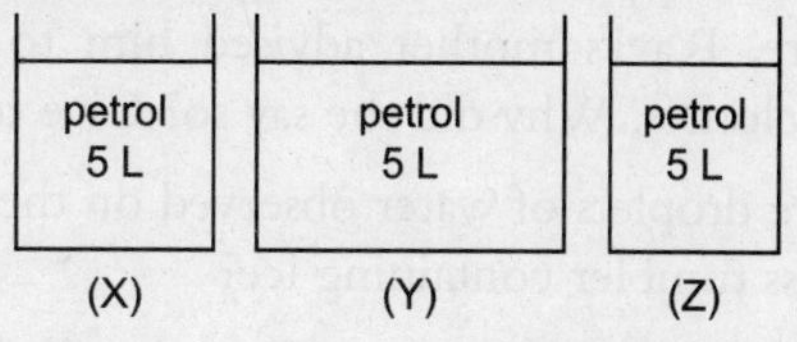

(a) X (b) Y
(c) Z (d) Cannot be predicted.

50. The interconversion involved in usage of 'odonil' in a washroom is______.

(a) sublimation (b) deposition
(c) melting (d) freezing

51. Dogs stretch out their tongues generally in summer because:

(a) evaporation leads to cooling

(b) of condensation of water vapour

(c) of freezing of saliva

(d) their body temperatures are high

52. A mixture contains three components namely camphor powder, common salt and water. These can be separated by:

(a) filtration and distillation.

(b) filtration, sedimentation and decantation.

(c) sublimation and distillation.

(d) sublimation, sedimentation and decantation.

53. Thermal expansion of solids is the least among the three states of matter due to:

(a) high kinetic energy of molecules of solids.

(b) close packing of molecules in solids.

(c) the vibratory motion and rotatory motion of molecules of solids.

(d) the large intermolecular space present in solids.

54. Water shows convex meniscus in narrow ____ and ____ tubes.

(a) glass, plastic

(b) glass, wax-coated glass

(c) wax-coated glass, plastic

(d) plastic, coloured glass

55. Among the following, a pair of a compound and an element, respectively is:

(a) iron powder and rust powder.

(b) rust powder and iron powder.

(c) lime and rust powder.

(d) rust powder and lime.

56. Rate of evaporation of water:

(a) is more in coastal areas than in non-coastal areas

(b) is more in non-coastal areas than in coastal areas

(c) is the same in both coastal and non-coastal areas

(d) Cannot be predicted

57. Which of the following pair of substances show sublimation?

(a) incense stick and odonil

(b) camphor and incense stick

(c) perfume and odonil

(d) naphthalene balls and camphor

Directions for questions from 58 to 60:

Match the entries given in Column A with the appropriate ones in Column B. More than one suitable content of Column B can also be considered correct for an entry in Column A and some content given in Column B may not be the appropriate one for any entry in Column A.

58.

Column A	Column B
A. Sodium	a. Homogeneous mixture
B. Sodium chloride	b. Element
C. Sulphur in water	c. Compound
D. Sugar in water	d. Heterogeneous mixture
	e. Impure compound

59.

Column A	Column B
A. Boiling	a. Water changes to ice
B. Melting	b. Water vapour changes to water
C. Condensation	c. Ice changes to water
D. Freezing	d. Water changes to water vapour
	e. Ice changes to water vapour

60.

Column A	Column B
A. Distillation	a. Mixture of sodium chloride and ammonium chloride
B. Filtration	b. Mixture of sodium chloride and water
C. Sublimation	c. Mixture of sawdust and water
D. Sedimentation	d. Mixture of iron and sulphur
E. Magnetic separation	e. Mixture of sand and water

Level 2: Review Your Concepts

61. Give an example of substances, formed is associated which have free movement and not just vibrating about a fixed position.

62. Look at the diagram shown below and write what A, B, C, D, E and F correspond to:

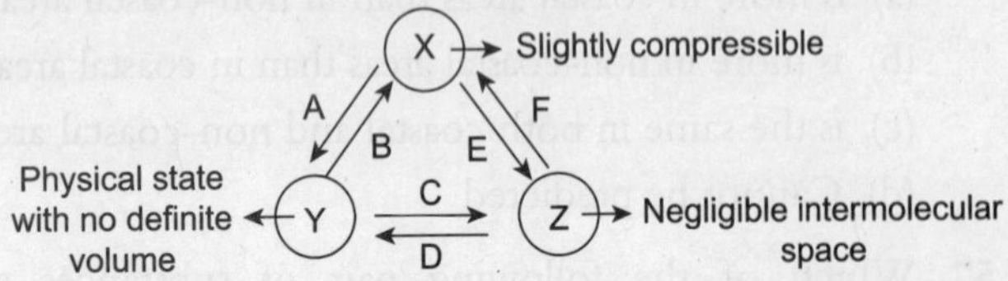

63. Two test tubes X and Y are filled with water and mercury, respectively. After these two liquids were poured, water drops on the inner walls of X were observed but no mercury drops in Y were seen. Give reasons.

64. Cotton clothes can be made more easily wet than synthetic clothes. Explain.

65. The thermal expansion of solids is the least among the three states of matter. Explain.

66. Camphor pellets should be preserved in air-tight containers. Give reasons.

67. Cotton clothes are more easily wettable in water than in oil. Give reasons.

68. During summer vacation Ravi decided to go to his grandparent's place at Delhi. Since it was summer, therefore, Ravi's mother advised him to carry only cotton clothes. Why did she say so? Give reason.

69. Why are droplets of water observed on the outer walls of a glass tumbler containing ice?

70. When Rita opened the perfume bottle in the bedroom without the permission of her mother, how did her mother came to know while watching TV in the drawing room?

71. Jack was getting late for the school, so, his mother advised him to pour hot milk from a glass into a saucer and then drink. Why did she say so? Give reason.

72. Why do we observe fog and mist in winter mornings?

73. When Vasu was running high temperature, his mother was nursing him by placing a wet cloth on his forehead till the temperature had gone down. Justify what purpose did the mother's action serve.

74. A student has a mixture consisting of charcoal and sulphur powder. He adds a certain reagent where he observes that one of the components goes into the solution state. Name the techniques by which the components can be separated.

75. Mother took her two daughters Bhavani and Shivani to a swimming pool in summer vacation. They both enjoyed swimming hours together. When they came out of swimming pool, both were shivering and fighting for the towel. Explain the reason for their shivering immediately after they came out of the swimming pool.

Level 3: Assess Your Concepts

76. How is milk powder prepared from milk?

77. Which characteristic property of mercury is exploited in its usage as a thermometric liquid? Is there any preferable metal for use in high temperature thermometers? Justify.

78. Why is mercury used in a thermometer? Is it suitable for measuring high temperatures? Name the liquid which can be used for the measurement of high temperatures. Give reasons.

79. Two thermometers A and B are dipped in water and alcohol, respectively taken in two containers of similar dimensions at room temperature. Compare the temperatures shown by these two thermometers giving appropriate reasons.

80. Naturally occurring diamonds are sometimes found in different colours. Give reasons.

AT

ANSWER KEYS

Crossword

Across

1. Mercury 3. Mixture 5. Element 7. Cohesive
9. Distillation

Down

2. Condensation 3. Molecules 4. Gaseous 6. Residue
8. Matter

Classroom Wing

Very Short Answer Type Questions

1. Loosely	2. increases	3. solidification	4. released	5. three
6. (d)	7. (d)	8. (d)	9. (d)	10. (a)
11. (c)	12. (a)	13. (c)	14. (b)	15. (c)
16. (c)	17. (d)	18. (a)	19. (d)	20. (c)
21. (c)	22. (d)	23. (a)	24. (b)	25. (c)
26. (c)	27. (b)	28. (b)	29. (b)	30. (d)
31. (c)	32. (d)	33. (d)	34. (b)	

35. A → c, B → d, C → d, D → b
36. A → b, B → e, d, C → a, D → c, E → f
37. A → d, B → e, C → a, D → c

Competition Wing

Level 1: Apply your Concepts

1. Filtration
2. Sublimation
3. compound
4. liquid, gas
5. gaseous
6. Evaporation, bulk phenomenon
7. Solid
8. homogeneous
9. Iodine
10. chemical methods
11. Graphite
12. Decrease
13. heterogeneous, homogeneous
14. magnetic separation
15. Evaporation, distillation
16. True

17. False	18. True	19. True	20. True	21. False
22. True	23. True	24. False	25. False	26. (c)
27. (c)	28. (d)	29. (a)	30. (c)	31. (d)
32. (a)	33. (a)	34. (a)	35. (a)	36. (d)
37. (d)	38. (b)	39. (a)	40. (a)	41. (d)
42. (a)	43. (d)	44. (c)	45. (c)	46. (d)
47. (a)	48. (b)	49. (b)	50. (a)	51. (a)
52. (a)	53. (b)	54. (c)	55. (b)	56. (b)

57. (d)
58. A → b, B → c, C → d, D → a
59. A → d, B → c, C → b, D → a
60. A → b, B → c, C → a, D → e, E → d

Hints and Explanations

CLASSROOM WING

Very Short Answer Type Questions

1. Since LPG is in a liquid state, the molecules are loosely packed.

2. The rate of evaporation is directly proportional to the surface area of a liquid.

3. solidification
The process involving the change of matter from liquid to solid on cooling is called solidification.

4. released
Freezing is the process of conversion of a liquid to solid. This can be carried out by extracting heat from a liquid.

5. three
Ozone is a triatomic molecule.

6. Generally, metals are solids having high tensile strength. They are also good conductors of heat.
Hence, correct option is (d).

7. Since ammonium chloride is a sublimable substance, it can be separated from chalk powder by sublimation.
Hence, correct option is (d).

8. Potassium is a soft metal.
Hence, correct option is (d).

9. Generally, non-metals are bad conductors of electricity and hence phosphorus is a bad conductor of electricity.
Hence, correct option is (d).

10. An atom is the smallest particle of an element which may or may not have independent existence.
Hence, correct option is (a).

11. Molecules of an element possess similar atoms and hence ozone is an element.
Hence, correct option is (c).

12. Evaporation can be defined as the change of state of a liquid to gas or vapour from the surface of the liquid below its boiling point.
Hence, correct option is (a).

13. As sawdust floats on water, it can be separated from water by filtration easily.
Hence, correct option is (c).

14. In compounds, the constituents are combined in a fixed weight ratio.
Hence, correct option is (b).

15. Mixture of water and sawdust is a heterogeneous mixture since sawdust is insoluble in water.
Hence, correct option is (c).

16. Milk is a heterogeneous mixture as the constituents are non-uniformly distributed.
Hence, correct option is (c).

17. NaCl is a compound. Every compound is a pure substance. Molten NaCl means NaCl in liquid state; hence, molten NaCl is a pure substance.
Hence, correct option is (d).

18. In gases, intermolecular forces of attraction are negligible and hence, they are highly compressible and diffuse very easily.
Hence, correct option is (a).

19. In gases, intermolecular space is more, so they undergo expansion by releasing pressure and hence, they diffuse into each other forming a homogeneous mixture.
Hence, correct option is (d).

20. In baking soda ($NaHCO_3$), the constitutions are combined chemically in a fixed weight ratio and hence, it is a compound.
Hence, correct option is (c).

21. Sodium and potassium have low boiling points.
Hence, correct option is (c).

22. An allotrope of carbon, namely diamond is the hardest substance.
Hence, correct option is (d).

23. Preparation of salt from sea water involves evaporation in which water undergoes evaporation leaving behind the salt.
Hence, correct option is (a).

24. (1) Carbon disulphide is added to the mixture

(5) Mixture is filtered and hot water is added to the residue

(3) Residue is filtered

(2) Carbon powder is separated

(4) KNO_3 is separated from its aqueous solution by heating it

Hence, correct option is (b).

25. (2) The mixture of camphor and sand is taken in the China Dish and an inverted funnel is kept on it

(1) The wet cloth is put over the funnel and the stem is closed with a cotton plug

(4) The mixture is heated gently where the vapours of camphor are formed

(3) The vapours are cooled and condensed to form the same solid and sand left behind in the dish

Hence, correct option is (c).

26. The constituents of a compound do not retain their properties. Hence, they can be separated by chemical methods. The constituents of a mixture retain their properties. Hence, they can be separated by physical methods.

Hence, correct option is (c).

27. Bromine is a liquid, and hence, it possesses stronger intermolecular forces of attractions.

Hence, correct option is (b).

28. In a solid, the molecules are closely packed due to strong forces of attraction, and hence, thermal expansion of solids is the least among the three states of matter.

Hence, correct option is (b).

29. Dogs stretch out their tongues in summer as evaporation of the saliva leads to cooling.

Hence, correct option is (b).

30. 4, 3, 2, 1

(i) ball

(ii) water

(iii) argon

(iv) dilute acid

Hence, correct option is (d).

31. Milk is a heterogeneous mixture in which fat particles are present in water.

Hence, correct option is (c).

32. 1, 3

(i) magnetic separation

(ii) sublimation

Hence, correct option is (d).

33. A $\rightarrow$ b Earthen pots work on the principle of evaporation.

B $\rightarrow$ a Purification of drinking water which contains suspended matter is based on the principle of filtration.

C $\rightarrow$ c Odonil, used in washrooms, works on the principle of sublimation.

Hence, correct option is (d).

34. Molecules of gas/vapour diffuse easily into each other.

Hence, correct option is (b).

35. Graphite is a good conductor of electricity.

Carbon fibre possesses high tensile strength.

Diamond possesses high density.

Bromine exists in the liquid state.

36. A $\rightarrow$ (b) Atom is the smallest particle of the matter.

B $\rightarrow$ (e, d) Solids are rigid and possess any number of free surfaces.

C $\rightarrow$ (a) Liquids do not have a definite shape and take the shape of the container.

D $\rightarrow$ (c) Gases have very weak intermolecular forces of attraction and hence, they are highly compressible.

E $\rightarrow$ (f) Molecule is the basic building block of matter.

37. A $\rightarrow$ (d) During boiling, the liquid is converted into gaseous state.

B $\rightarrow$ (e) During melting, solids melt into liquid.

C $\rightarrow$ (a) During condensation, gas is converted to liquid.

D $\rightarrow$ (c) During freezing, liquid freezes to solid.

38. X undergoes evaporation more rapidly than Y, which undergoes evaporation slowly.

39. Ozone is the odd one out.

Hydrogen atomicity $\rightarrow$ 2, Chlorine atomicity $\rightarrow$ 2

Nitrogen atomicity $\rightarrow$ 2, Ozone atomicity $\rightarrow$ 3

40. Since densities of lithium and sodium are less than water, they can float on water.

Hence, the (i) and (ii) are correct.

41. The number of atoms that constitute a molecule of an element is called **atomicity** of that element.

42. An element is a substance which is constituted of only one kind of atoms and cannot be further divided by any physical or chemical means.
A compound is a substance which is formed due to the chemical combination of two or more elements in a definite proportion by mass.

43. Mercury and gallium are two examples of metals which can exist in liquid state below 35°C.

44. Metalloids are elements which show the properties of both metals and non-metals.
Examples: germanium and arsenic

45. Noble metals like gold, platinum, silver are found in free state.

46. The process by which some solid substances directly change into the vapour state without passing through the intermediate liquid state is called sublimation. The solid obtained on cooling the vapour is called sublimate and the vapour formed is called sublime.

47. The process by which some solid substances directly change into the vapour state without passing through the intermediate liquid state is called **sublimation**.

48. The space between the constituent molecules of matter is called intermolecular space. The attractive forces that exist between the adjacent molecules of matter are called intermolecular forces of attraction.

49. The two factors on which the existence of matter in a particular state depend are temperature and pressure.

50. The process which involves the change in state of matter from solid to liquid by heating is called melting or fusion. The process which involves the conversion of a liquid state to a gaseous state from the bulk of the liquid by heating is called boiling.

51. All pure substances contain particles of only one kind having definite set of properties and their composition cannot be altered by any physical means so we can say that all pure substances are homogeneous in nature.

52. The constituents of compounds and mixture can be separated by chemical and physical methods, respectively.

53. The two examples of sublimable substances are camphor and iodine.

54. Bismuth and tungsten are poor conductors of electricity.

55. In the filtration process, the clear liquid that is collected in the beaker is known as a filtrate and the solid particles retained on the filter paper are known as a residue.

56. Phosphorus (P_4) and sulphur (S_8) are the two elements with atomicity more than three.

57. Liquids and gases are fluids.

Short Answer Type Questions

58. The correct order of thermal expansion is:
Z (gases) > Y (liquids) > X (solids)

59. Rate of evaporation of a liquid is directly proportional to the temperature and surface area of the liquid and is inversely proportional to humidity.
Hence, the correct order is DBCA.

60.

Compound	Mixture
Constituent atoms of elements combine chemically.	Constituent substances are mixed physically.
Constituent elements do not retain their properties in a compound.	The constituents retain their individual properties in a mixture.
Constituents can be separated only by chemical methods.	Constituents can be separated by physical methods.
These are homogeneous.	These can be either homogeneous or heterogeneous.

61. Mixture of sodium chloride and ammonium chloride is taken in a flat basin and a funnel is inverted over it. The outer surface of the funnel is wrapped with a water-soaked filter paper and the open end of the stem of the funnel is plugged with a piece of paper cotton to prevent vaporization. The basin is kept in a sand bath. The sand bath is placed over a wire mesh kept on a tripod stand and then is heated gently with the help of a Bunsen burner.
A white-coloured fume is observed which condenses as white powdery substance when it comes in contact with the colder wall of the funnel. The process of heating is continued till the evolution of white vapour is observed.
Since ammonium chloride is a sublimable substance, it sublimes and then condenses as a white powder. The substance left over on the basin is sodium chloride which does not sublime. Ammonium chloride is scrapped off from the walls of the funnel and thus the mixture is separated.

62. No, it is not possible to separate a mixture of volatile substance and water in which the solid remains in the dissolved state by distillation process as

volatile substance vaporizes on heating. The solid substance is made to dissolve in the liquid at high temperature to make a hot saturated solution. This solution on cooling-results in the crystallization of the solid substance. This method can be adopted for the separation of the constituents of solid liquid mixture

63. **Sedimentation and decantation**

In the mixture of sand and water, the heavier solid particles settle at the bottom and can be separated by this process.

Process: A mixture of sand and water is taken in a beaker and kept still for some time. The heavier sand particles settle down at the bottom. The clear water above it is gently poured off into another beaker with the help of a glass rod. The glass rod helps to pour off the liquid, without disturbing the solid settled at the bottom.

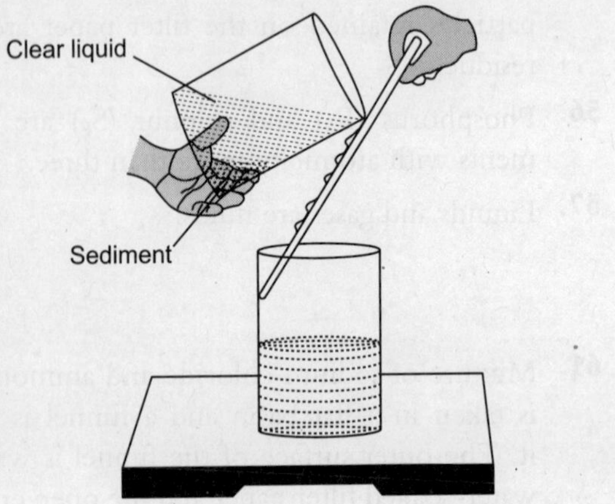

The water collected in the second beaker is clear and the sand particles are left behind in the first beaker.

64. The mixture in which different constituents are uniformly distributed throughout is called a homogeneous mixture. An example in this regard is a mixture of alcohol and water. The mixture in which different constituents are non-uniformly distributed throughout is called a heterogeneous mixture. An example in this regard is a mixture of sulphur and water.

65. Matter can also be classified based on its composition in the following way irrespective of the state in which it exists.

If the matter is made up of identical molecules, it is called a **pure substance**. The matter which is made up of different types of molecules is called a **mixture**. Molecules of matter are made up of still tinier particles called **atoms.** Atoms are the tiniest particles of matter which cannot exist independently. There are very few atoms which exist independently. These are the atoms of helium, neon, argon, krypton and xenon. They remain in the gaseous state in the atmosphere and are known as **noble gases**.

Pure substances can further be classified into **elements and compounds** based on the nature of constituent atoms present in their molecule.

If the molecules of a pure substance contain identical atom(s), it is called an **element**. The pure substance in which the molecules are made up of two or more different types of atoms is called a **compound**. Classification of matter based on its composition is schematically represented below:

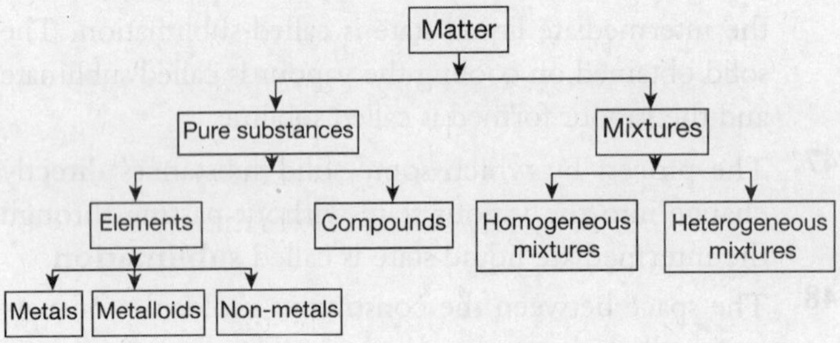

Element: An element is a substance which is constituted of only one kind of atoms and cannot be further divided by any physical or chemical means.

Examples: Hydrogen, oxygen, chlorine, sodium, potassium etc. Molecules of these substances consist of only one type of atoms. Molecules of different elements may contain different number of atoms.

Atomicity of an element: The number of atoms that constitute a molecule of an element is called **atomicity** of that element. A molecule of hydrogen is made up of two atoms and hence, its atomicity is two. Based on the atomicity, elements can be classified as follows:

(i) **Monoatomic elements**: The elements in which each molecule contains only one atom.
Examples: Cu, Ag, He, etc.

(ii) **Diatomic elements**: The elements in which each molecule contains two atoms.
Examples: H_2, O_2, N_2, etc.

(iii) **Polyatomic elements**: The elements in which each molecule contains more than two atoms.
Examples: O_3, P_4, S_8, etc.

Compounds: A compound is a substance which is formed due to the chemical combination of two or more elements in a definite proportion by mass. The constituents of a compound do not retain their properties and they can be separated only by chemical means.

Examples: Water, carbon dioxide, hydrochloric acid, sodium chloride, calcium carbonate, etc., are a few examples of compounds. A molecule of carbon dioxide is constituted of a carbon atom and two oxygen atoms. Two atoms of hydrogen and one atom of oxygen combine chemically to form a molecule of water.

Mixture: A mixture is a substance which is formed by mixing two or more substances (elements, compounds or both) physically in any proportion. No chemical reaction takes place during the formation of the mixture and all the constituents of the mixture retain their properties. Constituents of the mixture can easily be separated by physical means.

Examples: A solution of sugar and water is a mixture in which sugar and water both retain their properties and can be separated by a simple physical process, i.e., evaporation. Muddy water is another example of the mixture of mud and water which can easily be separated by filtration.

Elements and compounds are the substances in which the composition is uniform throughout the matter and hence, they are said to be **homogeneous**. However, the composition of a mixture, i.e., the proportion of its constituents may or may not be uniform throughout. Hence, the mixture may be homogeneous or heterogeneous.

Examples of homogeneous and heterogeneous mixtures: A mixture of alcohol and water is an example of a homogeneous mixture because of the constituents of this mixture is uniformly distributed. A mixture of sulphur and water is an example of a heterogeneous mixture because sulphur remains non-uniformly distributed in water.

66.

Liquid	Only one free surface	Only some liquids diffuse
Solid	Number of free surfaces	No diffusion
Gas	No free surfaces	Spontaneous and rapid diffusion.

67. Factors affecting the rate of evaporation are as follows:

Surface area: The rate of evaporation of a liquid is directly proportional to its surface area.

Temperature: With the increase of temperature, the rate of evaporation of a liquid increases.

Humidity: The rate of evaporation of a liquid is inversely proportional to the amount of moisture present in the atmosphere (humidity).

68. (a) **Element**: An element is a substance in a molecule which is constituted of only one kind of atoms and cannot be further divided by any physical or chemical means.

Examples: Hydrogen, oxygen, chlorine, sodium, potassium, etc. Molecules of these substances consist of only one type of atoms. Molecules of different elements may contain different number of atoms.

(b) **Mixture**: A mixture is a substance which is formed by mixing two or more substances (elements, compounds or both) physically in any proportion. No chemical reaction takes place during the formation of the mixture and all the constituents of the mixture retain their properties. Constituents of the mixture can easily be separated by physical means.

Examples: A solution of sugar and water is a mixture in which sugar and water both retain their properties and can be separated by a simple physical process, i.e., evaporation. Muddy water is another example of the mixture of mud and water which can easily be separated by filtration.

(c) **Compound**: A compound is a substance which is formed due to the chemical combination of two or more elements in a definite proportion by mass. The constituents of a compound do not retain their properties and they can be separated only by chemical means.

Examples: Water, carbon dioxide, hydrochloric acid, sodium chloride, calcium carbonate, etc. A molecule of carbon dioxide is constituted of a carbon atom and two oxygen atoms. Two atoms of hydrogen and one atom of oxygen combine chemically to form a molecule of water.

69. An atom is the smallest particle of matter which may or may not exist independently. A molecule is the smallest particle of matter which can have independent existence. Inert gases exist in atomic state. Oxygen, nitrogen, etc., exist in molecular form.

70. Malleability is the ability of a substance to roll into sheets. Generally, all metals are malleable. Ductility is the ability of substance to be drawn into thin wires. Carbon fibres are ductile in nature.

71. The attractive forces that exist between the adjacent molecules of a matter are called **intermolecular**

forces of attraction. Intermolecular forces of attraction can be of two types, i.e., cohesive and adhesive forces depending on the nature of the participant molecules.

72. The movement of gas molecules from a region of higher concentration to a region of lower concentration is called diffusion. *Example*: spreading of a perfume.

73. Classification of matter based on its composition is schematically represented below:

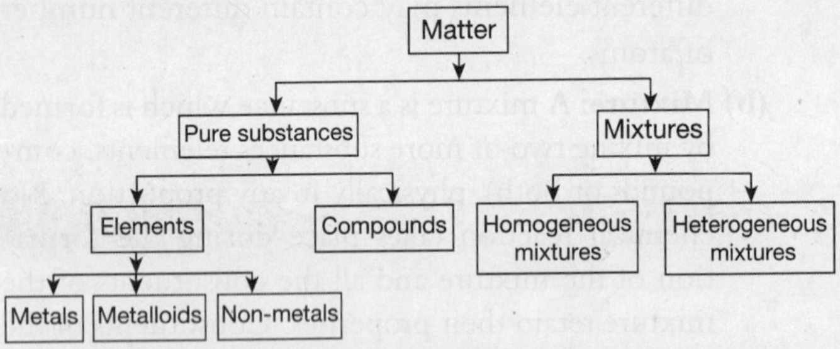

74. Separation of the components of a mixture of iron filings, sand and camphor

Procedure: The mixture of iron filing, sand and camphor spread evenly in basin. A strong bar magnet is brought close to the mixture repeatedly. The iron filings are attracted to the magnet. The iron filings that cling to the magnet can be shaved off from the surface using a piece of cardboard.

The remaining constituents are covered with an inverted funnel whose outside surface is wrapped with a moist filter paper and the open end of the steam of the funnel is plugged with a piece of paper or cotton to prevent vaporization. Then, the mixture is gently heated. Camphor undergoes sublimation and gets deposited on the cooler inner wall of the funnel and later on it is scrapped off. Sand is left behind in the basin. Thus, all the constituents of the given mixture are separated by magnetic separation followed by sublimation.

75. (a) Doctors advise to put strips of wet cloth on the forehead of a person having high temperature because, water in the wet cloth absorbs heat equivalent to the latent heat from patient's body in the process of evaporation and thus lowers the temperature of his body.

(b) When it comes to cooling effect, more the difference in energy content(heat) more is the transfer of energy. Since water at 0°C has more energy content, it'll extract relatively less energy from a body as compared to energy extracted by ice, hence giving less cooling effect

Essay Answer Type Questions

76.

Property	Solids	Liquids	Gases
Mass	Definite mass	Definite mass	Definite mass
Volume	Definite volume	Definite volume	No definite volume
Shape	Definite shape	No definite shape, take the shape of the container	No definite shape
Density	High density	Lesser density than solids	Least density
Compressibility	Incompressible	Slightly compressible	Highly compressible
Rigidity	Rigid (cannot flow)	Fluid (can flow)	Fluid (can flow)
Free surfaces	Any number of free surfaces	One free surface, i.e., only the upper surface	No free surfaces
Thermal expansion	Very low	Higher than solids	Much greater than both solids and liquids
Diffusion	Do not diffuse	Some liquids can diffuse spontaneously into another (examples are water and alcohol), but others do not diffuse. (examples are oil and water)	Gases diffuse spontaneously and rapidly.

77.

Property	Metals	Non-metals
State	Solids at room temperature. **Exceptions:** Mercury and gallium are liquids.	Mostly gases. **Exceptions**: Some of the solid non-metals are carbon, sulphur, phosphorus, iodine, whereas bromine is a liquid non-metal.
Melting and boiling points	Very high melting and boiling points. **Exceptions**: Sodium, potassium, mercury have low melting and boiling points. Gallium has a low melting point but a high boiling point.	Low melting and boiling points. **Exceptions**: Carbon, silicon and boron have high melting and boiling points.
Hardness	Generally hard. **Exceptions**: Sodium and potassium are soft.	Solid non-metals are brittle. **Exception**: Diamond is the hardest naturally occurring substance.
Density	Have high density **Exceptions**: Lithium, sodium and potassium have density lower than water (1 g/cm^3) have low density	**Exception**: Diamond
Conductivity	Good conductors of heat and electricity. **Exceptions**: Bismuth and tungsten are poor conductors of electricity.	Bad conductors of heat and electricity. **Exception**: Graphite and gas carbon are good conductors of electricity.
Lustre	Have lustre **Exceptions**: Iodine and graphite	No lustre
Tensile strength	High tensile strength **Exception**: Zinc has very less tensile strength	Do not have tensile strength. **Exception**: Carbon fibre, a recently developed allotrope of carbon.
Malleability and ductility	Generally malleable and ductile. **Exception**: Zinc is neither malleable nor ductile.	Non-malleable and non-ductile **Exception**: Carbon fibres are ductile.
Sonorousness	Sonorous	Non-sonorous
Occurrence	Found in combined state. **Exception**: Only noble metals are found in the free state.	Found in the free state as well as in the combined state.

78. (a) **Distillation process**

Process: The solution of copper sulphate is taken in a round bottom flask called distillation flask. A thermometer and a condenser, known as Liebig's condenser, are attached with the round bottom flask with the help of adapters. Liebig's condenser is a long glass tube enclosed in a jacket of glass. Cold water is circulated through the glass jacket continuously. The condenser leads to another flask called receiver to collect the liquid that gets separated from the solid during the process of distillation. The distillation flask is placed on a tripod stand and heated with the help of a Bunsen burner.

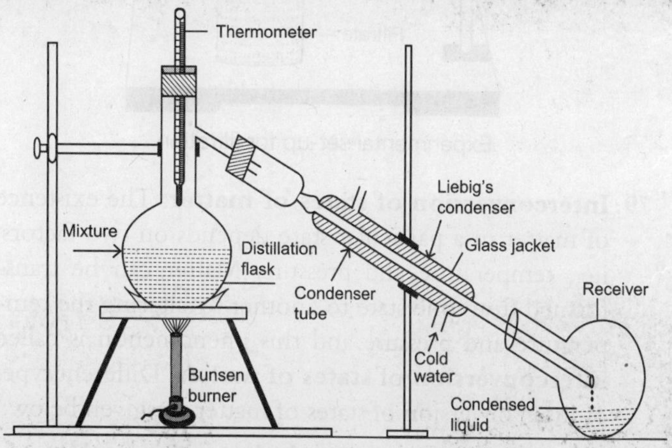

Experimental set-up for distillation

Observation: The solution starts boiling and water vapour obtained is passed through Liebig's condenser where it is converted to water due to condensation and is collected in the receiver. A solid residue is observed in the distillation flask.

Conclusion: Water present in the solution is vaporized leaving behind the non-volatile solid, i.e., copper sulphate in the distillation flask and thus constituents of the copper sulphate solution are separated.

(b) **Filtration**

All sorts of insoluble solids can be separated from the liquid in this process.

Process: A mixture of sawdust and water is taken in a beaker. A filter paper is folded in the form of a cone and fitted into a funnel by moistening it with a few drops of water. The mixture is poured gently into the filter cone and collected into another beaker.

Observation: The liquid collected is clear and transparent. Sawdust is found over the filter paper.

Conclusion: The mixture of sawdust and water is separated through the filtration process. The clear liquid that is collected in the other beaker is called a filtrate and solid particles retained on the filter paper are known as a residue.

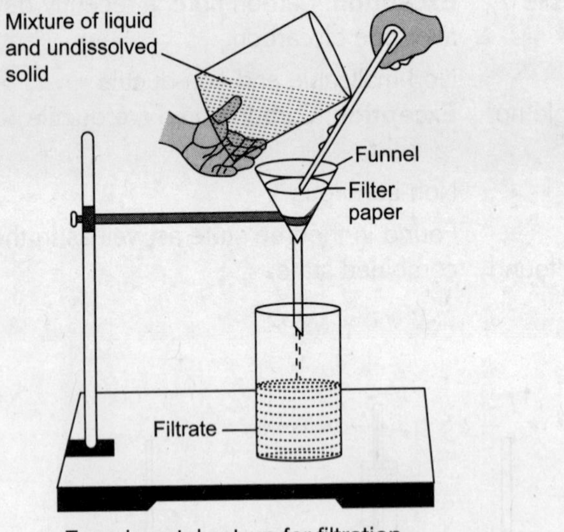

Experimental set-up for filtration

79. Interconversion of states of matter: The existence of matter in a particular state depends on two factors, i.e., temperature and pressure. Matter can be transformed from one state to another by altering the temperature and pressure and this phenomenon is called **interconversion of states of matter**. Different types of interconversion of states of matter are given below:

(i) **Melting**: The process which involves the change in state of matter from a solid to a liquid by heating is called melting or fusion. The temperature at which a solid changes into a liquid on heating at normal atmospheric pressure is called the melting point of that solid.

Example: Ice changes to water at 0°C under normal atmospheric pressure. Hence, 0°C is called the melting point of ice.

(ii) **Boiling**: The process which involves the change in state of matter from a liquid to a gas from the bulk of the liquid by heating is called boiling. The temperature at which the liquid changes into the gas from the bulk of the liquid by heating at normal atmospheric pressure is called the boiling point of that liquid.

Example: Water changes to water vapour at 100°C under normal atmospheric pressure. Hence, 100°C is called the boiling point of water.

(iii) **Condensation**: The process which involves the change of matter from a gas to a liquid on cooling is called condensation.

Example: Conversion of water vapour or steam to water.

(iv) **Solidification**: The process involving the change of matter from a liquid to a solid on cooling is called solidification or freezing. The temperature at which freezing occurs at normal atmospheric pressure is called the freezing point of that liquid.

Example: Water changes to ice at 0°C under normal atmospheric pressure. Hence, 0°C is called the freezing point of water.

Generally solids expand on melting and liquids contract on freezing.

(v) **Sublimation**: The process by which some solid substances directly change into the vapour state without passing through the intermediate liquid state is called **sublimation**. The solid obtained on cooling the vapour is called **sublimate** and the vapour formed is called **sublime**.

Examples: Camphor, iodine, etc., get converted to their respective vapour states directly under normal atmospheric pressure.

80. Separation of the components (KNO_3 [potassium nitrate] + carbon + sulphur) of gunpowder

Procedure: Carbon disulphide is added to a beaker containing gunpowder, and sulphur gets dissolved in carbon disulphide. This mixture is then filtered with the help of a filter paper. The filtrate obtained is taken in a flat vessel and exposed to air till carbon disulphide vaporizes leaving behind sulphur. The residue obtained contains carbon powder and nitre. It is taken in a beaker containing hot water. Nitre dissolves in hot water and this mixture is then filtered using a filter paper. Carbon powder is left on the filter paper as a residue which is collected after drying. The filtrate, on evaporation to dryness by heating, gives solid nitre. Thus, the constituents of gunpowder are separated.

81. (a) Rate of evaporation (transpiration) is maximum in the summer afternoons as temperature is maximum in the afternoon.
(b) Evaporation of a perfume takes heat from the body and we get a cooling sensation.
(c) Due to weak adhesive forces between waxy material and water, the leaves of submerged aquatic plants are protected from decay.
(d) Rate of evaporation is more in non-coastal areas since humidity is less. Rate of evaporation is less in coastal areas since humidity is high. Thus, sweat does not evaporate readily in coastal areas.

82. A mixture of sand and iodine (sublimable substance) can be separated by a simple physical process called sublimation process.

Sublimation: A mixture of sand and iodine is taken in a flat basin and a funnel is inverted over it. The outer surface of the funnel is wrapped with a water-soaked filter paper and the open end of the stem of the funnel is plugged with a piece of cotton to prevent vaporization. The basin is kept in a sand bath. The sand bath is placed over a wire mesh kept on a tripod stand and then is heated gently with the help of a Bunsen burner.

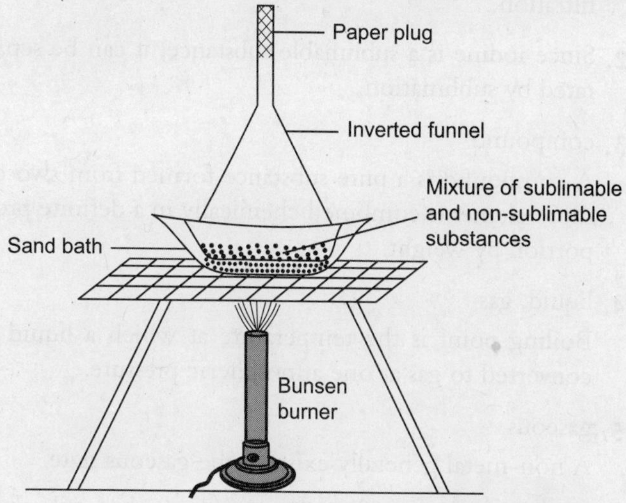

Experimental set-up for sublimation

Observation: A violet-coloured fume is observed which condenses as violet powdery substance when it comes in contact with the colder wall of the funnel. The process of heating is continued till the evolution of violet vapour is observed.

Conclusion: Since iodine is a sublimable substance, it sublimes and then condenses as a violet powder. The substance left over on the basin is sand which does not sublime. Iodine is scrapped off from the wall of the funnel and thus the mixture is separated.

83. The comparative study of three different states of matter with respect to the arrangement of molecules and other related parameters is presented below in a tabular form.

Parameter	Solids	Liquids	Gases
Packing of molecules	Very closely packed	Loosely packed	Very loosely packed
Intermolecular space	Negligible	More than that among the solid molecules	Maximum among the three states of matter
Intermolecular force of attraction	Maximum among the three states of matter	Less than that among the solid molecules	Negligible
Type(s) of movement of molecules	Vibrate to and fro about a fixed position	Vibrate to and fro, rotate around their own axis and move from one place to other within a certain limit	Vibrate to and fro, rotate around their own axis and move from one place to other randomly in all directions with much higher speed than that of the liquid molecules

Competition Wing

Level 1: Apply Your Concepts

1. Sawdust and water mixture can be separated by only filtration.
2. Since iodine is a sublimable substance, it can be separated by sublimation.
3. compound
   A compound is a pure substance formed from two or more elements combined chemically in a definite proportion by weight.
4. liquid, gas
   Boiling point is the temperature at which a liquid is converted to gas at one atmospheric pressure.
5. gaseous
   A non-metal generally exists in the gaseous state.
6. Evaporation is a surface phenomenon, whereas boiling is a bulk phenomenon.
7. Solid state is incompressible as the force of attraction is strong and intermolecular space is less.
8. A pure substance is homogeneous in nature.
9. Iodine is a lustrous non-metal.
10. The components of a compound are separated by chemical methods.
11. Graphite is a non-metal and is a good conductor of electricity.
12. Decrease in humidity increases the rate of evaporation.
13. A mixture of two solids is generally heterogeneous while a mixture of any number of gases is homogeneous in nature.
14. The mixture of an iron filing and sand can be separated by magnetic separation.
15. To separate soluble solids from a liquid the suitable methods are evaporation and distillation.
16. Gases have the maximum intermolecular spaces.
17. Metals are highly ductile and malleable.
18. Evaporation takes place from the surface of a liquid, and hence, it is a surface phenomenon.
19. Pure substances are made up of identical molecules, and hence, are homogeneous in nature.
20. Tellurium is a metalloid, and hence, it shows properties of both metals and non-metals.
21. Iodine is a lustrous non-metal.
22. As the density of sodium is less than that of water, it floats on water.
23. Ammonium chloride undergoes sublimation, and hence, it is a sublimable substance.
24. The constituents of a compound do not retain their properties, and hence, these cannot be separated by physical methods.
25. Sublimation is the process of the conversion of a solid to its gaseous state.
26. Pure substances → Elements → Metals → Monoatomic state.
   Hence, the correct order is CABD.
27. Steel is a homogeneous mixture. Solid–solid mixtures are either homogeneous or heterogeneous.
   Hence, the correct option is (c).
28. Sublimation → Iodine + sand; iodine undergoes sublimation on heating.
   Filtration → Sawdust + water; sawdust floats on water.
   Evaporation → NaCl + water; NaCl is soluble in water and undergoes evaporation on heating.
   Hence, correct option is (d).
29. Since water and petrol are immiscible liquids, they form a heterogeneous mixture.
   Hence, the correct option is (a).
30. A drop of water contains millions of molecules of water.
   Hence, correct option is (c).
31. Germanium has the properties of metals as well as non-metals, hence, it is a metalloid.
   Hence, correct option is (d).
32. The process is decantation as mud being heavier than water settles down at the bottom due to gravity and separates from water.
   Hence, correct option is (a).
33. Lime water is a saturated solution of calcium hydroxide, hence, it is a mixture.
   Hence, correct option is (a).
34. Water sticks to glass due to adhesive forces acting between water and glass.
   Hence, correct option is (a).

35. The temperature at which a solid gets converted into a liquid is called melting point.

Hence, correct option is (a).

36. Air is a homogeneous mixture of different gases.

Hence, correct option is (d).

37. During the formation of a mixture the constituent substances are mixed physically, and hence, there is no change in molecular composition during the formation of mixtures.

Hence, correct option is (d).

38. Bromine is a liquid, and hence, it possesses stronger intermolecular forces of attractions than gases.

Hence, correct option is (b).

39. Gases have the maximum intermolecular spaces, and hence, they diffuse in each other, forming a homogeneous mixture.

Hence, correct option is (a).

40. In washing soda (Na_2CO_3), the constituents are combined chemically in a fixed ratio of their weights, and hence, it is a compound.

Hence, correct option is (a).

41. Solids have strong intermolecular forces of attraction, and hence, carbon and potassium possess strong forces of attraction.

Hence, correct option is (d).

42. Soft metals are sodium and potassium

Hence, correct option is (a).

43. Carbon fibre, a recently developed allotrope of carbon is ductile and has high tensile strength.

Hence, correct option is (d).

44. Sand is insoluble in water, hence, it can be separated by filtration. Glucone-D is soluble in water, hence, it can be separated by distillation and water is collected separately.

Hence, correct option is (c).

45. Rate of evaporation is directly proportional to surface area of the liquid. This is because more number of surface molecules are exposed to atmosphere which gain kinetic energy and escape into atmosphere.

Hence, correct option is (c).

46. (2) A mixture of sawdust and water is taken in a beaker.
(3) A filter paper is folded in the form of a cone and fitted into a funnel by moistening it with a few drops of water.
(1) The mixture is poured gently into the filter cone and collected into another beaker which is called a filtrate.
(4) The solid retained on the filter paper is called a residue.

Hence, correct option is (d).

47. The force of attraction between similar molecules is called a cohesive force and that between dissimilar molecules is called an adhesive force. Adhesive forces act between water molecules and glass molecules. Due to stronger adhesive forces over cohesive forces, water shows concave meniscus in a narrow glass tube.

Hence, correct option is (a).

48. Iron is an element and rust is a compound of iron in which iron does not retain its properties. Hence, rust does not liberate hydrogen gas with dilute sulphuric acid and no effervescence is observed in container Y.

Hence, correct option is (b).

49. Petrol is a highly volatile liquid and undergoes evaporation, which causes cooling. Rate of evaporation is directly proportional to the surface area of the liquid. In the case of container 'Y,' the rate of evaporation is more, and hence, decrease in temperature is more.

Hence, correct option is (b).

50. Odonil undergoes sublimation, i.e., solid is converted into vapour state.

Hence, correct option is (a).

51. Tongues of dogs (upon exposure to atmosphere) enable the saliva to undergo evaporation which causes cooling. Hence, the body temperature decreases.

Hence, correct option is (a).

52. Since camphor is insoluble in water, therefore, it can be separated by filtration. Common salt from water can be separated by distillation.

Hence, correct option is (a).

53. In a solid, the molecules are closely packed due to strong forces of attraction, and hence, thermal expansion of solids is least among the three states of matter.

Hence, correct option is (b).

54. In the case of a wax-coated glass and plastic tube, cohesive forces are predominant over adhesive forces, and hence, water shows convex meniscus in a narrow wax-coated glass and plastic tubes.

Hence, correct option is (c).

55. Rust is a compound (hydrated ferric oxide). Iron powder is an element.

Hence, correct option is (b).

56. Rate of evaporation is inversely proportional to humidity. In non-coastal areas humidity is less when compared to coastal areas, and hence, rate of evaporation of water is more in a non-coastal area when compared to a coastal area.

Hence, correct option is (b).

57. Naphthalene balls and camphor undergo sublimation.

Hence, correct option is (d).

58. A $\rightarrow$ b Sodium is an element as it is made up of same atoms.

B $\rightarrow$ c NaCl is a compound because it is made up of sodium and chlorine in a fixed ratio by mass.

C $\rightarrow$ d Sulphur in water is a heterogeneous mixture as the component is non-uniformly distributed.

D $\rightarrow$ a Sugar in water is a homogeneous mixture as both the components are uniformly distributed.

59. A $\rightarrow$ d In boiling process, water changes into vapour.

B $\rightarrow$ c In melting process, ice changes into water.

C $\rightarrow$ b In condensation, water vapour changes into water.

D $\rightarrow$ a In freezing process, water changes into ice.

60. A $\rightarrow$ b In distillation process, the non-volatile component sodium chloride can be separated from water.

B $\rightarrow$ c Sawdust remains suspended in the water and separated by filtration.

C $\rightarrow$ a mixture of sodium chloride and ammonium chloride can be separated by sublimation as ammonium chloride is sublimable.

D $\rightarrow$ e Sand being heavier, settles down at the bottom and can be separated by sedimentation.

E $\rightarrow$ d Iron is magnetic and sulphur is non-magnetic in nature.

Level 2: Review Your Concepts

61. In gases, molecules possess all three types of molecular movements.

Some examples are: Water kept in a kettle and subjected to heating, Perfume coming out from a bottle etc.

62. X: Slightly compressible - This refers to liquids. Liquids are slightly compressible compared to solids which are incompressible.

Y: Physical state with no definite volume - This refers to gases. Gases do not have a definite volume; they fill the volume of their container.

Z: Negligible intermolecular space - This refers to solids. Solids have particles packed closely together with little to no space between them.

Using the above identifications:

A: Solid to Liquid

B: Liquid to Gas

C: Gas to Liquid

D: Liquid to Solid

E: Solid to Gas (sublimation)

F: Gas to Solid (deposition)

So:

A is Melting or Fusion

B is Vaporization or Boiling

C is Condensation

D is Freezing or Solidification

E is Sublimation

F is Deposition or Crystallization.

63. Between water and glass molecules, adhesive forces continually act which are predominant over cohesive forces, and hence, water droplets are observed on the inner walls of the glass tube X. In the case of mercury cohesive forces are more than adhesive forces, and hence, mercury droplets are not observed on the inner walls of 'Y.'

64. The force of attraction between similar molecules is called a cohesive force and that between dissimilar molecules is called an adhesive force. Between water and cotton molecules adhesive forces act which are predominant over cohesive forces. As a result cotton clothes can be easily made wet than synthetic clothes.

65. In solids, strong intermolecular forces of attraction are present between the molecules due to which they expand less on heating.

66. The process of conversion of a solid state to a vapour state directly without passing through the intermittent liquid state is called sublimation. Camphor undergoes sublimation at atmospheric pressure. As a result, camphor pellets should be preserved in air-tight containers.

67. Between water and cotton adhesive forces are more predominant over cohesive forces. But adhesive forces between water and oil are weak. As a result,

cotton clothes are more easily wettable in water than in oil.

68. Cotton has the property of absorbing sweat. When this is exposed to atmosphere sweat undergoes evaporation which causes cooling, and hence, we feel cool by wearing cotton clothes in summer.

69. Ice present in a glass tumbler starts melting by absorbing heat from the air around the glass. As a result, moisture present in the air gets condensed and forms tiny water droplets on the outer walls of the container.

70. Gas particles move with high speeds and the intermolecular spaces in gases are very large. These properties of gases allow a gas to diffuse easily into another. As a result, the smell of a perfume which is in vapour state reaches quickly to the other corner of the room.

71. The rate of evaporation depends on the surface area of liquids. The more is the surface area of the liquid, the more is the rate of evaporation of the liquid. This is due to increased number of surface molecules. When these surface molecules are exposed to atmosphere, they gain energy and escape into atmosphere. Hence, hot milk in the saucer gets cooled.

72. In winters, morning temperature is very low. As a result, moisture present in the atmosphere condenses and forms tiny droplets of water. These droplets appear as fog and mist.

73. Evaporation is the process of conversion of a liquid into a gas. During this process the energy required for the conversion of the liquid into the gas is taken from the surroundings, and as a result, the temperature of the surroundings decreases, i.e., evaporation causes cooling. When a wet cloth is placed on the forehead, water present in the cloth slowly undergoes evaporation, and hence, temperature of the body decreases.

74. The reagent is carbon disulphide which dissolves sulphur. Charcoal can be separated by filtration. Sulphur from the solution can be separated by evaporation.

75. Once we come out of the swimming pool in summer, water droplets present on the body undergo evaporation (slowly) which causes cooling, and as a result we feel shivering.

Level 3: Assess Your Concepts

76. Milk is sent through an atomiser and as a result it is converted into small droplets, consequently the surface area increases. Due to the increased surface area, rate of evaporation of water becomes more at room temperature. In this way, the entire water undergoes evaporation leaving behind fat particles which are converted into powder by adding other ingredients.

77. The properties of mercury that are exploited in its usage as a thermometric liquid are:

    (a) Low thermal expansion compared to other liquids (thermometers can be made small, compact and convenient to use)

    (b) Weaker adhesive forces between mercury and glass (Doesn't stick to the glass during its expansion and contraction with the change in temperature. Hence, is clearly visible)

    (c) Shiny surface of mercury (Facilitates easy reading)

    (d) Higher boiling point compared to other thermometric liquids (Facilitates its uses in measuring higher temperatures)

    Gallium is used for high temperature thermometers because of its low melting point and high boiling point.

78. Mercury expands on heating and has weak forces of attraction towards glass. Hence, it is used in thermometers. As gallium possesses high boiling point it is used for the measurement of high temperatures.

79. The rate of evaporation depends upon the nature of the liquid. In case of alcohol, the surface molecules possess high kinetic energy and as a result they easily escape into atmosphere, i.e., the rate of evaporation is more. As evaporation causes cooling, decrease in temperature in case of alcohol is more. Due to this reason, a decrease in the level of mercury is observed in the case of container B having alcohol but not in the case of A having water.

80. Naturally occurring diamonds are associated with some impurities. These impurities have characteristic colours and retain these colours in diamonds, hence, naturally occurring diamonds are found to be in different colours.

CHAPTER 2

Atomic Structure and Transformation of Matter

Remember

Before beginning this chapter, you should be able to:

- Classify materials around you
- Identify different states of matter solid, liquid, and gas

Key Ideas

After completing this chapter, you should be able to:

- learn about symbols of various elements.
- understand Dalton's atomic theory and different terms related to the structure of atom like atomic number, mass number, electronic configuration, etc.
- learn about valencies of different elements and radicals and the method of determining the formulae.
- explain the transformation of matter, types of reactions, and balance chemical equations.

Scientific Crypt

A Tribute to John Dalton (1766 – 1844)

John Dalton was an English chemist and physicist. He is best known for his work in the development of atomic theory which facilitated the development of Chemistry as a separate science.

John Dalton was born on September 7, 1766 at Eagles field in Cumberland, England. Dalton was born into a Quarter family and at the age of 15 he started assisting his elder brother in running a Quarter school in nearby Kendal. At the age of 26 he came to Manchester and was appointed as a teacher of Mathematics and natural philosophy at the "New College" in Manchester.

During his life time he was amazed by earth's atmosphere which led him to do significant study on behaviour of gases. In 1803 on the basis of his work on mixture of gases, he formulated a law which is known as Dalton's law of partial pressure.

Dalton's greatest achievement is the formulation of the atomic theory which was developed through a series of observations based on the experiment on mixture of gases. His work on atomic theory paved the way for the future scientists in the development of modern atomic theory. In his honour a street had been named as John Dalton street in the centre of Manchester.

FUN TIME

CROSSWORD

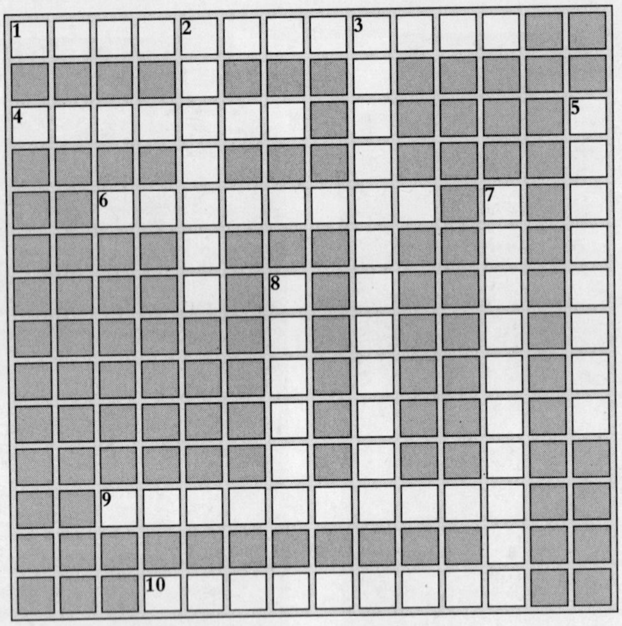

Across

1. Outermost shell of an atom.
4. A group of atoms having positive or negative charge.
6. _____ change involves change in the molecular composition of matter.
9. The sum of protons and neutrons.
10. The type of reaction due to the combination of two elements to form a new compound.

Down

2. The central part of the atom.
3. The Latin name of mercury.
5. The changes involved during melting of wax.
7. The symbol P is used for
8. Fundamental particle with positive charge.

INTRODUCTION

Matter and its basic constituents has been the great topic of interest for various scientific researches and studies from immemorial times. From those vigorous researches and experiments, it has been concluded that elements are the basic constituents of any matter, and the building block of an element is an atom. Since the contribution of element is vital for the study of matter, scientists all over the world started to name the elements for their convenience and for the purpose of exact identification. Consequently, the names of the elements were abbreviated to symbols in order to represent them in an easier and a more convenient way.

Symbolic Representation of Elements

In ancient days, alchemists were under the impression that some metals, such as iron could be converted into gold. However, this idea remained hypothetical and could not be realised in practice.

This hypothetical art of transmutation of some suitable metals into gold was called **alchemy**.

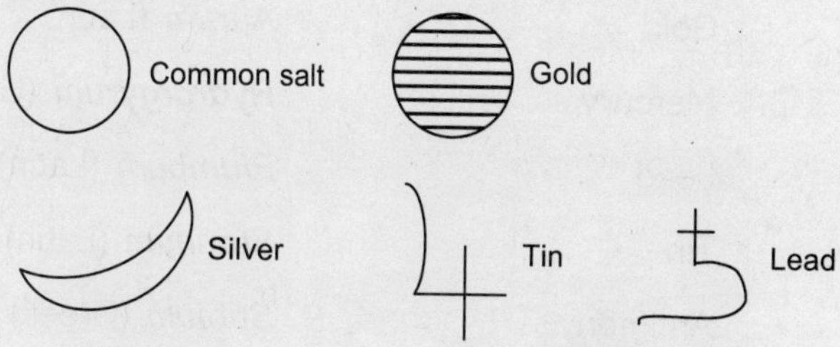

Figure 2.1 Examples of alchemist symbols

Symbols can be defined as the shorthand notations which represent a single atom of an element and generally consist of a letter or combination of letters derived from the name of the element. This system of writing symbols was suggested by Berzelius in the year 1814 to represent an atom of an element.

Important key points related to symbols of the elements are listed below.

1. In most cases, the first letter of the name of the element in capital letter is used as the symbol of the element.
2. When the names of two or more elements have the same initial letter (e.g., carbon and calcium), another letter from the name of the element is written in small letter along with the initial letter written in capital.

Table 2.1 Elements and their symbols as first letter of their names

Element	Symbol
Boron	B
Carbon	C
Fluorine	F
Hydrogen	H
Iodine	I
Nitrogen	N
Oxygen	O
Phosphorus	P
Sulphur	S
Vanadium	V
Uranium	U

Table 2.2 Elements and their symbols using two letters

Element	Symbol	Element	Symbol
Aluminium	Al	Chromium	Cr
Arsenic	As	Chlorine	Cl
Argon	Ar	Cobalt	Co
Barium	Ba	Palladium	Pd
Beryllium	Be	Platinum	Pt
Bromine	Br	Selenium	Se
Bismuth	Bi	Silicon	Si
Calcium	Ca	Strontium	Sr
Cadmium	Cd		

3. For some elements, the symbols are derived from their Latin, Greek or German names.

Table 2.3 Elements with symbols derived from their foreign names

Name of the element	Parent name	Symbol
Sodium	*Natrium* (Greek)	Na
Potassium	*Kalium* (Latin)	K
Iron	*Ferrum* (Latin)	Fe
Copper	*Cuprum* (Latin)	Cu
Silver	*Argentum* (Latin)	Ag
Gold	*Aurum* (Latin)	Au
Mercury	*Hydrargyrum* (Greek)	Hg
Lead	*Plumbum* (Latin)	Pb
Tin	*Stannum* (Latin)	Sn
Antimony	*Stibium* (Greek)	Sb
Tungsten	*Wolfram* (German)	W

Info Bytes!

The first systematic symbols for chemical elements were developed by Swedish chemist Jöns Jacob Berzelius in the early 19th century. He used one or two letters from the element's Latin name as its symbol.

The study of the atoms of different elements does not end with its nomenclature. The most important area of study of an atom is its structure. The term atom has been coined by the Greek philosophers. Indian philosopher, Maharshi Kannada named it as **Parmanu.**

In the 19th century, John Dalton, based on certain observations and experimental results, postulated a theory which regarded atoms as the fundamental building blocks of matter. This theory, based on the principle of indivisibility of atom, was well accepted throughout the century.

Dalton's Atomic Theory

In 1808, John Dalton proposed the atomic theory. Dalton's Atomic Theory is mainly based on the law of conservation of mass, the law of definite proportions and the law of multiple proportions which were formulated by Lavoisier.

The main postulates of Dalton's atomic theory are the following:

1. Matter is composed of tiny indivisible particles called **atoms**. They can neither be created nor destroyed nor transformed into atoms of another element.
2. Atoms of a given element are identical in all respects.
3. Atoms of different elements are different from each other in all respects.
4. Atoms of different elements take part in the chemical reaction and combine in a simple integral ratio to form compounds.
5. When elements react, the atoms may combine in more than one simple whole number ratio.

Dalton's atomic theory has been contradicted with the advancement of science and modified on the basis of further research and discoveries.

Konnect

Dalton himself had a unique condition called colour blindness. In fact, he was one of the first scientists to study colour blindness, which is sometimes referred to as 'Daltonism' in his honour!

Limitations of Dalton's Atomic Theory

Although Dalton's Atomic Theory built a strong ground for the scientists for the study of matter, it has some critical limitations also which are listed below:

1. With the discovery of subatomic particles, i.e., the electron, proton and neutron, it was concluded that atoms can be further divided.
2. Discovery of isotopes proved that atoms of the same element may possess different atomic weights, i.e., atoms of same elements may not be identical in all respects.

   Example: Isotopes of hydrogen are protium ($_1H^1$), deuterium ($_1H^2$) and tritium ($_1H^3$).
3. In some cases, atoms of different elements are found to have same mass number, i.e., atoms of different elements may be identical in this respect.

   Example: Calcium and argon are found to have the same mass number.

Though Dalton's atomic theory could not give convincing explanation to any of the above facts, it laid down the foundation for the development of modern atomic theory.

The basic postulate of Dalton's atomic theory which says that 'atoms are the tiniest particles of matter which take part in a chemical reaction, however accepted in modern atomic theory with experimental evidence.

However, discovery of radioactive elements led the scientists to focus on the divisibility aspect of the atom.

Later, experiments carried out by scientists like J. J. Thomson, Goldstein, Chadwick, etc., proved the presence of subatomic or fundamental particles in an atom. The changed perception that an atom is divisible made various scientists such as Rutherford, Bohr, Heisenberg, etc., to throw light on the structure of the atom precisely.

Structure of an Atom

An atom consists of three types of fundamental particles, namely, **protons, electrons and neutrons.**

Protons: Protons are **positively charged** particles carrying a charge of $+1.6 \times 10^{-19}$ Coulombs or $+4.8 \times 10^{-10}$ esu. The charge of one proton is taken as unit positive charge (+1). The mass of one proton is 1.67×10^{-27} kg. The mass of one proton is taken as 1 atomic mass unit (amu).

Electrons: Electrons are **negatively charged** particles carrying a charge equal to that of a proton, i.e., -1.6×10^{-19} coulombs or -4.8×10^{-10} esu. The charge of one electron is taken as unit negative charge (−1). The mass of an electron is very negligible and has a value of 9.1×10^{-31} kg.

The mass of an electron is $\frac{1}{1837}$ times that of the proton.

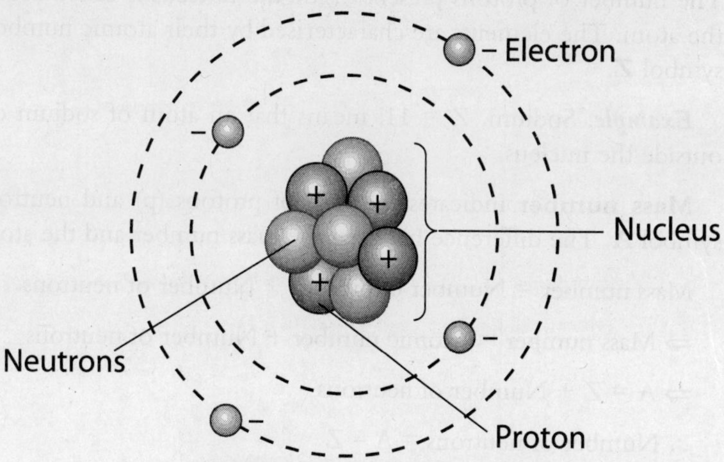

Figure 2.2 Structure of atom

Neutrons: Neutrons do not carry any charge. The mass of a neutron is only slightly greater than that of the proton that is equal to 1.72×10^{-27} kg. The mass of one neutron is also taken as 1 amu.

Various scientists proposed various ideas regarding the arrangement of fundamental particles in an atom which is called **structure of an atom**.

The modern concept of atom envisages the following arrangement of fundamental particles in an atom:

1. The protons and neutrons are concentrated in a small region at the centre of an atom. This central part is known as **nucleus**. The protons and neutrons present inside the nucleus are called **nucleons**.

2. The size of the nucleus is very small when compared to the size of the atom. This signifies the fact that there is a vast empty space in the atom.

3. Electrons revolve round the nucleus with high speed to overcome the strong electrostatic forces of attraction by the nucleus in definite fixed paths which are called **orbits or shells**.

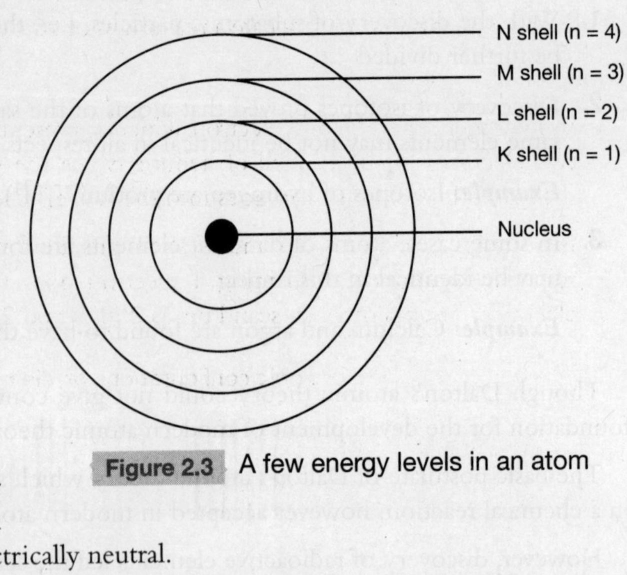

Figure 2.3 A few energy levels in an atom

4. In an atom, the number of electrons is equal to the number of protons inside the nucleus. Since the protons and electrons carry equal and opposite charges, an atom is electrically neutral.

5. The various orbits or shells are named as **K, L, M, N**... or **1, 2, 3, 4**...... and so on. The maximum number of electrons in the various orbits is 2, 8, 18, 32......, respectively. The energy of the orbit increases with the increase in distance from the nucleus.

6. The outermost shell is called **valence shell** and it can never have more than 8 electrons in any atom.

Atomic Number and Mass Number

The number of protons present inside the nucleus is called **atomic number.** It is equal to the number of electrons in the atom. The elements are characterised by their atomic numbers. The atomic number of an element is denoted by the symbol **Z**.

Example: Sodium, Z = 11, means that an atom of sodium contains 11 protons inside the nucleus and 11 electrons outside the nucleus.

Mass number indicates the sum of protons (p) and neutrons (n) present inside the nucleus. It is denoted by the symbol **A**. The difference between the mass number and the atomic number gives the number of neutrons.

Mass number = Number of protons + Number of neutrons

⇒ Mass number = Atomic number + Number of neutrons

⇒ A = Z + Number of neutrons

∴ Number of neutrons = A – Z

Example: Na → Z = 11, A = 23

Number of neutrons = A – Z = 23 – 11 = 12

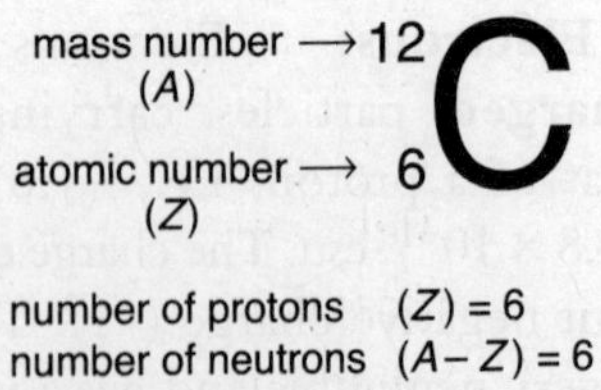

Figure 2.4 Depiction of Atomic number and mass number of carbon

The atomic number is the characteristic feature of each element. For the sake of convenience and universal application, all the elements are assigned unique symbols.
An element with its atomic number and mass number is represented as ${}_ZX^A$. The arrangement of electrons in various shells around the nucleus is called **electronic configuration**. In the building up of an atom, the electrons are added to the shells in increasing order of their energy.

Filling up of electrons in the shells follows certain rules. The maximum number of electrons in an orbit is equal to $2n^2$ where n denotes the number of the orbit or shell, i.e., 1, 2, 3, 4, etc. However, when the M shell is the valence shell, first it is filled with 8 electrons. The next 2 electrons go to the N shell and then the M shell gets filled with 10 more electrons because it can accommodate a maximum of 18 electrons as per the $2n^2$ formula.

Konnect

In Sanskrit, the word 'Anu' means 'atom'. Ancient Indian philosophers proposed ideas about the divisibility of matter and the existence of fundamental particles, or 'Anu', thousands of years ago.

Examples:

- In hydrogen, there is one electron which is present in the K shell and there are two electrons in the K shell of helium. Since the maximum capacity of the K shell is 2, the next electron goes into the L shell till it is filled with 8 electrons.
- In scandium, the K, L, M and N shells are filled with 2, 8, 8 and 2 electrons, respectively and the remaining 1 electron goes to the M shell. Hence, the electronic arrangement in scandium is 2, 8, 9 and 2.

Table 2.4 Electronic configurations of elements up to Z = 30

Element	Atomic number	Electronic configuration			
		K	L	M	N
Hydrogen	1	1			
Helium	2	2			
Lithium	3	2	1		
Beryllium	4	2	2		
Boron	5	2	3		
Carbon	6	2	4		
Nitrogen	7	2	5		
Oxygen	8	2	6		
Fluorine	9	2	7		
Neon	10	2	8		
Sodium	11	2	8	1	
Magnesium	12	2	8	2	
Aluminium	13	2	8	3	
Silicon	14	2	8	4	
Phosphorus	15	2	8	5	
Sulphur	16	2	8	6	
Chlorine	17	2	8	7	
Argon	18	2	8	8	
Potassium	19	2	8	8	1
Calcium	20	2	8	8	2
Scandium	21	2	8	9	2
Titanium	22	2	8	10	2
Vanadium	23	2	8	11	2
Chromium	24	2	8	13	1
Manganese	25	2	8	13	2
Iron	26	2	8	14	2
Cobalt	27	2	8	15	2
Nickel	28	2	8	16	2
Copper	29	2	8	18	1
Zinc	30	2	8	18	2

Geometrical Representation of an Element

The number and the arrangement of fundamental particles present in an atom can be shown diagrammatically by geometrical representation.

Examples: Oxygen (Z = 8)
Electronic arrangement = 2, 6

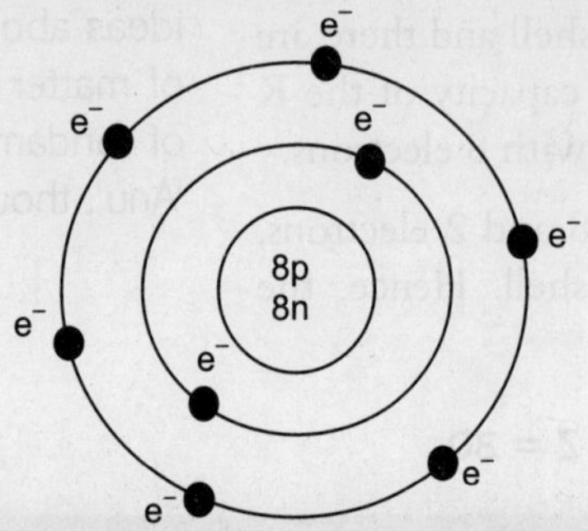

Phosphorus (Z = 15)
Electronic arrangement = 2, 8, 5

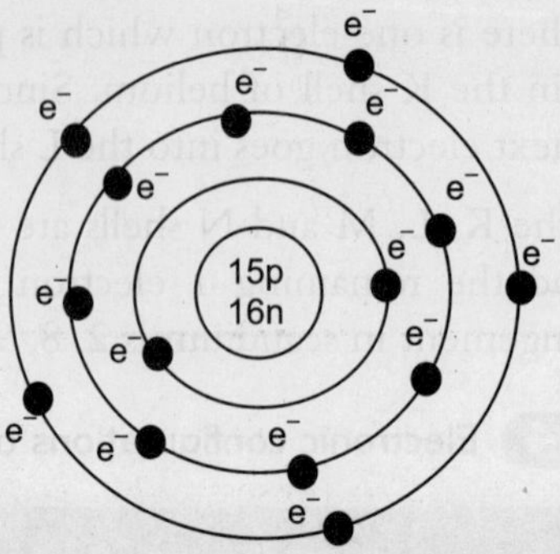

EXAMPLE 2.1 Calculate the number of neutrons in the following.

(a) $_{15}X^{31}$ **(b)** $_{92}U^{235}$ **(c)** $_{19}K^{39}$

SOLUTION

(a) Number of neutrons = 31 − 15 = 16
(b) Number of neutrons = 235 − 92 = 143
(c) Number of neutrons = 39 − 19 = 20

EXAMPLE 2.2 Give the electronic configuration and geometrical representation of the following elements.

(a) Flourine **(b)** Sodium **(c)** Chlorine **(d)** Carbon

SOLUTION

(a) Florine (Z = 9)
Electronic configuration = 2, 7

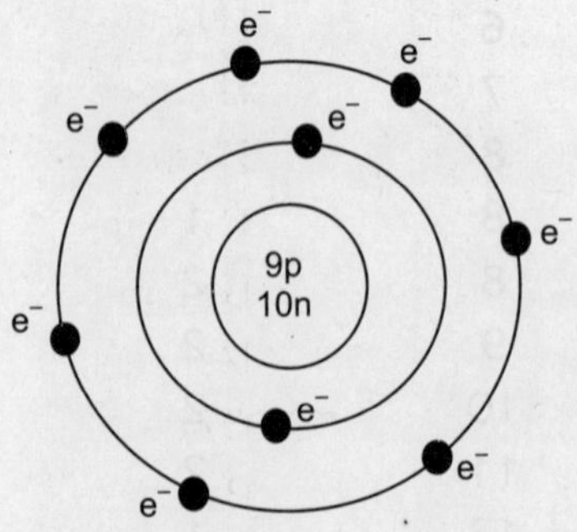

(b) Sodium (Z = 11)
Electronic configuration = 2, 8, 1

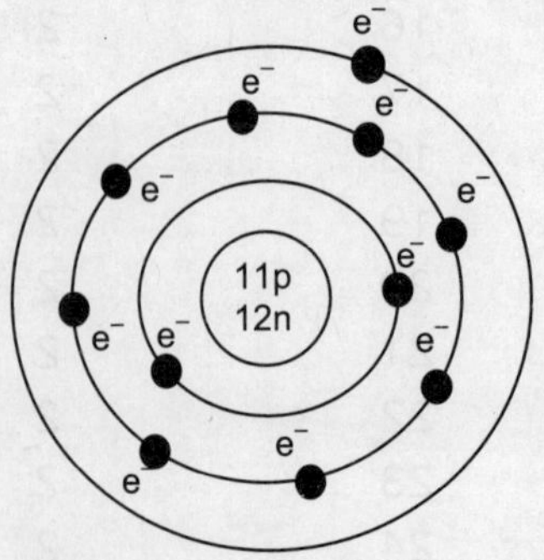

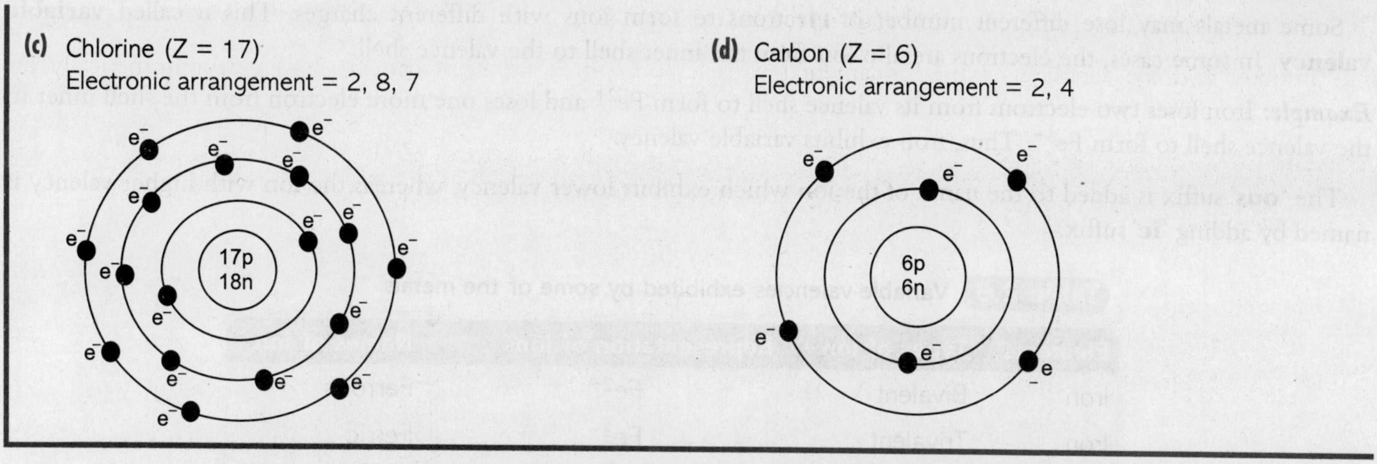

In nature, some elements are found to be quite stable as they are inactive towards chemical reactions. The atoms of these elements are found to possess eight electrons in their outermost shells. This condition is called **octet** and the resultant electronic configuration is called an **octet configuration**. For example, inert gases or noble gases namely neon, argon, krypton, xenon and radon possess the octet configuration. Among the noble gases, only helium has two electrons in the valence shell and the electronic configuration is called **duplet configuration**. Therefore, the octet or duplet configuration is considered to be responsible for the stability of elements.

The atoms of all other elements do not possess the octet or duplet configuration. Hence, the atoms of these elements have a tendency to gain this configuration either by gaining or losing electrons.

The atoms of different elements may lose or gain different number of electrons depending on their electronic arrangement. This gives rise to the concept of valency.

Valency

The number of electrons gained or lost by an atom of an element for attaining the stable octet or duplet configuration is called **valency**.

When an atom loses one or more electrons, the number of protons becomes more than the number of electrons and the ions so formed are left with a positive charge. This is called **positive valency**. When an atom attains stability by gaining one or more electrons, the number of electrons becomes more than the number of protons and the ion so formed becomes negatively charged. This is called **negative valency**.

The charge on the ion is corresponding to the number of electrons lost or gained. The ion may be monovalent, bivalent, trivalent and tetravalent which correspond to the valencies of 1, 2, 3 and 4, respectively.

Metals generally possess 1–3 electrons in their outermost shells and they tend to lose electrons to form positive ions called **cations**. Non-metals possess 4–7 electrons in their valence shells and they tend to gain electrons to form negative ions called **anions**.

Table 2.5 Valencies of different elements

Elements	Types of ion	Representation of ions	Names of ion
Sodium	Monovalent	Na^+	Sodium
Potassium	Monovalent	K^+	Potassium
Chlorine	Monovalent	Cl^-	Chloride
Fluorine	Monovalent	F^-	Fluoride
Iodine	Monovalent	I^-	Iodide
Hydrogen	Monovalent	H^-	Hydride
Hydrogen	Monovalent	H^+	Hydrogen
Zinc	Bivalent	Zn^{2+}	Zinc
Calcium	Bivalent	Ca^{2+}	Calcium
Barium	Bivalent	Ba^{2+}	Barium
Magnesium	Bivalent	Mg^{2+}	Magnesium
Oxygen	Bivalent	O^{2-}	Oxide
Oxygen	Bivalent	O_2^{2-}	Peroxide
Sulphur	Bivalent	S^{2-}	Sulphide
Aluminium	Trivalent	Al^{3+}	Aluminium
Chromium	Trivalent	Cr^{3+}	Chromium
Nitrogen	Trivalent	N^{3-}	Nitride
Phosphorus	Trivalent	P^{3-}	Phosphide

Some metals may lose different number of electrons to form ions with different charges. This is called **variable valency**. In some cases, the electrons are also lost from the inner shell to the valence shell.

Example: Iron loses two electrons from its valence shell to form Fe^{2+} and loses one more electron from the shell inner to the valence shell to form Fe^{3+}. Thus, iron exhibits variable valency.

The '**ous**' suffix is added to the name of the ion which exhibits lower valency, whereas the ion with higher valency is named by adding '**ic**' suffix.

Table 2.6 Variable valencies exhibited by some of the metals

Elements	Types of ion	Representation of ions	Names of ion
Iron	Bivalent	Fe^{2+}	Ferrous
Iron	Trivalent	Fe^{3+}	Ferric
Copper	Monovalent	Cu^{+}	Cuprous
Copper	Bivalent	Cu^{2+}	Cupric
Mercury	Monovalent	Hg^{+}	Mercurous
Mercury	Bivalent	Hg^{2+}	Mercuric
Tin	Bivalent	Sn^{2+}	Stannous
Tin	Tetravalent	Sn^{4+}	Stannic

The ions included in Tables 2.5 and 2.6 contain only one element. However, there are some charged species which contain more than one element.

A group of atoms possessing either positive or negative charge by losing or gaining one or more electrons is called **radical**. The positively charged radicals are ammonium radical (NH_4^+) and hydronium radical (H_3O^+). All other radicals are negatively charged.

Table 2.7 Some of the negatively– charged radicals

Formulae of radical	Names of radical
NO_2^-	Nitrite
NO_3^-	Nitrate
SO_3^{2-}	Sulphite
SO_4^{2-}	Sulphate
CO_3^{2-}	Carbonate
PO_4^{3-}	Phosphate
HCO_3^-	Bicarbonate or hydrogen carbonate
HSO_3^-	Bisulphite or hydrogen sulphite
HSO_4^-	Bisulphate or hydrogen sulphate
OH^-	Hydroxide
MnO_4^-	Permanganate
CrO_4^{2-}	Chromate
SiO_3^{2-}	Silicate
ZnO_2^{2-}	Zincate

In nature, a number of compounds are found. Some compounds are the combination of positive and negative ions or radicals. The following example explains the formation of NaCl from its constituent atoms.

Sodium (Z = 11) has the electronic configuration of 2, 8, 1. By losing one electron, it forms Na^+ ion which attains the configuration of neon, i.e., 2, 8. Chlorine (Z = 17) has the electronic configuration of 2, 8, 7. By gaining one electron, it forms Cl^- ion which attains the configuration of argon, i.e., 2, 8, 8. Since Na^+ and Cl^- ions carry opposite charges, a strong force of attraction binds the two ions together. Thus, the compound NaCl is formed.

The compounds are represented with the help of the shorthand notations called formulae which are derived from the symbols of the constituent elements. **Formula** represents a molecule of an element or compound and is a combination of the symbols of the constituent elements along with the number of atoms of individual elements present in a molecule.

Derivation of Formulae of Compounds from the Constituent Radicals

Whatever be the valencies of the constituent radicals, a chemical compound is always electrically neutral. That means, in a molecule of a compound, the positive valencies are balanced by the negative valencies.

Example: In a molecule of aluminium chloride, aluminium ion is trivalent and carries +3 charge and chloride ions are monovalent and carry −1 charge. In order to neutralise the +3 charge on the aluminium ion, three Cl^- ions are necessary. Thus, the formula can be written as $AlCl_3$.

The formula of a compound can be derived by using a shortcut method known as **criss-cross method.**

1. The positive radical is written first followed by the negative radical.

   Example: Ca^{+2}, Cl^-

2. The valencies of the ions or radicals are written below the radicals without positive or negative signs.

   Example: Ca^{+2}, Cl^-

   2 1

Table 2.8 Examples of different compounds with their molecular composition

Names of the compound	Formulae	Molecular compositions
Hydrochloric acid	HCl	1 hydrogen atom 1 chlorine atom
Nitric acid	HNO_3	1 hydrogen atom 1 nitrogen atom 3 oxygen atoms
Carbon dioxide	CO_2	1 carbon atom 2 oxygen atoms
Carbon monoxide	CO	1 carbon atom 1 oxygen atom
Sulphur dioxide	SO_2	1 sulphur atom 2 oxygen atoms
Sulphur trioxide	SO_3	1 sulphur atom 3 oxygen atoms
Nitrous oxide	N_2O	2 nitrogen atoms 1 oxygen atom
Nitrogen dioxide	NO_2	1 nitrogen atom 2 oxygen atoms
Nitrogen trioxide	N_2O_3	2 nitrogen atoms 3 oxygen atoms

(Continued)

Table 2.8 Continue

Nitrogen pentoxide	N_2O_5	2 nitrogen atoms 5 oxygen atoms
Phosphorus trioxide	P_2O_3	2 phosphorus atoms 3 oxygen atoms
Phosphorus pentoxide	P_2O_5	2 phosphorus atoms 5 oxygen atoms
Methane	CH_4	1 carbon atom 4 hydrogen atoms

3. The valencies should be interchanged and written as subscripts on right side of the respective ions.

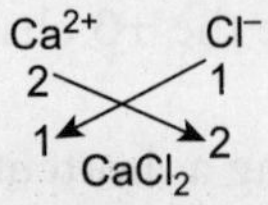

4. If the valencies have common factors, they are divided by the highest common factor.

Example:

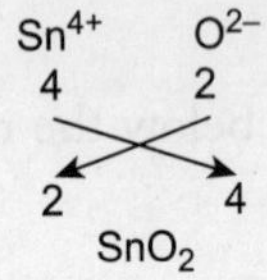

5. The radicals are enclosed in brackets; its number present in a molecule is more than one.

Example:

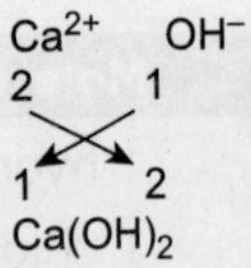

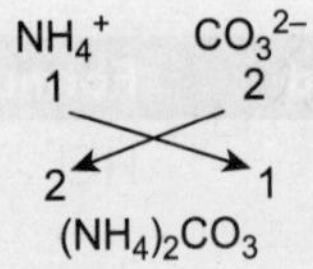

Nature is associated with a wide variety of chemical substances. Each substance has a definite molecular composition. Based on the molecular composition, the ratio of number of atoms of the constituent elements is indicated by a **chemical formula.**

Physical and Chemical Changes

The origin of the wide variety of chemical substances in different forms is attributed to the inherent tendency of the matter to undergo transformation. Matter can undergo transformation in two different ways as follows:

1. Transformation that involves the alteration in certain specific properties of matter like state, colour, texture, electrical conductivity, magnetic behaviour, etc., without the alteration of molecular composition is called **physical change.**

   Example: During melting of ice, solid ice melts to liquid water. In this transformation, the physical state of ice changes, but the molecular composition remains the same. Molecules of both ice and water are composed of two hydrogen atoms and one oxygen atom. Hence, this change is called physical change.

2. Transformation that takes place due to the alteration of molecular composition of matter is called **chemical change.**

Info Bytes!

Chemical equations are a way to depict chemical reactions in a concise manner. They show the exact number of atoms and molecules involved, ensuring the law of conservation of mass.

Example: Magnesium ribbon burns in presence of oxygen to form white-coloured powdery magnesium oxide. Magnesium is an element and contains only magnesium atoms. Oxygen is an element which consists of only oxygen atoms. But magnesium oxide is a compound and each molecule of it is composed of one magnesium atom and one oxygen atom.

Table 2.9 Comparative study of physical and chemical changes

Physical change	Chemical change
Molecular composition of the matter does not change.	Molecular composition of the matter changes.
No new substance is formed. Only the physical appearance or behaviour changes.	New substance is formed.
This change is called **temporary** or **reversible** because the previous form of the matter can easily be revived.	This change is called **permanent** or **irreversible** because the previous form of the matter cannot be revived by physical processes.

Table 2.10 Examples of physical and chemical changes

Physical changes	Chemical changes
Melting of wax	Burning of candle
Glowing of electric bulb	Electrolysis of water
Expansion of metals	Cooking of food
Changing of water into steam	Curdling of milk
Boiling of milk	Germination of seeds
Condensation of steam	Rusting of iron
Sublimation of camphor	Ripening of fruits
Freezing of water	Respiration
Liquifaction of gases	Blackening of silverware
Breaking of glass	Burning of LPG

Representation of a Chemical Change in Short Form Using Symbols and Formulae

The substances which undergo chemical change are called **reactants** and those formed as a result of the change are called **products**. The formulae of reactants are written on the left-hand side and the formulae of products are written on the right-hand side of an arrow. The different reactants and products are separated by a '+' sign. When a chemical change is represented in the form of an equation with the help of symbols and formulae of the reactants and the products, it is called **chemical equation**.

Example: $Mg + O_2 \rightarrow MgO$

Characteristics of Occurrence of Chemical Equations

In a chemical reaction, the conversion of reactants into products is often accompanied by certain features which can be observed.

Change in Colour

Some chemical reactions are marked by a change in colour. If two different-coloured liquids come together, they usually form a new colour. If a new colour appears after a couple of seconds or minutes, it can be recognised that a chemical reaction could have occurred.

Example: Lead nitrate solution + Potassium iodide $\longrightarrow$ Lead iodide + Potassium nitrate

Colourless Colourless Yellow coloured

The appearance of yellow colour indicates the occurrence of the chemical reaction in this case.

Ferrous sulphate $\xrightarrow{\Delta}$ Ferric oxide + Sulphur dioxide + Sulphur trioxide

Green coloured Reddish brown

Conversion of green colour to reddish brown colour indicates the progress of chemical reaction in this case.

However this is not always a chemical reaction indicator because there are many chemical reactions which occur without any characteristic change in colour.

Formation of a Precipitate

Some chemical reactions are characterised by the formation of an insoluble substance which stays behind, i.e., precipitate. A precipitate can be defined as a solid product which separates out from the solution during a chemical reaction.

Addition of barium chloride solution to an aqueous solution of sodium sulphate results in the formation of white precipitate of barium sulphate.

$$BaCl_2\,(aq) + Na_2SO_4(aq) \longrightarrow BaSO_4(s) + 2NaCl(aq)$$

Change in State

Some chemical reactions are characterised by a change in state. For example, when wax is burnt water vapour and carbon dioxide are formed. Now, molten wax is a liquid where as carbon dioxide is a gas. This means that during the combustion reaction of wax, the physical state changes from solid to liquid and then to gas.

Evolution of a Gas

Some chemical reactions are characterised by the evolution of a gas. This may be observed in the form of appearance of bubbles or colour of gas formed or smell of gas formed.

Lead nitrate $\xrightarrow{\Delta}$ Lead oxide + Nitrogen dioxide + Oxygen

Reddish brown vapours

Hydrogen and oxygen react to form water. However, a chemical equation should be written based on the principle that atoms can neither be created nor destroyed. This signifies the fact that the number of atoms of each element on either side must be equal. Such an equation is called **balanced chemical equation**.

The above example, $Mg + O_2 \rightarrow MgO$ is an unbalanced chemical equation. This is also called skeletal equation. A systematic procedure (as given below) should be followed for balancing the chemical equation.

Step I The number of times an element occurs on both sides is counted. The element which appears the least number of times is balanced first.

Step II Among the elements with same frequency of occurrence, the metallic element is balanced first followed by non-metallic element.

Step III Hydrogen and oxygen are balanced at the end.

A chemical change represented in this way is called a word equation.

The reaction of burning of magnesium in the presence of oxygen written in the form of a word equation.

Magnesium + Oxygen $\rightarrow$ Magnesium oxide

The names of the reactants and products are written in the form of their formulae for the sake of convenience. This is known as a **skeletal equation**.

In this equation, the formulae represent a molecule of an element or a compound. In this equation, the number of atoms of different elements on the reactants side may not be equal to those in the products side. This is called a skeletal equation.

All the chemical reactions obey the law of conservation of mass. Hence, the number of atoms of each element on the reactants side should be equal to those on the products side.

For this the chemical equation should be balanced by keeping the suitable coefficients for the various reactants and products involved in the chemical reaction.

Information obtained from a balance chemical equation:

- The physical states of reactants and products (s, l and g in brackets represent solid, liquid and gas respectively)
- The number of molecules of reactants and products taking part in the reaction
- The energy changes involved in the chemical reaction

Example: $C(s) + O_2(g) \rightarrow CO_2(g)$ + 394 kJ/mol

Examples:

1. $Mg + O_2 \rightarrow MgO$
$Mg + O_2 \rightarrow 2MgO$
$2Mg + O_2 \rightarrow 2MgO$

Reactant	Element	Product
1	Mg	1
2	O	1
1	Mg	2
2	O	2
2	Mg	2

2. $KClO_3 \rightarrow KCl + O_2$
$2KClO_3 \rightarrow KCl + 3O_2$
$2KClO_3 \rightarrow 2KCl + 3O_2$

Reactant	Element	Product
2	O	2
1	K	1
3	O	2
1	Cl	1
2	K	1
2	Cl	1
6	O	6
2	K	2
2	Cl	2
6	O	6

3. $Fe(OH)_3 + H_2SO_4$ (dil) $\rightarrow Fe_2(SO_4)_3 + H_2O$
$2Fe(OH)_3 + 3H_2SO_4 \rightarrow Fe_2\ (SO_4)_3 + H_2O$
$2Fe(OH)_3 + 3H_2SO_4 \rightarrow Fe_2(SO_4)_3 + 6H_2O$

Reactant	Element	Product
1	Fe	2
1	S	3
5	H	2
7	O	13
2	Fe	2
12	H	2
3	S	3
18	O	13
2	Fe	2
3	S	3
12	H	12
18	O	18

Types of Chemical Reactions

Depending on the way the products are formed from the reactants, the reactions are classified into four different types. Four different types of chemical reactions—chemical combination, chemical decomposition, chemical displacement and chemical double displacement are described below with the help of examples.

Chemical Combination

The reaction in which two substances, i.e., elements, compounds or both combine to form a new compound is called **chemical combination** reaction.

Representation: $X + Y \rightarrow XY$

Table 2.11 Types of chemical combinations with examples

Types	Examples
Element – element (synthesis)	$H_2 + Cl_2 \rightarrow 2HCl$
Element – compound	$2SO_2 + O_2 \rightarrow 2SO_3$
Compound – compound	$CaO + H_2O \rightarrow Ca(OH)_2$

Chemical Decomposition

The reaction in which a compound undergoes decomposition to form more than one substance in the presence of heat or light or electricity is called **chemical decomposition** reaction.

Representation: $AB \rightarrow A + B$

Table 2.12 Types of chemical decompositions with examples

Types	Examples
Thermal decomposition (in the presence of heat)	$2\,Pb(NO_3)_2 \xrightarrow{\Delta} 2PbO + 4NO_2 + O_2$
Photolytic decomposition (in the presence of light)	$2HOCl \xrightarrow{\text{light}} 2HCl + O_2$
Electrolytic decomposition (by passing electricity)	$2H_2O \xrightarrow{\text{electricity}} 2H_2 + O_2$

Chemical Displacement

The chemical reaction in which the more reactive element displaces the less reactive element from its salt solution of its aqueous solution is called **chemical displacement reaction**.

Representation:

- $X + YZ \rightarrow XZ + Y$

  X is a more reactive element than Y.
- $Y + XZ \rightarrow$ No reaction

  Y cannot displace X from its compound because it is less reactive than X.

Activity

When a few pieces of zinc are dipped in green-coloured ferrous sulphate solution, the colour disappears after some time and iron is found to be deposited. This phenomenon takes place because zinc is a more active metal than iron, and hence, it displaces iron from ferrous sulphate.

$Zn + FeSO_4 \rightarrow ZnSO_4 + Fe$

When copper is added to the ferrous sulphate solution, no change is observed. From this observation, it can be concluded that copper is a less active metal than iron.

$Cu + FeSO_4 \rightarrow$ No reaction

Some metals liberate hydrogen gas when they are treated with acids such as HCl and dilute H_2SO_4. Such metals are more active than hydrogen since they have the ability to displace hydrogen from acids. The metals which cannot displace hydrogen from acids are considered as less active metals than hydrogen.

Depending on the relative tendency of one metal to displace another metal from its compound, the metals are arranged in a series of decreasing order of reactivity. This is called **metal reactivity series.**

The more reactive metal displaces the less reactive metal from its compound.

Table 2.13 Metal reactivity series

Metal	Symbol	
Potassium	K	(Most reactive metal)
Sodium	Na	
Calcium	Ca	
Magnesium	Mg	
Aluminium	Al	
Zinc	Zn	Reactivity decreases
Iron	Fe	
Nickel	Ni	
Tin	Sn	
Lead	Pb	
Hydrogen	H	
Copper	Cu	
Mercury	Hg	
Silver	Ag	
Gold	Au	
Platinum	Pt	(Least reactive metal)

Chemical Double Decomposition/Double Displacement

The chemical reaction in which the two reactants (compounds) exchange their respective radicals and two new compounds are formed is called **double displacement reaction**.

Representation: $AB + XY \rightarrow AY + XB$

Where B and Y are the negative radicals which are exchanged to give AY and XB.

Example: $2KNO_3 + FeSO_4 \rightarrow K_2SO_4 + Fe(NO_3)_2$

In the above reaction, reactive K^+ (potassium ion) combines with SO_4^- (sulphate ion) and Fe^{2+} (ferrous ion) combines with NO_3^- (nitrate ion) to form two new compounds, K_2SO_4 and $Fe(NO_3)_2$.

During certain double displacement reactions, a solid substance is found to be deposited. The solid deposition is called precipitate and this type of reaction is called **precipitation reaction**.

Example: $NaCl + AgNO_3 \rightarrow NaNO_3 + AgCl \downarrow$

In the above reaction, during the exchange of radicals, silver chloride is formed which is insoluble in water. Therefore, it remains as a solid at the bottom of the container as **precipitate**.

Redox Reactions

Oxidation and reduction are the reactions which take place simultaneously. Usually, in a chemical reaction, if one substance undergoes oxidation, the other substance undergoes reduction. Therefore, these reactions are called **redox reactions.**

Info Bytes!

In redox reactions, one substance gets oxidized (loses electrons) while another gets reduced (gains electrons).

Oxidation: Addition of oxygen or removal of hydrogen is called oxidation.

Example:

$$2CO + O_2 \rightarrow 2CO_2$$

$$H_2S(g) + Cl_2(g) \rightarrow 2HCl(g) + S(s)$$

Reduction: Addition of hydrogen or removal of oxygen is called reduction.

Example:

$$CuO(s) + H_2(g) \rightarrow Cu(s) + H_2O(l)$$

$$H_2O(g) + C(s) \rightarrow H_2(g) + CO(g)$$

EXAMPLE 2.3

Derive the formulae of the following compounds.

(a) Calcium hydroxide **(b)** Copper(II) chloride

SOLUTION

(a) Calcium hydroxide

$Ca^{+2}OH^{-}$

$\therefore$ Formula is $Ca(OH)_2$

(b) Copper(II) chloride

$Cu^{+2}\ Cl^{-}$

$\therefore$ Formula is $CuCl_2$.

EXAMPLE 2.4

Give the necessary chemical equations and balance them.

(a) Reaction of red hot iron with steam to give Fe_3O_4 and hydrogen gas.

(b) Burning magnesium ribbon in an atmosphere of nitrogen.

(c) Displacement of copper from its sulphate salt solution by zinc.

SOLUTION

(a) $\underset{\text{(Steam)}}{3Fe + 4H_2O} \longrightarrow \underset{\text{Ferrosoferric oxide}}{Fe_3O_4} + 4H_2$

(b) $3Mg + N_2 \longrightarrow Mg_3N_2$

(c) $CuSO_4 + Zn \longrightarrow ZnSO_4 + Cu$

EXAMPLE 2.5

Explain the observable changes taking place during reactions of zinc with the aqueous solutions of HCl and $AgNO_3$, respectively.

SOLUTION

Zinc on reacting with HCl liberates hydrogen gas. The solution becomes clear due to the formation of zinc chloride.

$Zn + 2HCl \rightarrow ZnCl_2 + H_2\uparrow$

Zinc reacting with $AgNO_3$ solution displaces silver because zinc is more reactive than silver. Hence, the clear solution of $AgNO_3$ turns cloudy due to the formation of silver metal, and a solution of zinc nitrate is formed.

$Zn + 2AgNO_3(aq) \rightarrow Zn(NO_3)_2 + 2Ag$

As the reaction proceeds, tiny silver crystals will settle at the bottom, and the solution's colour might change depending on the concentration of the remaining silver nitrate and the newly formed zinc nitrate.

EXAMPLE 2.6 In the table given below, some compounds are listed. In each case identify the positive and negative radicals present in the compound.

	Compounds	Positive radical	Negative radical
(a)	SiO_2		
(b)	CuS		
(c)	H_2O_2		
(d)	BaO_2		
(e)	MgS		
(f)	$NaAlO_2$		
(g)	MnO_2		
(h)	LiH		
(i)	$KMnO_4$		
(j)	$CaSiO_3$		
(k)	CaF_2		
(l)	$HOCl$		
(m)	$CaCO_3$		

SOLUTION

	Compounds	Positive radical	Negative radical
(a)	SiO_2	Si^{4+}	O^{2-}
(b)	CuS	Cu^{2+}	S^{2-}
(c)	H_2O_2	H^+	O_2^{2-}
(d)	BaO_2	Ba^{2+}	O_2^{2-}
(e)	MgS	Mg^{2+}	S^{2-}
(f)	$NaAlO_2$	Na^+	AlO_2^-
(g)	MnO_2	Mn^{4+}	O^{2-}
(h)	LiH	Li^+	H^-
(i)	$KMnO_4$	K^+	MnO_4^-
(j)	$CaSiO_3$	Ca^{2+}	SiO_3^{2-}
(k)	CaF_2	Ca^{2+}	F^-
(l)	$HOCl$	H^+	ClO^-
(m)	$CaCO_3$	Ca^{2+}	CO_3^{2-}

POINTS TO REMEMBER

- ✔ An atom contains a small central positive part known as nucleus.
- ✔ Nucleus contains protons and neutrons which are together called nucleons.
- ✔ Electrons revolve round the nucleus in circular paths called orbits or shells.
- ✔ The orbits are named as K, L, M, N ------- and their energies increase with the increase in distance from the nucleus.
- ✔ The outermost shell of an atom is called valence shell.
- ✔ Metals contain less number of electrons in their valence shells and non-metals contain more number of electrons in their valence shells. Therefore, they form positive and negative ions, respectively.
- ✔ A group of atoms possessing either positive or negative charge is called radical.
- ✔ The formula of a compound should be written in such a way that the positive and negative charges are neutralised.
- ✔ Physical and chemical changes can be distinguished with respect to the change in molecular composition.
- ✔ Element–element combination reactions are called synthesis reactions.
- ✔ Displacement reactions are the reactions which involve displacement of a less active element from its compound by a more active element.
- ✔ In a double decomposition reaction, if one of the products formed is an insoluble solid, it is called precipitation reaction.

DW

PRACTICE QUESTIONS CLASSROOM WING

Very Short Answer Type Questions

Directions for questions from 1 to 5:
Fill in the blanks.

1. Name of the radical PO^{-3}_4 is ______.
2. Formulae of sodium sulphite and sodium sulphate are, respectively ______ and ______.
3. Generally ______ changes are reversible because there is no change in the ______ of the substance.
4. Decomposition of solid ammonium chloride is associated with ______ changes.
5. The number of atoms of a molecule or compound is balanced on either side of a chemical equation by keeping appropriate ______.

Directions for questions from 6 to 39:
For each of the questions, four choices have been provided. Select the correct alternative.

6. The number of electrons present in the K shells of hydrogen and helium are:
   (a) 2 and 1, respectively
   (b) 2 in both the elements
   (c) 1 and 2, respectively
   (d) 1 in both the elements
7. The charge possessed by permanganate is the same as ______ radical.
   (a) magnesium (b) bisulphate
   (c) sulphate (d) potassium
8. If the formulae of respective chlorides of X and Y are XCl_3 and YCl_4, respectively, then the valencies of X and Y are:
   (a) 3 and 2 (b) 3 and 4
   (c) 1 and 1 (d) 1 and 4
9. The formula of a compound when a positive radical 'A' with valency 2 and negative radical 'B' with valency 1 combine is ______.
   (a) B_2A (b) A_2B
   (c) AB_2 (d) AB
10. Sugar gets charred when treated with conc. H_2SO_4. This is an example of ______.
    (a) physical change
    (b) chemical change
    (c) simultaneous physical and chemical changes
    (d) chemical combination reaction
11. Melting of wax is a ______.
    (a) chemical change
    (b) decomposition reaction
    (c) both physical and chemical change
    (d) physical change
12. Corrosion of a metal involves change in ______.
    (a) chemical composition
    (b) only colour and shape
    (c) only density
    (d) malleability and ductility
13. Formation of clouds, mist and fog are the examples of ______.
    (a) chemical combination of O_2 and H_2O.
    (b) physical change which involves condensation of water vapour.
    (c) physical change which involves sublimation.
    (d) chemical change which involves absorption of huge amounts of energy.
14. The reaction $AgNO_3 + NaCl \rightarrow AgCl + NaNO_3$ is a ______ reaction.
    (a) chemical displacement
    (b) chemical combination
    (c) double displacement
    (d) decomposition
15. Which of the following elements is chemically inactive?
    (a) Nitrogen (b) Neon
    (c) Hydrogen (d) Copper
16. The formula of chloride of a corresponding metal is MCl_2. What is the valency of the metal?
    (a) 4 (b) 3
    (c) 1 (d) 2
17. What will be the formulae of the sulphate and sulphite of a trivalent metal?
    (a) $M_2(SO_4)_3$, $M_2(SO_3)_3$
    (b) MSO_4, $M_2(SO_3)_3$
    (c) M_2SO_4, M_2SO_3
    (d) MSO_4, MSO_3

18. Identify the atomic numbers of the pair of elements which possesses same number of electrons in the L and M shells.
(a) 12, 18 (b) 19, 20
(c) 18, 16 (d) 17, 18

19. Which of the following is a physical change?
(a) Dissolution of lime in water
(b) Dissolution of CO_2 in water at high pressure
(c) Dissolution of concentrated acid in water
(d) Electrolysis of water

20. Which of the following is not a chemical change?
(a) Passing of steam over red hot coke.
(b) Colour change of dil. nitric acid upon long standing.
(c) Absorption of moisture by P_2O_5.
(d) Absorption of moisture by $CaCl_2$.

21. Arrange the following points in a sequence for derivation of formulae of compounds.
(1) The valencies of the ions or radicals are written below the radicals without positive and negative sign.
(2) If the valencies have common factors, then they are divided by the highest common factor.
(3) The magnitude of valencies should be interchanged and written as subscripts on the right side of the respective ions.
(4) The positive radical followed by negative radical are written with their charges.
(5) If the radicals more than one atom, they are enclosed in brackets and the appropriate valency (more than one) written as subscripts outside the bracket.
(a) 2, 3, 4, 5, 1
(b) 4, 1, 3, 2, 5
(c) 1, 2, 3, 4, 5
(d) 4, 1, 2, 3, 5

22. What will be the formula of the sulphate of a trivalent metal that is M^{+3}?
(a) $M_2(SO_4)_3$
(b) MSO_4
(c) M_2SO_4
(d) MSO_3

23. Match the element in column A with the electronic configuration given in column B.

Column A	Column B
(A) Chlorine	(a) 2, 2
(B) Scandium	(b) 2, 8, 7
(C) Manganese	(c) 2, 8, 9, 2
(D) Beryllium	(d) 2, 8, 13, 2

(a) A → c, B → d, C → a, D → b
(b) A → d, B → a, C → b, D → c
(c) A → b, B → c, C → d, D → a
(d) A → d, B → a, C → c, D → b

24. The atomic numbers of three elements A, B and C are 10, 18 and 8, respectively. Identify the element which is chemically reactive.
(a) A (b) B
(c) C (d) both A and B

25. Heating solid ammonium chloride involves change in the ________.
(a) physical state only.
(b) physical state as well as chemical composition.
(c) colour only.
(d) both colour and volume only.

26. Arrange the following points in a sequence to draw the geometrical representation of $_{20}Ca^{40}$.
(1) Protons and neutrons are shown in the nucleus.
(2) Writing the electronic configuration of the atom.
(3) Arrange the electrons in shells around the nucleus following the electronic configuration.
(4) Calculation of the number of protons and neutrons.
(5) Identification of the atomic number and mass number of the atom.
(a) 5, 4, 3, 2, 1 (b) 5, 4, 1, 2, 3
(c) 1, 2, 3, 4, 5 (d) 3, 1, 2, 4, 5

27. Four types of reactions are given below in a particular order.
(a) Displacement reaction
(b) Combination reaction
(c) Double displacement
(d) Decomposition reaction

Follow this sequence to arrange the following reactions:
(a) A + B → AB.
(b) AB → A + B
(c) AB + C → CB + A
(d) AC + BD → AD + BC
(a) cadb (b) bacd
(c) bdac (d) acbd

28. Identify the coefficients of the products CuO and NO_2 formed respectively when hydrated copper nitrate is thermally decomposed.

$2Cu(NO_3)_2 . 6\,H_2O \rightarrow CuO + NO_2 + 6H_2O + O_2$

(a) 3, 4 (b) 2, 4
(c) 4, 5 (d) 2, 3

29. If the formula of a metal ion is M^{+2}, then the formula of its dihydrogen phosphate is

(a) $M_2(PO_4)_3$ (b) $MHPO_4$
(c) $M(H_2PO_4)_2$ (d) M_2HPO_4

30. Match the elements in column A with the valency exhibited by the element given in column B.

Column A	Column B
(A) Neon	(a) 4
(B) Oxygen	(b) 3
(C) Potassium	(c) 2
(D) Boron	(d) 1
(E) Silicon	(e) 0

(a) A → b B → c, C → d, D → e, E → a
(b) A → b, B → c, C → a, D → e, E → d
(c) A → e, B → d, C → a, D → b, E → c
(d) A → e, B → c, C → d, D → b, E → a

31. Identify the number of neutrons present in a pair of elements with atomic numbers 20 and 13, if their mass numbers are 40 and 27, respectively.

(a) 20 and 13
(b) 20 and 13
(c) 17 and 20
(d) 20 and 14

32. Tripositive ion, i.e., X^{3+} has 13 protons and 14 neutrons. Calculate the number of electrons present in the M shell of the neutral atom.

(a) 2 (b) 1
(c) 3 (d) 5

33. Which of the following is a chemical change?

(a) Formation of clouds
(b) Formation of rust
(c) Manufacture of milk powder from milk
(d) Formation of black coating on the walls of a tube light

34. The atomic numbers of the elements X, Y and Z are 2, 10 and 16, respectively. Identify the element which does not exist in monoatomic state.

(a) X (b) Z
(c) Y (d) X and Y

35. If a solid non-metal 'X' forms an oxide of type X_2O_5, then the valency of X is:

(a) 3 (b) 5
(c) 6 (d) 4

36. Assertion (A): The total mass of the protons of a boron atom is 6185 times the total mass of electrons.

Reason (R): Mass of one proton is 1837 times the mass of electron.

(a) Both A and R are true and R is the correct explanation for A.
(b) Both A and R are true but R is not the correct explanation for A.
(c) A is true and R is false.
(d) A is false and R is true.

37. Assertion (A): Sodium forms a monovalent ion.

Reason (R): Sodium loses only one electron from the second last shell.

(a) Both A and R are true and R is the correct explanation for A.
(b) Both A and R are true but R is not the correct explanation for A.
(c) A is true and R is false.
(d) A is false and R is true.

38. The difference in the number of electrons between the K and L and L and M shells is the same for an atom of an element X (M shell is the valence shell). And the difference of value is the number of valence electrons in the M shell of the other element Y. The electronic configurations of stable ions of X and Y are, respectively:

(a) 2, 8, 2 and 2, 8, 6
(b) 2, 8 and 2, 8
(c) 2, 8 and 2, 8, 8
(d) 2, 8, 8 and 2, 8, 8

39. The number of neutrons is equal to the number of protons present in the nucleus of two elements X and Y and their dinegative ions possess 8 electrons in the L and M shells, respectively. Then the ratio of mass numbers of the two elements is:

(a) 1 : 2
(b) 2 : 3
(c) 3 : 4
(d) 2 : 5

Directions for questions from 40 to 42:
Match the entries given in Column A with the appropriate ones in Column B. More than one suitable content of Column B can also be considered correct for an entry in Column A and some content given in Column B may not be the appropriate one for any entry in Column A.

40. Match entries in Column A with those in Column B.

Column A (Elements)	Column B (Clues)
(i) Oxygen	(A) 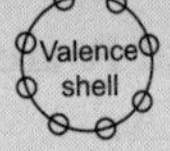
(ii) Neon	(B) 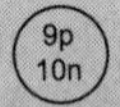
(iii) Potassium	(C) 
(iv) Hydride ion	(D) 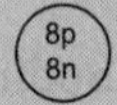
(v) Fluorine	(E) 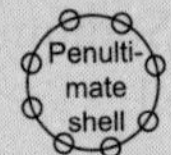

41.

Column A Name of radical	Column B Charge
A. Zincate	a. −3
B. Stannic	b. +1
C. Nitride	c. +2
D. Potassium	d. +4
	e. −2

42.

Column A	Column B
A. $X + Y \rightarrow XY$	a. Displacement reaction
B. $X + YZ \rightarrow XZ + Y$	b. Combination reaction
C. $AB + XY \rightarrow AY + XB$	c. Decomposition reaction
D. $AB \rightarrow A + B$	d. Double displacement reaction

Directions for questions from 43 to 62:
Answer the following questions.

43. The number of protons and neutrons in atom B is x and y, respectively. Write the correct representation of the atom.

44. Find the odd one out with respect to valency: Ferrous, Mercurous, Stannous, Cupric.

45. Which of the following: He, K^{+2}, Na, F^{-1} has an octet configuration in the valence shell?

46. Which of the following processes associated with copper, are chemical and which are physical changes?

(i) Alloying

(ii) Sonorousness

(iii) Formation of green patches

(iv) Conduction of electricity

47. Study the equation given below and find out the relation between c and d.

$$aC_3H_8 + bO_2 \rightarrow cCO_2 + dH_2O$$

48. Name two metals that can exhibit variable valency. Also give the names of radicals.

49. What is meant by synthesis reaction? Give an example.

50. $A + BC \rightarrow AC + B$, in this equation, compare the reactivities of A and B.

51. What is meant by electrolytic decomposition? Give an example.

52. Give reason for the stability of inert gases.

53. What is a valence shell? What is the maximum number of electrons it can have in an atom?

54. An atom is electrically neutral. Justify.

55. What is photolytic decomposition? Give an example.

56. Identify physical and chemical changes among the following:

(a) Boiling of milk

(b) Ripening of fruits

(c) Curdling of milk

(d) Melting of a candle

(e) Rusting of iron

(f) Blackening of silverware

57. Why should a chemical equation be balanced?

58. Dissolution of calcium oxide in water is which type of reaction?

59. In a double decomposition reaction, one of the products is insoluble. What type of reaction is that?

60. Potassium chlorate on strong heating gives potassium chloride and oxygen. What type of reaction is this?

61. Balance the following chemical equations:
(i) $NH_3 + Br_2 \rightarrow N_2 + NH_4Br$
(ii) $FeS_2 + O_2 \rightarrow Fe_2O_3 + SO_2$

62. In the following table, some compounds are listed. In each case, identify the positive and negative radicals present in the compound.

No.	Compounds	Positive radical	Negative radical
(i)	$CaSiO_3$		
(ii)	H_2SO_3		

Short Answer Type Questions

63. Arrange the following elements in the decreasing order of the number of electrons in their respective L shells.
(a) Boron (b) Lithium
(c) Helium (d) Oxygen
(e) Calcium

64. Arrange the following negative radicals in the decreasing order of the number of oxygen atoms present in a single radical.
(a) Chromate (b) Silicate
(c) Hydroxyl (d) Nitrite

65. Calculate the number of neutrons in the following:
(a) ${}_{15}X^{31}$ (b) ${}_{92}U^{235}$ (c) ${}_{19}K^{39}$

66. For each of the following reactions identify the products formed and balance the reaction.
(a) $NaCl + AgNO_3 \rightarrow$
(b) $Zn + HCl \rightarrow$

67. Define radical. Give some examples of bivalent negative radicals.

68. How do you distinguish a physical change from a chemical change?

69. In an atom of an element, K and N shells have the same number of electrons. The number of electrons in L and M shells is also the same. Determine the formula of the compound formed by this element and fluorine.

70. Mention different types of combination reactions with examples.

71. What is meant by thermal decomposition? Give an example.

72. Define double decomposition reaction. Give an example.

73. What is a chemical displacement reaction? Mention the condition required for it.

74. Distinguish between cations and anions.

75. In the following table, some commonly used positive and negative radicals are listed. Use the criss-cross method to obtain the formulae of the compound that is formed using the given radicals. Name the compound thus obtained.

No.	Positive radicals	Negative radicals	Formula	Name of the compound
1.	Al^{3+}	PO_4^{3-}		
2.	Ca^{2+}	NO_3^-		
3.	NH_4^+	SO_4^{2-}		
4.	Al^{3+}	C^{4-}		

76. Distinguish between atomic number and mass number with an example.

77. Draw the geometrical representation of sulphur.

78. Derive the formulae of the following compounds.
(a) Ammonium nitrate
(b) Ferrous sulphate

79. How do you distinguish metals and non-metals with respect to electronic arrangement?

80. Write the electronic configurations of the following elements.
(a) Magnesium (b) Silicon
(c) Sulphur (d) Argon

81. Explain the formation of sodium chloride.

82. Write the symbols of the following elements.
(a) Cadmium (b) Bismuth
(c) Silicon (d) Argon

83. Explain the observable change taking place during reaction of iron with the aqueous solutions of H_2SO_4 and $CuSO_4$, respectively.

84. A dipositive ion of an element X has 10 electrons and a dinegative ion of an atom of another element Y has 10 electrons. Calculate the number of electrons and protons in the respective atoms.

Essay Answer Type Questions

85. Explain in detail the modern structure of atom.

86. Give the electronic configuration and geometrical representation of the following elements.
   (a) Fluorine
   (b) Sodium
   (c) Chlorine
   (d) Carbon

87. Classify the chemical reactions into various types depending on the way the products are formed by giving suitable examples.

88. Mention the postulates and limitations of Dalton's atomic theory.

89. Write the steps in balancing a chemical equation with an example.

90. What is valency? Write short note on different types of valencies of cations with examples.

91. In the given chemical double displacement reaction $AB + XY \rightarrow AY + XB$, cation present in the reactant XY is barium ion and the anion present in the reactant AB is sulphate radical. In the product, AY, the cation has three protons and the number of electrons in the uni-negative anion is equal to the number of protons of argon atom. Identify the reactants and the products. Write the balanced chemical equations.

PRACTICE QUESTIONS COMPETITION WING

Level1: Apply your Concepts

Directions for questions from 1 to 15:
Fill in the blanks.

1. The symbol of calcium is ______.
2. Magnesium attains an octet configuration by ______ electrons.
3. The electronic arrangement of an atom with two electrons in the first shell is called ______ if the first shell is the valence shell.
4. Two molecules of sulphur trioxide are indicated by ______.
5. ______ is the suffix used while naming the salt of a metal with lower valency.
6. The symbol of cobalt is ______.
7. The mass of an electron is ______ times that of mass of a proton.
8. The maximum number of electrons that can be accommodated in the outermost orbit is equal to ______.
9. The valency of argon is ______.
10. In the formation of sodium chloride, each chlorine gains ______ electron.
11. The formula of a zincate radical is ______.
12. The combining capacity of the metal which can exhibit more than one valency is called ______.
13. Blackening of silverware is a ______ change.
14. $2HOCl \rightarrow 2HCl + O_2$ is a ______ decomposition reaction.
15. Atomic number of a metal having 12 neutrons and mass number 23 is ______.

Directions for questions from 16 to 25:
State whether the following statements are true or false.

16. Due to the charring of sugar, it cannot retain its chemical properties.
17. The valency of helium is zero.
18. The name of CrO_4^{-2} radical is dichromate ion.
19. Rusting of iron is an example of both physical and chemical change.
20. Sublimation of camphor is a physical change.
21. The central part of the atom called nucleus accounts for the mass of an atom.
22. Both protons and neutrons possess the same magnitude of charge but opposite signs.
23. The maximum number of electrons in the L shell is two.
24. An atom is electrically neutral.
25. In phosphide ion, the total number of electrons is equal to 12.

Directions for questions from 26 to 61:
For each of the questions, four choices have been provided. *Select the correct* alternative.

26. **Assertion (A):** In one molecule of calcium hydroxide, two hydroxyl radicals are present.
    Reason (R): The electronic configuration of calcium is 2, 8 and 2.
    (a) Both A and R are true and R is the correct explanation of A.
    (b) Both A and R are true, but R is not the correct explanation of A.
    (c) A is true and R is false.
    (d) A is false and R is true.
27. **Assertion (A):** Atomic number is the fundamental property of an atom.
    Reason (R): Isotopes have the same atomic number.
    (a) Both A and R are true and R is the correct explanation of A.
    (b) Both A and R are true, but R is not the correct explanation of A.
    (c) A is true and R is false.
    (d) A is false and R is true.
28. Among the noble gases which gas does not have an octet configuration?
    (a) Neon (b) Helium
    (c) Argon (d) Xenon

29. Which among the following pairs of elements forms cation and anion, respectively?
(a) Sulphur and neon
(b) Chlorine and sodium
(c) Potassium and phosphorus
(d) Aluminium and lithium

30. Which is a negative radical among the following?
(a) Silicate (b) Ammonium
(c) Ferrous (d) Chromium

31. Which among the following reactions is not balanced?
(a) $2KClO_3 \rightarrow 2KCl + 3O_2$
(b) $2Fe(OH)_3 + 4H_2SO_4 \rightarrow Fe_2(SO_4)_3 + 6H_2O$
(c) $2Pb(NO_3)_2 \rightarrow 2PbO + 4NO_2 + O_2$
(d) $2KNO_3 + FeSO_4 \rightarrow K_2SO_4 + Fe(NO_3)_2$

32. Among the following reactions, identify the synthesis reaction.
(a) $2SO_2 + O_2 \rightarrow 2SO_3$
(b) $C + O_2 \rightarrow CO_2$
(c) $CaO + H_2O \rightarrow Ca(OH)_2$
(d) $2H_2O \rightarrow 2H_2 + O_2$

33. Identify a useful change among the following chemical changes.
(a) Blackening of silverware.
(b) Rusting of iron.
(c) Curdling of milk.
(d) All the above.

34. Which among the following is not a characteristic of a physical change?
(a) The change is temporary.
(b) No new substance is formed.
(c) Molecular formula of a compound changes.
(d) Change of state of matter takes place without any change in molecular composition.

35. Among the following types of chemical reactions, application of metal reactivity series is involved with which reaction?
(a) Chemical combination
(b) Chemical displacement
(c) Chemical decomposition
(d) Double decomposition

36. If a solid non-metal X forms oxide of type X_2O_5, then the formula of its corresponding chloride is:
(a) XCl_3 (b) XCl_5
(c) X_2Cl_5 (d) X_3Cl_2

37. If the formula of a metal nitrite is $M(NO_2)_2$, then the formula of its dihydrogen phosphate is:
(a) $M_2(PO_4)_3$ (b) $MHPO_4$
(c) $M(H_2PO_4)_2$ (d) M_2HPO_4

38. Identify the number of neutrons present in a pair of elements with atomic numbers 20 and 13, if their mass numbers are 40 and 27, respectively.
(a) 20 and 13
(b) 20 and 13
(c) 17 and 20
(d) 20 and 14

39. Heating solid ammonium chloride involves change in the ______.
(a) physical state only.
(b) physical state as well as chemical composition.
(c) colour only.
(d) both colour and volume only.

40. Which of the following is a chemical change?
(a) Formation of clouds.
(b) Formation of rust.
(c) Manufacture of milk powder from milk.
(d) Formation of black coating on the walls of a tube light.

41. Arrange the following sequence in order to derive the formula of zinc oxide.
(1) The valencies of ions formed by zinc and oxygen are written below without positive and negative sign.
(2) The positive ion, i.e., Zn^{2+} followed by the negative ion, i.e., oxide (O^{2-}) ion are written with their charges.
(3) The valencies of zinc and oxide ion have common factors, and hence, they are divided by their highest common factor.
(4) The magnitude of valencies of the ions should be interchanged and written as subscripts on right side of the respective ions.
(a) 2, 1, 4, 3 (b) 1, 2, 3, 4
(c) 2, 1, 3, 4 (d) 3, 1, 2, 4

42. X and Y are non-metals in which the M shell is valence shell. Y is precedent to X. X shows uninegative valence. Identify the formulae of the compounds formed when X and Y react with the divalent metal M.
(a) MX_2, MY (b) MX, MY_2
(c) M_3X_2, M_2Y_3 (d) M_2X_3, M_3Y_2

43. Identify the formula of the corresponding hydride of a non-metal X which attains an octet configuration by gaining three electrons.
(a) XH (b) XH_2
(c) XH_3 (d) X_2H_4

44. Identify the chemically reactive element if the number of positively-charged particles in the elements A, B, C are 10, 18, 8, respectively.
(a) A (b) B
(c) C (d) both A and B

45. If a dispositive ion of an element X consists of 12 protons and 12 neutrons and another dispositive ion of an element Y consists of 18 electrons and twice the number of electrons of dispositive ion X is the number of neutrons of Y, then, the mass number would be in the ratio of:
(a) 1 : 2 (b) 3 : 5
(c) 12 : 19 (d) 2 : 3

46. If a uninegative ion has 10 neutrons and 9 protons, then the electronic configuration of the atom of the element is:
(a) 2, 8, 1 (b) 2, 7
(c) 2, 8 (d) 2, 8, 8

47. Mass of total positive charge present in an atom is 55110 times to that of mass of electron. Write the electronic configuration of the element.
(a) 2, 8, 9, 2
(b) 2, 8, 18, 1
(c) 2, 8, 18, 2
(d) 2, 8, 8, 2

48. The ratio of difference in the number of electrons between the K and M shells is 3 : 2 for X and Y elements, respectively. X possesses stable electronic configuration and M is the valence shell for both X and Y. Give the electronic configurations of X and Y.
(a) 2, 8, 5 and 2, 8, 4
(b) 2, 8, 8 and 2, 8, 6
(c) 2, 8, 8 and 2, 6, 6
(d) 2, 8, 6 and 2, 8, 4

49. $2KMnO_4 + H_2SO_4 + H_2C_2O_4 \rightarrow K_2SO_4 + 2MnSO_4 + 10CO_2 + 8H_2O$

Potassium permanganate oxidises oxalic acid in an acidic medium as per the above chemical reaction. Identify the coefficients of H_2SO_4 and $H_2C_2O_4$ in the above equation.
(a) 3, 5 (b) 4, 4
(c) 5, 3 (d) 4, 2

50. Heating of a mixture consisting of potassium nitrate, carbon and sulphur involves which of the given chemical changes?
(a) Decomposition and combination
(b) Double decomposition
(c) Combination and displacement
(d) Displacement and decomposition

51. Observe the reactions given below and answer the following question.

$CuSO_4 + X \rightarrow XSO_4 + Cu$;
$CuSO_4 + Y \rightarrow YSO_4 + Cu$;
$XSO_4 + Y \rightarrow$ No reaction;
$CuSO_4 + Z \rightarrow$ No reaction

Arrange Cu, X, Y and Z in the ascending order of reactivity.
(a) X, Y, Z, Cu
(b) Cu, Y, X, Z
(c) Cu, X, Z, Y
(d) Z, Cu, Y, X

52. A metal M shows variable valencies 2 and 3. Calculate the ratio of oxygen atoms present in their corresponding sulphates.
(a) 1 : 3 (b) 3 : 1
(c) 3 : 4 (d) 3 : 2

53. Identify the formula of the corresponding hydride of a non-metal X which attains an octet configuration by gaining two electrons.
(a) XH (b) XH_3
(c) XH_4 (d) XH_2

54. Identify the element which does not exist in monoatomic state if the number of valence electrons in the valence shells, 1, 2, 3 of the X, Y, Z elements are 2, 8, 6, respectively.
(a) X (b) Z
(c) Y (d) X and Y

55. The number of neutrons is equal to the number of protons present in the nucleus of two elements and their respective dinegative ions possess 8 electrons in the L and M shells, respectively. Then the ratio of mass numbers of the two elements is:
(a) 1 : 2 (b) 2 : 3
(c) 3 : 4 (d) 2 : 5

56. Tripositive ion of an element has 13 protons and 14 neutrons. Calculate the ratio of number of electrons present in the K and M shells of the neutral atom.
(a) 2 : 3 (b) 2 : 1
(c) 1 : 1 (d) 2 : 5

57. The ratio of number of electrons present in four shells of an element is 1 : 4 : 4 : 1, fourth shell is the valence shell. Then mass of total positive charge present in the atom is ______ times to that of mass of electron
(a) 36,740
(b) 27,555
(c) 18,370
(d) 55,110

58. The difference in the number of electrons between K and L and L and M shells is the same for an atom of element X (M shell is the valence shell) and the difference value is the number of valence electrons in the M shell of the other element Y. Give the electronic configurations of their stable ions.
(a) 2, 8, 2 and 2, 8, 6
(b) 2, 8 and 2, 8
(c) 2, 8 and 2, 8, 8
(d) 2, 8, 8 and 2, 8, 8

59. The colour change of $CuSO_4$ solution can be observed when it is made to react with:
(a) silver
(b) silver chloride solution
(c) zinc
(d) gold

60. Identify the ratio of the coefficients of the products CuO, NO_2 and H_2O formed respectively when hydrated copper nitrate is thermally decomposed.
$Cu(NO_3)_2.6H_2O \rightarrow CuO + NO_2 + H_2O + O_2$
(a) 2 : 3 : 1
(b) 1 : 2 : 3
(c) 1 : 1.5 : 1
(d) 3 : 2 : 1

61. Which of the following chemical change is a photolytic decomposition reaction?
(a) Decomposition of HOCl on standing
(b) Formation of hydrogen chloride from their constituent elements
(c) Decomposition of limestone
(d) Both (a) and (b)

Directions for questions from 62 to 64:
Match the entries given in Column A with the appropriate ones in Column B. More than one suitable content of Column B can also be considered correct for an entry in Column A and some content given in Column B may not be the appropriate one for any entry in Column A.

62.

Column A	Column B
A. $4SO_2$	a. Three atoms of oxygen
B. $2Na^+$	b. Three oxygen molecules
C. $3O_2$	c. Eight molecules of chlorine
D. $8Cl_2$	d. Eight chlorine atoms
	e. Two sodium atoms
	f. Four sulphur dioxide molecules
	g. Two sodium ions

63.

Column A Names of the radical	Column B Charges
A. Aluminium	a. –1
B. Stannous	b. +3
C. Bisuphite	c. +2
D. Silicate	d. +4
	e. –2

64.

Column A	Column B
A. $2Pb(NO_3) \rightarrow PbO + 4NO_2 + O_2$	a. Combination reaction
B. $Zn + FeSO_4 \rightarrow ZnSO_4 + Fe$	b. Double decomposition reaction
C. $NaCl + AgNO_3 \rightarrow NaNO_3 + AgCl$	c. Decomposition reaction
D. $S + O_2 \rightarrow SO_2$	d. Displacement reaction

Level 2: Review Your Concepts

65. Identify the given atom.

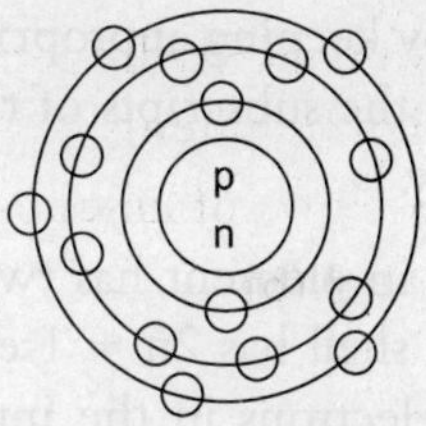

66. A stable neutral atom X contains two completely-filled orbits. Find out its mass number if it consists of 10 neutrons.

67. Write the number of constituent atoms for each of the following:
(i) Nitrogen pentoxide (ii) Sulphuric acid
(iii) Calcium hydroxide (iv) Ferric hydroxide

68. Apply the law of conservation of mass on the following reaction and identify the substance (reactant or product) associated with the lowest coefficient.

$CuO + NH_3 \rightarrow Cu + H_2O + N_2$

69. Predict the valencies of the elements with atomic numbers 7, 15, 16, 18, 19 and justify. Also give the formulae of hydrides formed by the above elements if any.

70. In a chemical laboratory, a student took two test tubes A and B. Lead nitrate solution is taken in thest tube "A" and sulphuric acid is taken in the test tube "B". Sodium chloride solution and lithium hydroxide solutions are added to the test tubes "A" and "B" respectively. Predict the products and identify the types of reactions.

71. In an atom, the L and M shells have the same number of electrons. The N shell has one electron less than the K shell. Explain the formation of compound by this element and oxygen atom.

72. Explain the formation of the compound formed by two elements with Z = 20 and Z = 17.

73. An atom of an element has the electrons distributed in four shells. If the electrons present in I and IV shells is in 1 : 1 ratio, and the ratio of electrons in II and III shells is also 1 : 1. Predict its valency and justify. Write the formulae of (a) nitride (b) silicate (c) chloride.

74. A negative ion of an atom of element X has 18 electrons and 16 protons. Calculate the number of electrons and protons in its corresponding atom. Also calculate the number of neutrons, if the mass number is 2 units more than double the number of protons.

75. If the formula of metal sulphite of a metal M is MSO_3, give the formula of its:
(a) phosphate
(b) hydrogen phosphate
(c) chloride

76. In a chemical laboratory, a student broke the thermometer while performing an experiment. Immediately, the mercury which was spilled over was removed by the lab incharge by sprinkling sulphur on it. The teacher asked the students to predict the type of change/reaction associated with the above process. Explain with appropriate reasons.

77. Asha's mother asked her daughter Asha to boil the milk and after some time, she told Usha, Asha's sister, to add a little curd in the same lukewarm milk. Next day, their father while teaching 'transformation of matter' to his daughters wanted to relate the given activity. So, he asked them, 'what type of change was involved in the activities performed by you yesterday?' Predict the answer given by them and justify.

78. What is the valency of iron in the products formed when iron is exposed to humid air for a long time?

79. Give the necessary chemical equations for the following and balance them.
(a) Reaction of a red hot iron with steam to give Fe_3O_4
(b) Burning magnesium ribbon in an atmosphere of nitrogen
(c) Displacement of copper from the solution of its sulphate by zinc

80. In a science fair, a student took two test tubes labelled A and B filled with copper sulphate solution, then he put magnesium ribbon in test tube A and silver foil in test tube B. Predict the observation and justify.

Level 3: Assess Your Concepts

81. An atom of an element X has three completely filled shells. The ratio of electrons in 1 and 4 shells is 1 : 1. Find the atomic number of X. Also write the formulae of its bicarbonate, chromate and phosphide.

82. A metal (M) and a non-metal (X) form a compound with the formula M_4X_3. Predict the electronic arrangements of M and X assuming that M has three occupied shells and X has two occupied shells. Also derive the formulae of (a) sulphate, (b) dihydrogen phosphate and (c) hydroxide of ion of M.

83. Two metals A and B possess the same number of electrons in the L shell and they differ by 1 unit in the number of electrons present in valence shell and number of valence electrons is greater in B than A. The ions formed get the configuration of the nearest inert gases namely argon and neon, respectively. Give the probable electronic configurations of the metals corresponding to A and B and also give the formulae of their corresponding nitrite, nitrate, sulphite and bisulphite.

84. Number of atoms on either side of a chemical equation is balanced by keeping appropriate coefficients and not by changing the subscripts of the elements in the formulae. Justify.

85. An atom of an element has two shells with electrons. The valence shell has 2n + 1 electrons where n is the number of electrons in the inner shell. This element can form a radical X with hydrogen and two radicals Y and Z with oxygen, Z has more number of oxygen than Y. Identify the element and the radicals. Write the reaction taking place between solutions of two salts, AgZ and XCl. Identify the type of reaction.

86. In the given compound XY, the charges on cation and the anion are equal to the charges of cupric ion and sulphate radical respectively. And the total number of electrons in the cation is equal to the number of protons of neon atom and the number of electrons in the anion is equal to the total of the number of electrons present in K, L and M shells of potassium atom. Identify the compound XY.

ANSWER KEYS

Crossword

Across

1. Valence shell 4. Radical 6. Chemical 9. Mass number
10. Synthesis

Down

2. Nucleus 3. Hydrargyrium 5. Physical 7. Phosphorus
8. Proton

Classroom Wing

Very Short Answer Type Questions

1. phosphate 2. Na_2SO_3, Na_2SO_4 3. physical, molecular composition
4. both physical and chemical changes 5. coefficients 6. (c) 7. (b)
8. (b) 9. (c) 10. (b) 11. (d) 12. (a)
13. (b) 14. (c) 15. (b) 16. (d) 17. (a)
18. (b) 19. (c) 20. (d) 21. (b) 22. (a)
23. (c) 24. (c) 25. (b) 26. (b) 27. (a)
28. (b) 29. (c) 30. (d) 31. (d) 32. (c)
33. (b) 34. (b) 35. (b) 36. (d) 37. (c)
38. (c) 39. (a) 40. (i) → (D), (ii) → (A), (iii) → (E), (iv) → (c), (v) → (B)
41. A → e, B → d, C → a, D → b 42. A → b, B → a, C → d, D → c

Competition Wing

Level 1: Apply your Concepts

1. Ca 2. losing two 3. duplet configuration 4. $2SO_3$
5. Ous 6. Co 7. $\frac{1}{1837}$ 8. 8 9. zero
10. one 11. ZnO_2^{-2} 12. variable valency 13. chemical change 14. photolytic
15. 11 16. True 17. True 18. False 19. False
20. True 21. True 22. False 23. False 24. True
25. False 26. (c) 27. (b) 28. (b) 29. (c)
30. (a) 31. (b) 32. (b) 33. (c) 34. (c)
35. (b) 36. (b) 37. (c) 38. (d) 39. (b)
40. (b) 41. (c) 42. (a) 43. (c) 44. (c)
45. (b) 46. (b) 47. (c) 48. (b) 49. (a)
50. (a) 51. (d) 52. (a) 53. (d) 54. (b)
55. (a) 56. (a) 57. (a) 58. (c) 59. (c)
60. (b) 61. (a) 62. A → f, B → g, C → b, D → c
63. A → b, B → c, C → a, D → e 64. A → c, B → d, C → b, D → a

Hints and Explanations

CLASSROOM WING

Very Short Answer Type Questions

1. phosphate
   PO_4^{3-} is called phosphate
2. Na_2SO_3, Na_2SO_4
   Na_2SO_3 and Na_2SO_4 are the formulae of sodium sulphite and sodium sulphate, respectively.
3. physical, molecular composition
   Most of the physical changes can be reversed since there does not involve change in molecular composition of the substance.
4. both physical and chemical changes
   $NH_4Cl(s) \rightarrow NH_4Cl(g) \rightarrow NH_3 + HCl$
   Hence, it involves both physical and chemical changes.
5. coefficients
   The number of atoms on either side of the chemical equation is balanced by keeping appropriate coefficients.
6. H (Z = 1) electronic configuration = 1; He (Z = 2) electronic configuration = 2
   Hence, the correct option is (c)
7. $MnO_4^- \rightarrow$ the charge of permanganate is –1 which is same as bisulphate ion (HSO_4^-)
   Hence, the correct option is (b)
8. XCl_3, $YCl_4 \rightarrow$ the valencies of X and Y are 3 and 4.
   Hence, the correct option is (b)
9. 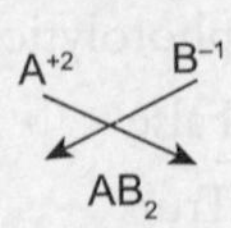

   Hence, the correct option is (c)
10. When sucrose (sugar) is treated with conc. H_2SO_4, coke is formed due to the removal of water molecules.
    $$C_{12}H_{22}O_{11} \xrightarrow{\text{conc. } H_2SO_4} 12C + 11H_2O$$
    Hence, it is a chemical change.
    Hence, the correct option is (b)
11. Melting of wax is a physical change.
    Hence, the correct option is (d)
12. Corrosion of any metal is a chemical change.
    Hence, the correct option is (a)
13. Formation of clouds, mist, etc., represent the examples of physical changes.
    Hence, the correct option is (b)
14. $AgNO_3 + NaCl \rightarrow AgCl + NaNO_3$ is a double displacement reaction.
    Hence, the correct option is (c)
15. Inert gases like He, Ne, Ar are chemically inactive.
    Hence, the correct option is (b)
16. MCl_2
    Since the valency of chlorine is 1, the valency of metal is 2.
    Hence, the correct option is (d)
17. 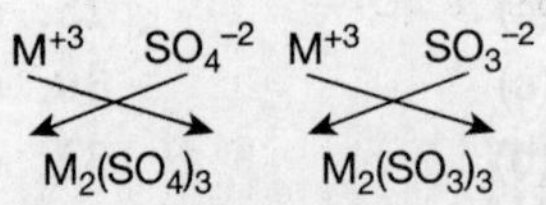

    Hence, the correct option is (a)
18.

Atomic number (Z)	Electronic configuration
19	2, 8, 8, 1
20	2, 8, 8, 2

    Hence, the correct option is (b)
19. Dissolution of any acid in water makes an acid dilute. Hence, it involves only a physical change.
    Hence, the correct option is (c)
20. Anhydrous $CaCl_2$ absorbs moisture till it becomes saturated and changes its physical state. Hence, it is a deliquescent substance.
    Hence, the correct option is (d)
21. (i) The positive radical followed by negative radical is written with their charges.
    (ii) The valencies of the ions or radicals are written below the radicals without positive and negative sign.
    (iii) The magnitude of valencies should be interchanged and written as subscripts on the right side of the respective ions.

(iv) If the valencies have common factors, then they are divided by the highest common factor.

(v) If the radicals contain more than one atom, they are enclosed in brackets and the appropriate valency (more than one) is written as subscript outside the bracket.

Hence, the correct option is (b)

22. M^{+3} SO_4^{-2}

$M_2(SO_4)_3$

Hence, the correct option is (a)

23. A → b Atomic number of chlorine is 17, electronic configuration is 2, 8, 7.

B → c Atomic number of scandium is 21, electronic configuration is 2, 8, 9, 2.

C → d Atomic number of manganese is 25, electronic configuration is 2, 8, 13, 2.

D → a Atomic number of beryllium is 4, electronic configuration is 2, 2.

Hence, the correct option is (c)

24.

Elements	Atomic numbers	Electronic configurations
A	10	2, 8
B	18	2, 8, 8
C	8	2, 6

Hence, C is chemically reactive. A and B are chemically inert because of stable octet configuration.

Hence, the correct option is (c)

25. $NH_4Cl_s \xrightarrow{\Delta} NH_4Cl_g \xrightarrow{\Delta} NH_{3g} + HCl_g$

It involves both sublimation (physical change) and chemical decomposition (chemical change)

Hence, the correct option is (b)

26. (i) Identification of the atomic number and mass number of the atom.

(ii) Calculation of the number of protons and neutrons.

(iii) Protons and neutrons are shown in the nucleus.

(iv) Writing the electronic configuration of the atom.

(v) Arrange the electrons in shells around the nucleus following the electronic configuration.

Hence, the correct option is (b)

27. (i) AB + C → CB + A

(ii) A + B → AB

(iii) AC + BD → AD + BC

(iv) AB → A + B

Hence, the correct option is (a)

28. $2Cu(NO_3)_2 \cdot 6H_2O \xrightarrow{\Delta} 2CuO + 4NO_2 + O_2 + 6H_2O$

Coefficients of CuO and NO_2 are, respectively 2 and 4.

Hence, the correct option is (b)

29. Valency of metal is 2.

M^{+2} $H_2PO_4^{-1}$

$M(H_2PO_4)_2$

Hence, the correct option is (c)

30. A → e Atomic number of neon is 10 and electronic configuration 2, 8, valency = 0.

B → c Atomic number of oxygen is 8 and electronic configuration 2, 6, valency = 8 – 6 = 2.

C → d Atomic number of potassium is 19 and electronic configuration is 2, 8, 8, valency = 1.

D → b Atomic number of boron is 5 and electronic configuration is 2, 3, valency = 3.

E → a Atomic number of silicon is 14 and electronic configuration is 2, 8, 4, valency = 4.

Hence, the correct option is (d)

31. A – Z = number of neutrons.

(1) 40 – 20 = 20

(2) 27 – 13 = 14

Hence, the correct option is (d)

32. Electronic configuration of neutral atom is

K	L	M
2	8	3

Hence, the correct option is (c)

33. Formation of rust is a chemical change in which iron when exposed to humid atmosphere forms hydrated ferric oxide ($Fe_2O_3 \cdot xH_2O$).

Hence, the correct option is (b)

34.

Element	X	Y	Z
Valence shell	K	L	M
	(1)	(2)	(3)
Number of valence electrons	2	8	6
Element	He	Ne	S

Sulphur (S) does not exist in monoatomic state due to its greater chemical reactivity.

Hence, the correct option is (b)

35. $\overset{+5}{X_2}\overset{-2}{O_5}$

Valency of non-metal is 5.

Hence, the correct option is (b)

36. Mass of one proton is 1837 times the mass of an electron. Hence, the total mass of protons in boron is 9185 times (5 × 1837) the total mass of electrons.

Hence, the correct option is (d)

37. Sodium loses only one electron from its outermost shell or valence shell and forms monovalent ion.

Hence, the correct option is (c)

38. (X) K L M (Y) K L M

2 8 X 2 8 6

$$\frac{8-2}{8-X}=\frac{1}{1}$$

$8 - X = 8 - 2$

$X = 2$

Stable ion of X is X^{+2} and of Y is Y^{-2}.

X^{+2} : 2, 8 Y^{-2} : 2, 8, 8

Hence, the correct option is (c)

39. The electronic configuration of the dinegative ion with 8 in electrons in the L valence shell is:

$X^{-2} \rightarrow$ 2, 8

X → 2, 6 (Z), mass number is 16 for X.

The electronic configuration of the dinegative ion with 8 electrons in the M shell is

Y^{-2} → 2, 8, 8

Y → 2, 8, 6 (Z)

Mass number is 32 (A) for Y.

Ratio of mass number is 16 : 32 ⇒ 1 : 2

Hence, the correct option is (a)

40. (i) Oxygen → (D)

8p and 8n are in the nucleus.

(ii) Neon → (A)

8 electrons are in the valence shell.

(iii) Potassium → (E)

8 electrons are in the penultimate shell.

(iv) Hydride ion → (C)

2 electrons are in the valence shell.

(v) Fluorine → (B)

9p and 10n are in the nucleus.

41. A → e Charge on zincate ion is −2.

B → d Charge on stannic ion is +4.

C → a Charge on nitride ion is −3.

D → b Charge on potassium ion is +1.

42. A → b X + Y → XY is a combination reaction.

B → a Y + YZ → XZ + Y is a displacement reaction.

C → d AB + XY → AY + XB in a double displacement reaction.

D → c AB → A + B is a of decomposition reaction.

43. The correct representation of the atom is $_{x}B^{x+y}$.

44. The valency of mercurous ion is +1 while the valency of other radicals is +2.

45. F^{-1} has octet configuration in the valence shell.

46. Formation of green patches on copper is a chemical change whereas others are physical changes.

47. $C_3H_8 + 5O_2 \rightarrow 3CO_2 + 4H_2O$

$\therefore 4c = 3d$

48. Copper and iron

Copper: Cuprous Cu^{+}

Cupric Cu^{2+}

Iron: Ferrous Fe^{2+}

Ferric Fe^{3+}

49. Synthesis is a combination chemical reaction in which two elements combine to give one single compound.

Example: $H_2 + Cl_2 \rightarrow 2HCl$

50. A is more reactive than B.

51. Electrolytic decomposition is a chemical decomposition in which a single reactant is decomposed into more than one product by the passage of electricity.

Example: $2H_2O \rightarrow 2H_2 + O_2$

52. Inert gases hzave 8 electrons in their valence shell and hence, they are stable. Helium, an inert gas, has 2 electrons in the first shell which is its valence shell. It is stable because the first shell cannot accommodate more than two electrons.

53. The outermost shell is called valence shell and it can never have more than 8 electrons in any atom.

54. In an atom, the number of electrons is equal to the number of protons inside the nucleus. Since the protons and electrons carry equal and opposite charges, an atom is electrically neutral.

55. A chemical decomposition reaction which takes place in presence of light is called photolytic decomposition reaction.

Example: $2HOCl \rightarrow 2HCl + O_2$

56.

Physical change	Chemical change
Boiling of milk, melting of candle	Ripening of fruits, curdling of milk, rusting of iron, blackening of silverware

57. In order to satisfy the law of conservation of mass (atoms cannot be created or destroyed), a chemical equation should be balanced.

58. Dissolution of calcium oxide in water is a compound–compound combination reaction.

59. It is called precipitation reaction.

60. It is a decomposition reaction.

61. (i) $NH_3 + O_2 \rightarrow NO + H_2O$

$4NH_3 + 5O_2 \rightarrow 4NO + 6H_2O$

(ii) $FeS_2 + O_2 \rightarrow Fe_2O_3 + SO_2$

$4FeS_2 + 11O_2 \rightarrow 2Fe_2O_3 + 8SO_2$

62.

No.	Compounds	Positive radical	Negative radical
(i)	$CaSiO_3$	Ca^{2+}	SiO_3^{2-}
(ii)	H_2SO_3	H^+	SO_3^{2-}

Short Answer Type Questions

63.

Element	Electronic configuration
(a) Boron	2, 3
(b) Lithium	2, 1
(c) Helium	2, 0
(d) Oxygen	2, 6
(e) Calcium	2, 8, 8, 2

∴ The order is EDABC.

64. (a) Chromate → CrO_4^{-2}

(b) Silicate → SiO_3^{-2}

(c) hydroxyl → OH^-

(d) Nitrite → NO_2^{1-}

∴ The order is ABDC.

65. (a) Neutrons = 31 − 15 = 16

(b) Neutrons = 235 − 92 = 143

(c) Neutrons = 39 − 19 = 20

66. (a) $NaCl + AgNO_3 \rightarrow NaNO_3 + AgCl$

(b) $Zn + 2HCl \rightarrow ZnCl_2 + H_2 \uparrow$

67. A group of atoms possessing either positive or negative charge by losing or gaining one or more elect-rons is called a radical. The positively charged radicals are ammonium radical (NH_4^+) and hydronium radical (H_3O^+). All other radicals are negatively charged.

SO_3^{-2}, SO_4^{-2}, CO_3^{-2} are some examples of bivalent negative radicals.

68. The given table gives the comparative study of physical and chemical changes.

Physical change	Chemical change
Molecular composition of the matter does not change.	Molecular composition of matter changes.
No new substance is formed. Only the physical appearance or behaviour changes.	New substance is formed.
This change is called temporary or reversible because the previous form of matter can easily be revived.	This change is called permanent or irreversible because the previous form of matter cannot be revived by physical processes.

69. Calcium has two electrons in both K and N shells and eight electrons in both L and M shells. Calcium can form stable Ca^{2+} ion. Fluorine can form stable F^- ion. Therfore, the compound formed by the calcium and fluorine is CaF_2 (calcium fluoride).

70.

Types	Examples
Element–element (synthesis)	$H_2 + Cl_2 \rightarrow 2HCl$
Element–compound	$2SO_2 + O_2 \rightarrow 2SO_3$
Compound–compound	$CaO + H_2O \rightarrow Ca(OH)_2$

71. The chemical decomposition which takes place in presence of heat is called thermal decomposition.

Example: $2Pb(NO_3)_2 \rightarrow 2PbO + 4NO_2 + O_2$

72. The chemical reaction in which the two reactants (compounds) exchange their respective radicals and two other new compounds are formed is called a double decomposition reaction.

Example: $NaCl + AgNO_3 \rightarrow NaNO_3 + AgCl$

73. The chemical reaction in which the more reactive element displaces the less reactive element from its compound is called a chemical displacement reaction.

$X + YZ \rightarrow XZ + Y$

X is a more reactive element than Y.

$Y + XZ \rightarrow$ No reaction

Y cannot displace X from its compound since it is less reactive than X.

74.

Cations	Anions
Positively charged ions are called cations.	Negatively charged ions are called anions.
Generally metals form cations by losing electrons.	Generally non-metals form anions by gaining electrons.

75. (1) $AlPO_4 \rightarrow$ aluminium phosphate

(2) $Ca(NO_3)_2 \rightarrow$ calcium nitrate

(3) $(NH_4)_2SO_4 \rightarrow$ ammonium phosphate

(4) $Al_4C_3 \rightarrow$ aluminium carbide

76. **Atomic number:** The number of protons present inside the nucleus is called atomic number. It is equal to the number of electrons in a neutral atom. The elements are characterized by their atomic numbers. Atomic number is denoted by 'Z'.

Example: In sodium, Z = 11, means that an atom of sodium contains 11 protons in the nucleus and 11 electrons outside the nucleus.

Mass number: Mass number indicates the sum of protons and neutrons present inside the nucleus. It is denoted by 'A'.

Example: In sodium, Z = 11, A = 23, indicates that an atom of sodium contains 11 protons and (23 − 11) = 12 neutrons.

77. Sulphur Z = 16

Electronic configuration 2, 8, 6

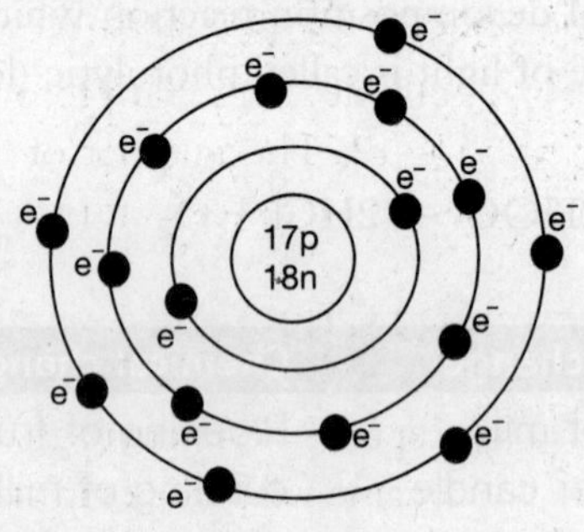

78. (a) ammonium nitrate

$NH_4^+ NO_3^-$

∴ Formula is NH_4NO_3

(b) ferrous sulphate

$Fe^{+2} SO_4^{-2}$

∴ Formula is $FeSO_4$

79. Metals generally possess 1 – 3 electrons in their outermost shells and they tend to lose electrons to form positive ions called cations. Non-metals possess 4 – 7 electrons in their valence shells and they tend to gain electrons to form negative ions called anions.

80. (a) Magnesium (Z = 12) → (2, 8, 2)

(b) Silicon (Z = 14) → (2, 8, 4)

(c) Boron (Z = 5) → (2, 3)

(d) Argon (Z = 18) → (2, 8, 8)

81. Sodium (Z = 11) has electronic configuration of 2, 8, 1. By losing one electron, it forms Na^+ ion which attains the configuration of neon that is 2, 8. Chlorine (Z = 17) has electronic configuration of 2, 8, 7. By gaining one electron, it forms Cl^- ion which attains the configuration of argon, i.e., 2, 8, 8. Since Na^+ and Cl^- ion carry opposite charges, a strong force of attraction binds the two ions together. Thus, the compound sodium chloride is formed.

82. (a) Cadmium → Cd (b) Bismuth → Bi

(c) Silicon → Si (d) Argon → Ar

83. Fe on treatment with H_2SO_4 liberates hydrogen gas.

$Fe + H_2SO_4 \rightarrow \rightarrow FeSO_4 + H_2$

The solution turns green due to the formation of $FeSO_4$.

As Fe is more reactive than Cu, it displaces Cu from $CuSO_4$ solution. Hence, blue colour of $CuSO_4$ solution disappears.

$Fe + CuSO_4(aq) \rightarrow FeSO_4 + Cu$

84. A dispositive ion of an atom of an element "X" has 10 electrons. So the atom "X" is magnesium.

Dinegative ion of an atom of an element "Y" has 10 electrons. So the atom 'Y' is oxygen.

The number of both electrons and protons present in a magnesium atom is 12. The number of both electrons and protons present in an oxygen atom is 8.

Essay Answer Type Questions

85. The modern concept of atom envisages the following arrangement of fundamental particles in an atom.

(i) The protons and neutrons are concentrated in a small region at the centre of an atom. This central part is known as **nucleus**. The protons and neutrons present inside the nucleus are called **nucleons**.

(ii) The size of the nucleus is very small when compared to the size of the atom. That means, there is vast empty space in the atom.

(iii) Electrons revolve round the nucleus in definite fixed paths which are called **orbits or shells**.

(iv) In an atom, the number of electrons is equal to the number of protons inside the nucleus. Since the protons and electrons carry equal and opposite charges, an atom is electrically neutral.

(v) The various orbits or shells are named as **K, L, M, N**.... or **1, 2, 3, 4**..... and so on. The maximum number of electrons in the various orbits is 2, 8, 18, 32 .... respectively. The energy of the orbit increases with increase in distance from the nucleus.

(vi) The outermost shell is called **valence shell** and it can never have more than 8 electrons in any atom.

86. (a)

Fluorine, Z = 9

Electronic arrangement = 2, 7

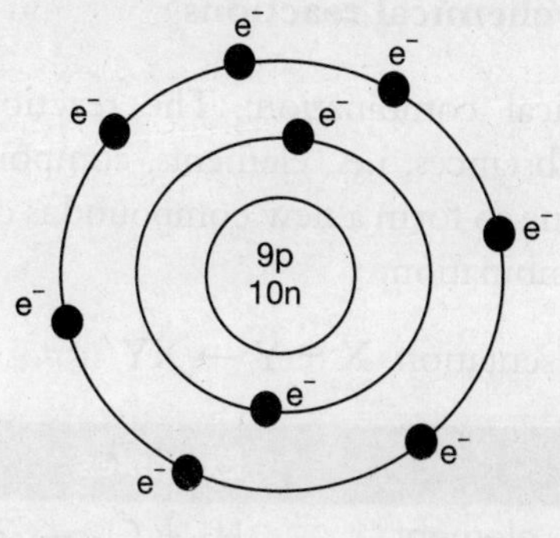

(b)

Sodium, Z = 11

Electronic arrangement = 2, 8, 1

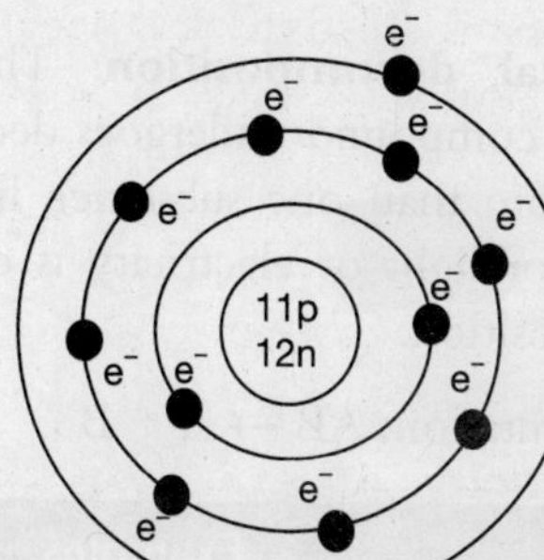

(c)

Chlorine, Z = 17

Electronic arrangement = 2, 8, 7

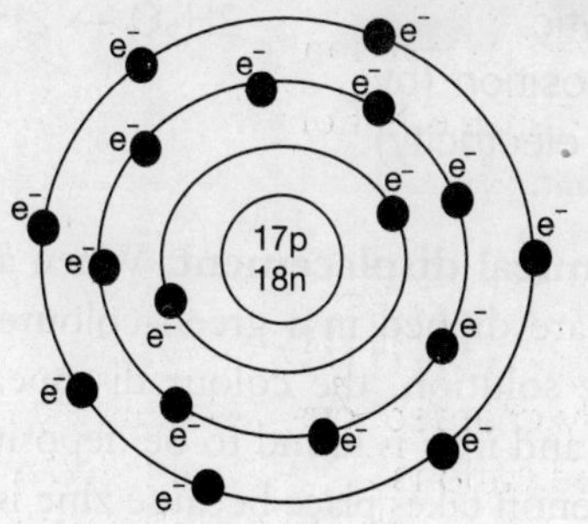

(d)

Carbon, Z = 6

Electronic arrangement = 2, 4

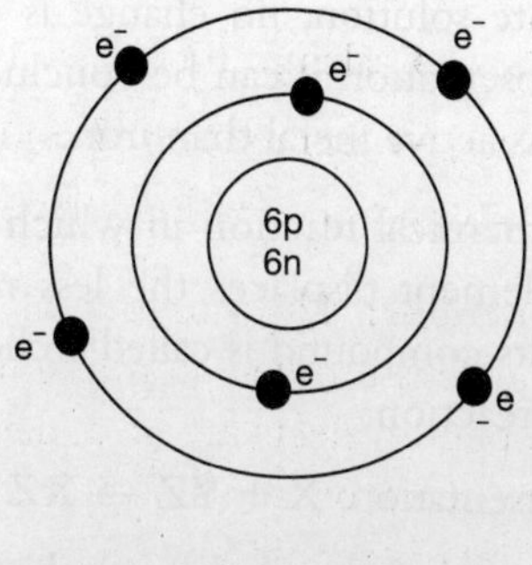

87. Types of chemical reactions

(i) Chemical combination: The reaction in which two substances, i.e., elements, compounds or both combine to form a new compound is called chemical combination.

Representation: $X + Y \rightarrow XY$

Types	Examples
Element–element (synthesis)	$H_2 + Cl_2 \rightarrow 2HCl$
Element–compound	$2SO_2 + O_2 \rightarrow 2SO_3$
Compound–compound	$CaO + H_2O \rightarrow Ca(OH)_2$

(ii) **Chemical decomposition**: The reaction in which a compound undergoes decomposition to form more than one substance in the presence of heat or light or electricity is called chemical decomposition.

Representation: $AB \rightarrow A + B$

Types	Examples
Thermal decomposition (in presence of heat)	$2 Pb(NO_3)_2 \rightarrow 2PbO + 4NO_2 + O_2$
Photolytic decomposition (in presence of light)	$2HOCl \rightarrow 2HCl + O_2$
Electrolytic decomposition (by passing electricity)	$2H_2O \rightarrow 2H_2 + O_2$

(iii) **Chemical displacement**: When a few pieces of zinc are dipped in a green-coloured ferrous sulphate solution, the colour disappears after some time and iron is found to be deposited. This phenomenon takes place because zinc is a more active metal than iron and hence, it takes away the other constituent, i.e., iron from ferrous sulphate and iron gets separated.

Whereas, when copper is added to the ferrous sulphate solution, no change is observed. From this observation it can be concluded that copper is a less active metal than iron.

The chemical reaction in which the more reactive element displaces the less reactive element from its compound is called a chemical displacement reaction.

Representation: $X + YZ \rightarrow XZ + Y$

X is a more reactive element than Y.

$Y + XZ \rightarrow$ No reaction

Y cannot displace X from its compound since it is less reactive than X.

Examples:

$Zn + FeSO_4 \rightarrow ZnSO_4 + Fe$

$Cu + FeSO_4 \rightarrow$ no reaction

(iv) **Chemical double decomposition/double displacement**: The chemical reaction in which the two reactants (compounds) exchange their respective radicals and two other new compounds are formed is called a double displacement reaction.

Representation: $AB + XY \rightarrow AY + XB$

Where B and Y correspond to the negative radicals which are exchanged to give AY and XB.

Example: $2KNO_3 + FeSO_4 \rightarrow K_2SO_4 + Fe(NO_3)_2$

In the above reaction, reactive K^+ (potassium ion) combines with SO^{4-} (sulphate ion) and Fe^{+2} (ferrous ion) combines with NO^{3-} (nitrate ion) to form two new compounds, K_2SO_4 and $Fe(NO_3)_2$. During certain double displacement reactions, a solid substance is found to be deposited. The solid deposition is called precipitate and this type of reaction is called precipitation reaction.

Example: $NaCl + AgNO_3 \rightarrow NaNO_3 + AgCl$

In the above reaction, during the exchange of radicals, silver chloride is formed which is insoluble in water. Therefore, it remains as a solid at the bottom of the container as precipitate.

88. The main postulates of Dalton's atomic theory are:

(i) Matter is composed of tiny indivisible particles called **atoms**. They cannot be created or destroyed or transformed into atoms of another element.

(ii) Atoms of a given element are identical in all respects.

(iii) Atoms of different elements are different from each other in all respects.

(iv) Atoms of different elements take part in a chemical reaction and combine in a simple integral ratio to form compounds.

(v) When elements react, the atoms may combine in more than one simple whole number ratio.

Dalton's atomfic theory has been contradicted with the advancement of science and modified on the basis of further research and discoveries.

Limitations of Dalton's Atomic Theory

(i) With the discovery of subatomic particles, i.e., the electron, proton and neutron, it was concluded that atoms can be further divided.

(ii) Discovery of isotopes proved that atoms of the same element may possess different atomic weights, i.e., atoms of same elements may not be identical in all respects. For example, isotopes of hydrogen, namely, protium ($_1H^1$) and deuterium ($_1H^2$).

(iii) In some cases, atoms of different elements are found to have same mass number, i.e., atoms of different elements may be identical. For example, calcium and argon are found to have same mass number.

89. *Example:* $Mg + O_2 \rightarrow MgO$ is an unbalanced chemical equation. This is called a skeletal equation. A systematic procedure should be followed for balancing the chemical equation.

Step I: The number of times an element occurs on both sides is counted. The element which appears the least number of times should be balanced first.

Step II: Among the elements with same frequency of occurrences, the metallic element is balanced first followed by non-metallic element.

Step III: Hydrogen and oxygen are balanced at the end.

Examples:

R P

$Mg + O_2 \rightarrow MgO$

1 – Mg – 1

2 – O – 1

$Mg + O_2 \rightarrow 2MgO$

1 – Mg – 2

2 – O – 2

$2Mg + O_2 \rightarrow 2MgO$

90. Valency: The number of electrons gained or lost by an atom of an element for attaining stable octet or duplet configuration is called valency.

When an atom loses one or more electrons, the number of protons in it becomes more than the number of electrons and hence, the ions formed are left with positive charge. This is called positive valency.

When an atom attains stability by gaining one or more electrons, the number of electrons in it becomes more than the number of protons and hence, the ion formed becomes negatively charged. This is called negative valency.

The charge on the ion is corresponding to the number of electrons lost or gained. They may be monovalent, bivalent, trivalent and tetravalent which correspond to the valencies, 1, 2, 3, 4, respectively.

The following table represents the valencies of different elements:

Elements	Types of ion	Representation of ions	Names of ion
Sodium	Monovalent	Na^+	Sodium
Chlorine	Monovalent	Cl^-	Chloride
Hydrogen	Monovalent	H^+	Hydrogen
Zinc	Bivalent	Zn^{2+}	Zinc
Magnesium	Bivalent	Mg^{2+}	Magnesium
Oxygen	Bivalent	O^{2-}	Oxide
Oxygen	Bivalent	$O_2{}^{2-}$	Peroxide
Aluminium	Trivalent	Al^{3+}	Aluminium
Nitrogen	Trivalent	N^{3-}	Nitride

Some metals like iron, copper, etc. exhibit more than one valency called variable valency by losing different number of electrons.

91. The given chemical double displacement reaction is $AB + XY \rightarrow AY + XB$.

In the reactant XY; X^{2+} is barium ion (Ba^{2+})

In the reactant AB; B^{2-} is sulphate radical ($SO_4{}^{2-}$)

In the product AY; A^+ ion is lithium ion (Li^+) because it has three protons.

Y ion is chloride ion (Cl^-) because it has eighteen electrons.

Reactants AB, and XY are lithium sulphate and barium chloride respectively. Products AY, and XB are lithium chloride and barium sulphate respectively.

The balanced chemical reaction is

$Li_2SO_4 + BaCl_2 \rightarrow 2LiCl + BaSO_4$

Competition Wing

Level 1: Apply Your Concepts

1. Symbol of calcium is Ca
2. Electronic arrangement of Mg is 2, 8, 2. By losing two electrons, it attains an octet configuration.
3. Duplet configuration is observed in helium which possesses two electrons in the first shell.
4. $2SO_3$ means 2 molecules of SO_3.
5. 'ous' is the suffix used to name the salt of the corresponding metal with lower valency.
6. The symbol of cobalt is Co.
7. The mass of an electron is $\frac{1}{1837}$ times that of mass of a proton.
8. Eight is the maximum number of electrons that can be accommodated in the valence shell.
9. The valency of argon is zero.
10. Chlorine gains an electron while sodium loses an electron to form NaCl.
11. The formula of zincate radical is ZnO_2^{2-}
12. Certain metals like Fe, Cu, Sn, etc., exhibit more than one valency in their compounds called variable valency.

    Examples: $FeCl_2$, $FeCl_3$
13. Blackening of silverware is a chemical change.
14. $2HOCl \rightarrow 2HCl + O_2$ is photolytic decomposition reaction.
15. Atomic number = mass number − number of neutrons

    Atomic number = 23 − 12 = 11
16. True. Charring of sugar is a chemical change. Hence, in this process, it cannot retain its chemical properties.
17. Helium possesses stable duplet configuration with 2 electrons in the first shell. Hence, its valency is zero.
18. $Cr_2O_7^{2-}$ is called dichromate ion.
19. Rusting of iron is a chemical change in which iron gets corroded in humid air.
20. Sublimation of camphor is a physical change.
21. Nucleus consists of both protons and neutrons and it accounts for the mass of the atom.
22. Neutrons carry no charge, i.e., they are neutral, but all protons are positively charged.
23. The maximum number of electrons in the L shell is eight.
24. An atom is electrically neutral due to the presence of equal number of positively and negatively charged particles.
25. P^{3-} = 15 + 3 = 18 electrons
26. The formula of calcium hydroxide is $Ca(OH)_2$. However, the electronic configuration is 2, 8, 8, and 2.

    Hence, the correct option is (c).
27. Atomic number is unique for each element. Isotopes have the same atomic number, but different mass numbers.

    Hence, the correct option is (b).
28. Helium has a duplet configuration.

    Hence, the correct option is (b)
29. Potassium loses one electron to form cation and phosphorous gains three electrons to form anion.

    Hence, the correct option is (c)
30. Silicate is a negative radical, i.e., SiO_3^{-2}.

    Hence, the correct option is (a)
31. Second reaction is wrongly balanced. Correct balancing is as follows:

    $2Fe(OH)_3 + 3H_2SO_4 \rightarrow Fe_2(SO_4)_3 + 6H_2O$

    Hence, the correct option is (b)
32. $C + O_2 \rightarrow CO_2$ is an example of synthesis reaction.

    Hence, the correct option is (b)
33. Curdling of milk results in the formation of curd which is a useful change.

    Hence, the correct option is (c)
34. In a physical change, molecular composition, i.e., molecular formula remains the same.

    Hence, the correct option is (c)

35. In displacement reactions, application of metal reactivity series is involved.

Hence, the correct option is (b)

36. + 5 – X_2O_5

Since the valency of chloride ion is 1, the formula of the above chloride would be

X^{+5} Cl^{-1}

XCl_5

Hence, the correct option is (b)

37. $M(NO_2)_2$, hence, valency of metal is 2.

M^{+2} $H_2PO_4^{-1}$

$M(H_2PO_4)_2$

Hence, the correct option is (c)

38. A – Z = n

(1) 40 – 20 = 20

(2) 27 – 13 = 14

Hence, the correct option is (d)

39.

$$NH_4Cl(s) \xrightarrow{\Delta} NH_4Cl(g) \xrightarrow{\Delta} NH_3(g) + HCl(g)$$

It involves both sublimation (physical change) and chemical decomposition (chemical change)

Hence, the correct option is (b)

40. Formation of rust is a chemical change. When iron is exposed to humid atmosphere, it forms hydrated ferric oxide ($Fe_2O_3.xH_2O$).

Hence, the correct option is (b)

41. (i) The positive ion, i.e., Zn^{+2} followed by the negative ion, i.e., O^{-2} are written with their charges.

(ii) The valencies of ions formed by zinc and oxygen and are written below without positive and negative signs.

(iii) The valencies of zinc and oxide have common factors, and hence, they are divided by the highest common factor.

(iv) The magnitude of the valencies of the ions should be interchanged and written as subscripts on right side of the respective ions.

Hence, the correct option is (c)

42. Electronic configuration of X is 2, 8, 7

Electronic configuration of Y is 2, 8, 6

∴ Valencies of X and Y are 1 and 2, respectively.

$M^{2+}X^{-}$ $M^{2+}Y^{2-}$

MX_2 MY

Hence, the correct option is (a)

43. X should possess five valence electrons since its valency is 3. Hence, its corresponding hydride is X^{3-} $H^{1+} \Rightarrow XH_3$

Hence, the correct option is (c)

44.

Element	'Z'	Electronic configuration
A	10	2, 8
B	18	2, 8, 8
C	8	2, 6

Hence, C is chemically reactive. A and B are chemically inert because of stable octet configuration.

Hence, the correct option is (c)

45. X^{+2} = No. of protons = 12 (Z)

Neutrons = 12

No. of electrons = 10

A = 12 + 12 = 24

Y^{+2} = 18 electrons

Y = 20 electrons or 20 protons (Z)

A = 20 + 20 = 40

$A_x : A_y$

24 : 40

3 : 5

Hence, the correct option is (b)

46. X^- = 9 protons (Z)

10 neutrons

10 electrons

$$X \xrightarrow{+1e^{-1}} X^{-1}$$

(9 electrons) (10 electrons)

Therefore, the electronic configuration of an atom is 2, 7.

Hence, the correct option is (b)

47. We know that mass of a proton is 1837 times that of an electron.

∴ Atomic number of the element $= \frac{55110}{1837} = 30$

∴ Electronic configuration of the element is 2, 8, 18 and 2.

Hence, the correct option is (c)

48. X : Y

3 : 2

2, 8, 8   2, 8, x

$\frac{8-2}{x+2} = \frac{3}{2}$; X = 6

$\therefore$ X → 2, 8, 8 and Y → 2, 8, 6

Hence, the correct option is (b)

49. $2KMnO_4 + 3H_2SO_4 + 5H_2C_2O_4 \rightarrow K_2SO_4 + 2MnSO_4 + 10CO_2 + 8H_2O$

Hence, the correct option is (a)

50. Gunpowder is a mixture of KNO_3, sulphur and coke. When it is heated, KNO_3 undergoes decomposition to produce O_2 and KNO_2. S and C burn in the presence of O_2 producing SO_2 and CO_2.

$$2KNO_3 \xrightarrow{\Delta} 2KNO_2 + O_2$$

$$S + O_2 \rightarrow SO_2$$

$$C + O_2 \rightarrow CO_2$$

Hence, the type of chemical changes involved is decomposition and combination.

Hence, the correct option is (a)

51. $CuSO_4 + X \rightarrow XSO_4 + Cu$

$\therefore$ X is more reactive than Cu

$CuSO_4 + Y \rightarrow YSO_4 + Cu$

$\therefore$ Y is more reactive than Cu

$XSO_4 + Y \rightarrow$ No reaction

$\therefore$ X is more reactive than Y

$CuSO_4 + Z \rightarrow$ No reaction

$\therefore$ Z is less reactive than Cu

$\therefore$ order is Z < Cu < Y < X

Hence, the correct option is (d)

52. Let the metal be X. The compounds possible are XSO_4 and $X_2(SO_4)_3$. The number of oxygen atoms present is 4 and 12, respectively. Ratio of oxygen atoms is 4 : 12 = 1 : 3

Hence, the correct option is (a)

53. X attains an octet configuration after gaining two electrons. Hence, the valency is 2 and valency of hydrogen is 1. $X^{-2}H^{+1} \Rightarrow XH_2$

Hence, the correct option is (d)

54.

Element	X	Y	Z
Valence shell	K	L	M
	(1)	(2)	(3)
No. of valence electrons	2	8	6
Elements	He	Ne	S

Sulphur does not exist in monoatomic state due to its greater chemical reactivity.

Hence, the correct option is (b)

55. The electronic configuration of the of the dinegative ion with 8 electrons in valence shell (L shell) is

X^{-2} → 2, 8

X → 2, 6 (Z), mass number is 16,

Y^{-2} → 2, 8, 8

Y → 2, 8, 6 (Z)

Mass number is 32 (A) for Y.

Ratio of mass numbers = 16 : 32; 1 : 2

Hence, the correct option is (a)

56. Electronic configuration of neutral atom is:

K	L	M
2	8	3

Therefore, the ratio of the electrons present in the K and M shells is 2 : 3.

Hence, the correct option is (a)

57. The electronic configuration of the element is

K	L	M	N
2	8	8	2

Therefore, the atomic number is 20. We know that mass of proton is 1837 times that of electron.

Therefore, total positive charge present in nucleus is 20 × 1837 = 36,740.

Hence, the correct option is (a)

58. (X) K L M   (Y) K L M

2 8 X   2 8 6

$\frac{8-2}{8-X} = \frac{1}{1}$

8 − X = 8 − 2

X = 2

Stable ion of X is X^{2+} and of Y is Y^{2-}.

X^{2+} : 2, 8 Y^{2-} : 2, 8, 8

Hence, the correct option is (c)

59. $CuSO_4 + Zn \rightarrow ZnSO_4 + Cu$
blue colourless

Hence, the correct option is (c)

60. $2Cu(NO_3)_2.6H_2O \rightarrow 2CuO + 4NO_2 + O_2 + 6H_2O$

Coefficients of CuO, NO_2 and H_2O are respectively 2, 4 and 6.

∴ Ratio is 1 : 2 : 3

Hence, the correct option is (b)

61. Decomposition of limestone takes place at higher temperatures. Hence, it is a thermal decomposition reaction. Formation of HCl takes place in presence of light. But it is not a decomposition reaction. HOCl on standing in presence of light decomposes to give HCl and O_2.

Hence, the correct option is (a)

62. A → f $4SO_2$ represents four sulphur dioxide molecules

B → g $2Na^+$ represents two sodium ions

C → b $3O_2$ represents three molecules of oxygen

D → c $8Cl_2$ represents 8 molecules of chlorine

63. A → b Charge on aluminium ion is +3

B → c Charge on of stannous ion is +2

C → a Charge on of bisulphate is –1

D → e Charge on silicate ion is –2

64. A → c Lead nitrate is decomposed into PbO, NO_2 and O_2

B → d Zinc displaces iron from $FeSO_4$

C → b Mutual exchange of ions takes place when NaCl and $AgNO_3$ react

D → a Sulphur combines with oxygen to form sulphur dioxide

Level 2: Review Your Concepts

65. The electronic configuration of the given atom is 2, 8, 5. Therefore, it is phosphorus.

66. Electronic configuration of X is 2, 8

A – Z = number of neutrons

A – 10 = 10

∴ mass number (A) is = 20

67. $N_2O_5 \rightarrow 7$

$H_2SO_4 \rightarrow 7$

$Ca(OH)_2 \rightarrow 5$

$Fe(OH)_3 \rightarrow 7$

68. $3CuO + 2NH_3 \rightarrow 3Cu + N_2 + 3H_2O$

N_2 has the lowest coefficient, i.e., 1.

69.

Atomic number	Element	Electronic configuration	Valency
7	Nitrogen	2, 5	3
15	Phosphorus	2, 8, 5	3
16	Sulphur	2, 8, 6	2
18	Argon	2, 8, 8	0
19	Potassium	2, 8, 8, 1	1

Since N and P need three more electrons to attain an octet configuration, their valencies are 3.

Similarly, the valencies of other elements with atomic numbers 16, 18, 19 are 2, 0 and 1, respectively.

Except argon, all other elements form hydrides.

Phosphorus – PH_3, Potassium – KH

Nitrogen – NH_3

Sulphur – H_2S

Argon does not form any compound

70. In test tube "A", when sodium chloride solution is added to lead nitrate solution Pb^{2+}(Lead ion) combine with Cl^-(chloride ion) and Na^+(sodium ion) combine with $NO^-{}_3$ (Nitrate ion) to form $PbCl_2$ (lead chloride) and $NaNO_3$(sodium nitrate) in which $PbCl_2$ is insoluble in water. So this reaction is precipitation reaction (chemical double displacement reaction).

In test tube "B", when lithium hydroxide solution is added to Sulphuric acid, lithium sulphate and water are formed. So this reaction is a chemical double displacement reaction as well as neutralisation reaction.

71. The electronic arrangement of the element could be 2, 8, 8, 1. It corresponds to Z = 19 and the element is potassium. Oxygen (Z = 8) has the electronic arrangement of 2, 6. Potassium loses one electron to form K^+ ion, oxygen requires 2 electrons to complete its octet. Therefore, it takes 2 electrons from two potassium atoms and forms K_2O.

72.

Elements	Atomic numbers	Electronic configurations
Ca	20	2, 8, 8, 2
Cl	17	2, 8, 7

Ca loses two electrons to attain an octet configuration while Cl gains an electron to attain the same.

Hence, the formula of the compound is

$Ca^{2+}\ Cl^{-}$

$CaCl_2$

73. K L M N
2 8 8 2

Hence, the valency of an atom of an element (M) with above electronic configuration is 2 and by losing two electrons it attains an octet configuration.

(a) Formula of its nitride is $M^{2+}N^{3-} \rightarrow M_3N_2$

(b) Formula of its silicate is $M^{2+}SiO_3^{2-} \rightarrow MSiO_3$

(c) Formula of its chloride is $M^{2+}Cl^{-} \rightarrow MCl_2$

74. 16 protons mean that the atomic number of the element (X) is 16. This signifies that the electronic configuration is 2, 8, 6. It has to gain two electrons to attain an octet configuration. Hence, the dinegative ion possesses 18 electrons.

$(X^{2-}) = 16 + 2 = 18.$

A – Z = number of neutrons

Mass number = 2 + 2 (number of protons)

= 2 + 2 (16) = 34

∴ Number of neutrons = 34 – 16 = 18

Hence, number of neutrons = 18

75. In MSO_3, the valency of sulphite is 2. Hence, the valency of M is also 2.

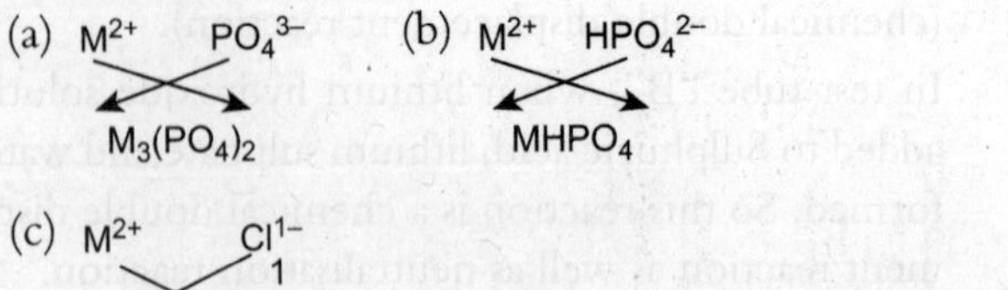

76. When mercury gets spilled on the floor or any surface, it can be collected by sprinkling sulphur powder because Hg reacts with S to form HgS.

$Hg + S \rightarrow HgS$

It is an element–elèment combination, i.e., a synthesis reaction.

77. During boiling of milk, the fat particles being lighter than water rise up when some amount of water vaporizes. This layer of fat becomes thick and forms a coating over milk upon cooling. Since it involves partial separation of the components of milk, boiling of milk is a physical change. Curdling of milk involves partial conversion of lactose sugar into lactic acid. Since there is change in molecular composition, curdling of milk is a chemical change.

78. When Fe is exposed to humid air for a long period of time, it gets rusted.

Rust: $Fe_2O_3.x\ H_2O$

Valency of Fe is 3

79. (a) $3Fe + 4H_2O \rightarrow Fe_3O_4 + 4H_2$
Steam (ferroso-ferric oxide)

(b) $3Mg + N_2 \rightarrow Mg_3N_2$

(c) $CuSO_4 + Zn \rightarrow ZnSO_4 + Cu$

80.

A	B
$CuSO_4$	$CuSO_4$
+	+
Mg	Ag
↓	↓
$MgSO_4$ + Cu	No reaction

The blue-coloured $CuSO_4$ solution in test tube A disappears, and thus, a colourless solution of $MgSO_4$ is formed. This is due to higher reactivity of Mg than Cu. Hence, Mg can displace Cu from $CuSO_4$ solution, and hence, blue-coloured $CuSO_4$ slowly turns colourless. Ag, being less reactive than Cu, cannot displace Cu from $CuSO_4$, and hence, the solution remains blue in colour.

Level 3: Assess Your Concepts

81. The electronic arrangement of X must be 2, 8, 18, 2. So, the atomic number of X should be 30. The element X is Zn which can form Zn^{+2} ion by losing 2 electrons from the N shell.

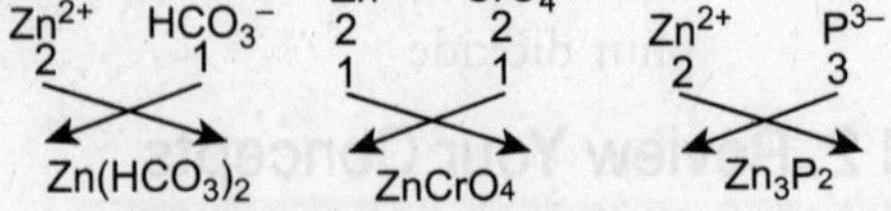

82. Formula M_4X_3 corresponds to $M^{3+}\ X^{4-}$. M has three occupied shells K, L and M. The number of electrons in valence shell is equal to 3. The electronic arrangement could be 2, 8, 3 which corresponds to Z = 13, i.e., aluminium. X has two occupied shells K and L and the L shell must have 4 electrons. The electronic arrangement could be 2, 4 which corresponds to Z = 6, i.e., carbon.

(a) $Al^{3+}SO_4^{2-}$

(b) Al^{3+} $H_2PO_4^-$
(c) Al^{3+} OH^-
$Al_2(SO_4)_3$ $Al(H_2PO_4)_3$ $Al(OH)_3$

83.

Shell	A	B
L	8	8
Electronic configuration	2, 8, 8, 1	2, 8, 2
Metal	K	Mg
Formulae	(i) KNO_2	$Mg(NO_2)_2$
	(ii) KNO_3	$Mg(NO_3)_2$
	(iii) K_2SO_3	$MgSO_3$
	(iv) $KHSO_3$	$Mg(HSO_3)$

Or

	A	B
Electronic configuration	2, 8, 8, 2	2, 8, 3
Metal	Ca	Al
Formulae	(i) $Ca(NO_2)_2$	$Al(NO_2)_3$
	(ii) $Ca(NO_3)_2$	$Al(NO_3)_3$
	(iii) $CaSO_3$	$Al_2(SO_3)_3$
	(iv) $Ca(HSO_3)_2$	$Al(HSO_3)_3$

84. If subscripts are changed, then the molecular formulae, i.e., composition of the compound is changed.

Hence, the number of atoms on either side of a chemical equation is balanced by keeping appropriate coefficients.

85. K shell can have only 2 electrons. That means $n = 2$ and the number of electrons in the L shell is $2n + 1$ which is equal to 5. The electronic arrangement, i.e., 2, 5 corresponds to nitrogen. Nitrogen can form NH_4^+ radical (x) with hydrogen. Y is NO_2^- and Z is NO_3^-.

$AgNO_3 + NH_4Cl \rightarrow AgCl + NH_4NO_4$

This is a double decomposition reaction where silver chloride being insoluble settles at the bottom.

Therefore, this is a precipitation reaction.

86. The charges on cupric ion [Cu^{2+}] and sulphate radical [SO_4^{2-}] are +2 and –2 respectively. In the given compound XY, the cation present is X^{2+} and the anion present is Y^{2-}. The number of protons of neon atom is 10 and the total of the number of electrons present in K, L and M shells of potassium atom is 18. X^{+2} has 10 electrons, hence it is magnesium ion and Y^{2-} has 18 electrons so it is sulphide ion. The compound XY is MgS (magnesium sulphide)

CHAPTER

3

Acids, Bases and Salts

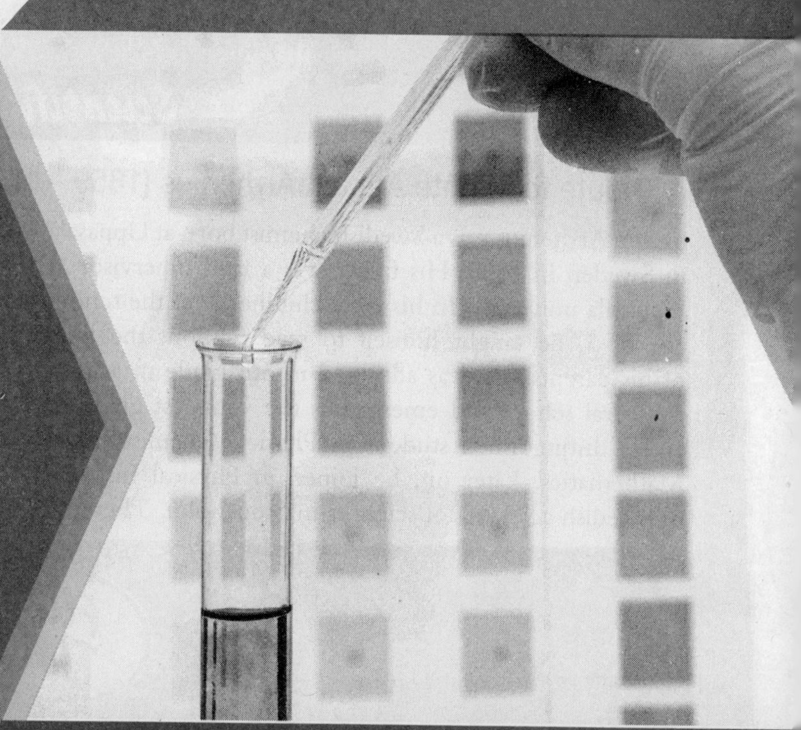

Remember

Before beginning this chapter, you should be able to:

- classify matter on the basis of physical and chemical properties.
- define terms such as atoms, molecules, atomic numbers, etc.
- understand the chemical reactions.

Key Ideas

After completing this chapter, you should be able to:

- define terms such as acids, bases, indicators, acidity, basicity, etc.
- learn about the methods of preparation, properties and uses of acids and bases.
- describe the action of indicators on acids and bases.
- learn about neutralisation, different types of salts, their methods of preparation, properties and uses.

Scientific Crypt

A Tribute to Svante August Arrhenius (1859 – 1927)

Svante Arrhenius was a Swedish chemist born at Uppasala in Sweden in 1859. His father was a land supervisor at Uppasala university. In his early childhood, at the tender age of 3, he taught himself to read without the help of his parents. He was admitted in 5th grade in a local cathedral school and emerged as the youngest graduate and a distinguished student in Physics, Chemistry and Mathematics. Later on, he joined in Physical Institute of Swedish academy of sciences in Stockholm. There he pursued study on various topics including the theory of acids and bases. In 1903, he was awarded Nobel prize in Chemistry for his work on electrolytes. He was made a fellow of Royal Swedish academy of sciences and also member of Nobel committee on Physics and Chemistry. He had many more achievements in the field of Chemistry and attained eventuality in 1927 and was buried at Uppasala.

FUN TIME

CROSSWORD

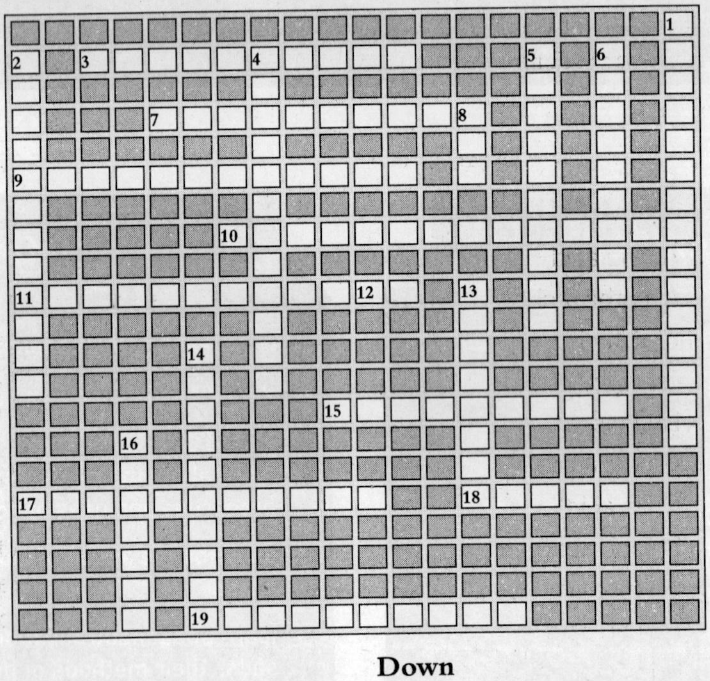

Across

3. Salt which is used for purification of water.
7. Type of salt formed between carbonic acid and potassium hydroxide.
9. Acids obtained from plants or animals.
10. Reaction between acid and base.
11. Salts which can not give reactions of individual ions.
15. Type of salt formed between nitric acid and calcium hydroxide.
17. The nature of substances which do not undergo any change in physical state on absorbing moisture.
18. Number of water molecules present in each molecule of green vitriol
19. Common name of a base used for removal of hair from skin

Down

1. Salt which is used for removal of microorganisms from water.
2. _______ nature is associated with substances which lose water of crystallisation on exposure to air
4. The salts which possess fixed number of water molecules attached to crystals.
5. Acid present in tomato
6. Acids which possess hydrogen and non-metal.
8. Number of water molecules associated with a molecule of washing soda.
12. Acid which is a component of baking powder.
13. Acids which possess hydrogen, oxygen and non-mental.
14. Salts which contain more than one acidic or basic radicals.
16. Acidic salts are formed by _______ neutralisation between acid and base.

INTRODUCTION

We are very much familiar with the classification of substances on the basis of their physical state as solids, liquids and gases. In the same way, they can be classified on the basis of chemical composition as elements, compounds and mixtures. This chapter will deal with another important categorisation of some chemical compounds into acids, bases and salts.

We know that some fruits such as oranges, lemons and grapes and other food materials, such as tamarind, have a sour taste. The term, **acid**, (derived from '*acidus*' [Latin]; used for expressing sour taste) has been given to the substances which are responsible for the sour taste of the food materials discussed earlier. In the same way, the substances which possess bitter taste like bitter gourd and slippery touch like soaps are called **bases.**

Classification of Acids

Based on the Source of Origin

Many acids are obtained from the parts of plants and some acids are produced by animals also. These are called **organic acids** due to the fact that their primary sources of origin are living systems. They can also be synthesised in a laboratory (Table 3.1).

Table 3.1 Organic Acids

Acids	Sources
Acetic acid	Vinegar
Ascorbic acid	Lemons
Citric acid	All citrus fruits
Tartaric acid	Tamarind, grapes
Lactic acid	Curd
Maleic acid	Grapes
Oleic acid	Olive oil
Stearic acid	Mustard oil
Palmitic acid	Palm oil
Formic acid	Sting of ants and insects
Uric acid	Urine
Oxalic acid	Tomato
Butyric acid	Rancid butter

Konnect

The ancient Indian sage and philosopher, Charaka, who lived around 300 BCE, recognized the sour taste as one of the basic tastes. This is a testament to the fact that ancient India was already familiar with acidic substances long before modern classifications!

The acids which are synthesised from the minerals obtained from the earth's crust are called **mineral acids** or **inorganic acids.**

These mineral acids can be further classified on the basis of various characteristics (Table 3.2).

Table 3.2 Mineral Acids

Chemical Names	Common Names	Formulae
Hydrochloric acid	Muriatic acid	HCl
Sulphuric acid	Oil of vitriol or king of chemicals	H_2SO_4
Nitric acid	Aqua fortis	HNO_3

Some Common Mineral Acids Used in Laboratories

Based on the constituent elements in the acids, they are classified as hydracids and oxyacids. The acids which contain hydrogen and another non-metal are called **hydracids**. The acids which contain oxygen along with hydrogen and non-metal are called **oxyacids.**

Classification of Bases

Based on their ionization capacity, bases are classified into two types: strong bases and weak bases.

Strong Bases: These are bases which ionize completely when mixed with water. E.g. NaOH, KOH.

Weak Bases: These are bases which ionize partially in aqueous solution. Eg. NH_4OH, $Ca(OH)_2$.

On the basis of their acidity, bases are classified into three types:

Monoacidic base: One molecule gives one hydroxide ion when dissolved in water, E.g. NaOH, KOH.

Diacidic base: One molecules gives two hydroxide ions when dissolved in water. E.g., $Ca(OH)_2$, $Mg(OH)_2$

Triacidic base: One molecules gives two hydroxide ions when dissolved in water. E.g., $Al(OH)_3$, $Fe(OH)_3$

Acids, Bases and Their Types

An **acid** is defined as a substance which on dissolution in water furnishes H^+ ions as the only positively charged ions. A **base** is defined as a substance which on dissolution in water furnishes OH^- ions as the only negatively charged ions.

The splitting up of a substance into ions when dissolved in water is called **ionisation.**Various acids and bases differ with respect to the extent of ionisation, and hence, they are classified on the basis of ionisation.

Strong Acids and Strong Bases

The acids and bases which undergo complete ionisation when dissolved in water and furnish large concentration of $\mathbf{H^+}$ or $\mathbf{OH^-}$ ions, respectively are called **strong acids** and **strong bases.**

Examples:

Strong Acids

$HCl \rightarrow H^+ + Cl^-$

$H_2SO_4 \rightarrow 2H^+ + SO_4^{2-}$

$HNO_3 \rightarrow H^+ + NO_3^-$

Strong Bases

$NaOH \rightarrow Na^+ + OH^-$

$KOH \rightarrow K^+ + OH^-$

Info Bytes!

Historical Use of Acids—Ancient Indian metallurgy techniques used acidic solutions, like those derived from plants, to refine and extract metals.

Weak Acids and Weak Bases

The acids and bases which ionise partially and furnish less concentration of H^+ and OH^- ions, respectively are called **weak acids** and **weak bases.**

Examples:

Weak Acids

$CH_3COOH \rightleftharpoons CH_3COO^- + H^+$

$H_2CO_3 \rightleftharpoons 2H^+ + CO_3^{2-}$

$H_3PO_4 \rightleftharpoons 3H^+ + PO_4^{3-}$

Weak Bases

$Ca(OH)_2 \rightleftharpoons Ca^{2+} + 2OH^-$

$Al(OH)_3 \rightleftharpoons Al^{3+} + 3OH^-$

Hydracids are named as hydro ……ic acid by including the name of the non-metal.

Examples:

HCl	Hydrochloric acid
HBr	Hydrobromic acid
HI	Hydroiodic acid
H_2S	Hydrosulphuric acid

Oxyacids

Oxyacids are named based on the number of oxygen atoms present in the acid. Generally, most of the non-metals form two types of oxyacids. The acid containing less number of oxygen atoms is called **ous acid**. The acid containing more number of oxygen atoms is called **ic acid** (Table 3.3).

Table 3.3 Naming of Acids

Names of Non-metal	Formulae of Oxyacid	Names of Oxyacid
Sulphur	H_2SO_3	Sulphurous acid
	H_2SO_4	Sulphuric acid
Nitrogen	HNO_2	Nitrous acid
	HNO_3	Nitric acid
Chlorine	$HClO_2$	Chlorous acid
	$HClO_3$	Chloric acid
Carbon	H_2CO_3	Carbonic acid
Phosphorus	H_3PO_3	Phosphorous acid
	H_3PO_4	Phosphoric acid

All oxides and hydroxides of metals are basic in nature. Therefore, the bases are named by suffixing oxide term or hydroxide term to the positive radical.

Examples:

NaOH	Sodium hydroxide
NH_4OH	Ammonium hydroxide

The bases which are soluble in water are called **alkalies**.

Konnect

All alkalies are bases but not all bases are alkalies.

Solubility of Acids and Bases in Water

Since all the acids and alkalies are soluble in water, the solutions of these substances in water are called **aqueous solutions**. Depending on the relative proportions of water and acid or base present in the solution, the acids and bases are categorised as concentrated and dilute acids or bases.

Concentrated acids or bases contain lesser proportion of water in contrast to the **dilute** acids or bases which contain larger proportion of water.

Actual concentration of H^+ or OH^- ions in an aqueous solution of an acid or base respectively depends upon the number of H^+ or OH^- ions furnished by one molecule of an acid or base, respectively on ionisation. This is given by **basicity** of an acid, i.e., the number of H^+ ions furnished by one molecule of acid and **acidity** of a base, i.e., the number of OH^- ions furnished by one molecule of base.

Acids and bases can also be classified on the basis of **basicity** of acids and **acidity** of bases (Tables 3.4 and 3.5).

Table 3.4 Classification of Acids Based on Basicity

Types of Acid	Basicity	Examples
Monobasic acid	1	$HCl \rightarrow H^+ + Cl^-$
		$HNO_3 \rightarrow H^+ + NO_3^-$
		$CH_3COOH \rightleftharpoons H^+ + CH_3COO^-$
Dibasic acid	2	$H_2SO_4 \rightarrow 2H^+ + SO_4^{2-}$
		$H_2CO_3 \rightleftharpoons 2H^+ + CO_3^{2-}$
		$H_2C_2O_4 \rightleftharpoons 2H^+ + C_2O_4^{2-}$
Tribasic acid	3	$H_3PO_4 \rightleftharpoons 3H^+ + PO_4^{3-}$

Table 3.5 Classification of Bases Based on Acidity

Types of base	Acidity	Examples
Monoacidic base	1	$NaOH \rightarrow Na^+ + OH^-$
		$KOH \rightarrow K^+ + OH^-$
		$NH_4OH \rightleftharpoons NH_4^+ + OH^-$
Diacidic base	2	$Ca(OH)_2 \rightleftharpoons Ca^{2+} + 2OH^-$
		$Ba(OH)_2 \rightleftharpoons Ba^{2+} + 2OH^-$
Triacidic base	3	$Al(OH)_3 \rightleftharpoons Al^{3+} + 3OH^-$

Methods of Preparation of Acids and Bases

There are various methods to prepare acids and bases. Some of those are listed below.

Acids

1. **By Direct Combination of Elements:** Acids can be prepared by taking two elements like hydrogen gas and chlorine gas. They directly combine and give hydrogen chloride gas (HCl) which dissolves in water and forms hydrochloric acid.

   Example: $H_2 + Cl_2 \rightarrow 2HCl$

2. **From Non-metals:** Non-metallic elements, on heating with oxygen, give corresponding oxides. Some oxides on dissolution in water give the corresponding acids, and hence, such non-metallic oxides are called **acidic oxides**.

   Example:

   $C + O_2 \rightarrow CO_2$ $\quad$ $CO_2 + H_2O \rightarrow H_2CO_3$

   $S + O_2 \rightarrow SO_2$ $\quad$ $SO_2 + H_2O \rightarrow H_2SO_3$

   $2SO_2 + O_2 \rightarrow 2SO_3$ $\quad$ $SO_3 + H_2O \rightarrow H_2SO_4$

   The oxides which are insoluble in water are called **neutral oxides**, for example, NO and CO.

Konnect

The process of fermenting rice and other grains to produce alcoholic beverages in India relies on the action of acids. The concept of fermentation has been in practice for centuries!

Bases

1. **From Metals:** Metals on heating with oxygen give metal oxides which are basic in nature. These metal oxides on dissolution in water give corresponding bases.

   Examples:

   $4Na + O_2 \rightarrow 2Na_2O$ $Na_2O + H_2O \rightarrow 2NaOH$

   $2Mg + O_2 \rightarrow 2MgO$ $MgO + H_2O \rightarrow Mg(OH)_2$

2. **Preparation of Slaked Lime from Quick Lime**: When quick lime (calcium oxide) reacts with water, it forms slaked lime (calcium hydroxide) with the liberation of heat.

$$\underset{\text{(Quick lime)}}{CaO} + H_2O \rightarrow \underset{\text{(Slaked lime)}}{Ca(OH)_2} + \text{Heat}$$

Slaked lime is not readily soluble in water and gets settled down at the bottom. The water collected over the slaked lime is called **lime water**.

Physical Properties of Acids and Bases

Some of the physical properties of acids and bases are listed in Table 3.6.

Table 3.6 Physical Properties of Acids and Bases

Properties	Acids	Bases
Colour	Mineral acids are colourless liquids but sometimes sulphuric acid becomes yellow due to impurities. Some organic acids are white-coloured solids. **Example:** Benzoic acid	Bases are colourless except the hydroxides of iron and copper
Taste	Sour	Bitter
Touch	–	Slippery
Solubility	Soluble in water	Some bases are soluble in water

Info Bytes!

The Taj Mahal, one of the world's seven wonders located in Agra, India, has been affected by acid rain. The pollutants in the air react with water to form acids which corrode the white marble of the monument.

Chemical Properties of Acids and Bases

Some of the important chemical properties of acids and bases are listed in Table 3.7 and Table 3.8 respectively.

Table 3.7 Chemical Properties of Acids

Reactions	Examples
Reaction with Metals: Some metals displace hydrogen from strong acids (HCl, H_2SO_4, etc.). These are called **active metals**	$Zn + H_2SO_4 \rightarrow ZnSO_4 + H_2$ $Mg + 2HCl \rightarrow MgCl_2 + H_2$
Reaction with Metal Oxides: All dilute mineral acids react with metallic oxides to form their respective metallic salts and water	$ZnO + H_2SO_4 \rightarrow ZnSO_4 + H_2O$ $CaO + 2HNO_3 \rightarrow Ca(NO_3)_2 + H_2O$
Reaction with Metal Carbonates: This reaction also comes under neutralisation but accompanied by the release of CO_2 gas along with the formation of salt and water	$CaCO_3 + 2HCl \rightarrow CaCl_2 + H_2O + CO_2$ $MgCO_3 + H_2SO_4 \rightarrow MgSO_4 + CO_2 + H_2O$

Table 3.8 Chemical Properties of Bases

Reactions	Examples
Action of Heat: Some hydroxides melt on strong heating. They do not undergo decomposition	NaOH, KOH
Other metal hydroxides undergo decomposition on strong heating	$Ca(OH)_2 \xrightarrow{\Delta} CaO + H_2O$ $2Al(OH)_3 \xrightarrow{\Delta} Al_2O_3 + 3H_2O$
Ammonium hydroxide decomposes rapidly to give ammonia gas and water upon slight heating	$NH_4OH \xrightarrow{\Delta} NH_3 + H_2O$

Comparative Study of Properties of Acids and Bases

A comparative study of properties of acids and bases is provided in Table 3.9.

Table 3.9 Comparative Study of Properties of Acids and Bases

Parameter	Properties	Examples
Corrosive action on skin	All acids and some alkalies show corrosive action on skin as they form painful blisters when they come in contact with skin.	H_2SO_4 absorbs water from skin tissues. HNO_3 reacts with skin proteins to form a pulp-like mass. NaOH and KOH are called caustic soda and caustic potash, respectively due to their causticizing action on skin.
Reactions between acids and bases	All acids react with alkalies (metal hydroxides) to form salt and water.	$2KOH + H_2SO_4 \rightarrow K_2SO_4 + 2H_2O$ $Ca(OH)_2 + 2HNO_3 \rightarrow Ca(NO_3)_2 + 2H_2O$

EXAMPLE 3.1

Why is NaOH called caustic soda?

SOLUTION

NaOH has a strong corrosive action on the skin, and therefore, it is called caustic soda.

EXAMPLE 3.2

Give an example of a tribasic acid. How is it obtained from the corresponding non-metal? Give balanced equations.

SOLUTION

Phosphoric acid is a tribasic acid. When phosphorus burns in the presence of oxygen, it forms phosphorus pentoxide. On dissolution in water, phosphorus pentoxide forms phosphoric acid.

$P_4 + 5O_2 \rightarrow 2P_2O_5$

$P_2O_5 + 3H_2O \rightarrow 2H_3PO_4$

Thus, phosphoric acid is obtained.

Neutralisation

The reaction between an acid and a base invariably gives salt and water and is called **neutralisation**. In a neutralisation reaction, one H^+ ion of acid is neutralised by one OH^- ion of base. When all the H^+ ions in the acidic solution are neutralised by same number of OH^- ions of basic solution, it is called **complete neutralisation**. The relative amounts of acid and base required for complete neutralisation depend upon the total number of H^+ and OH^- ions produced by the respective acid and base.

Konnect

In traditional Indian medicine, Ayurveda, the concept of balancing the body's pH is fundamental, and it is believed that a balanced diet consisting of both acidic and alkaline foods ensures good health.

Applications of Neutralisation in Daily Life

- **Addition of Lime to Soils:** Usually, soils are acidic in nature due to the minerals present in the earth's crust, acid rain etc., Acidic soils are generally not suitable for most of the crops. Addition of lime to soil reduces the acidity and makes the soil neutral or basic which is ideal for many crops. Reverse is done when the soil is too basic. In this case organic matter or compost is added which releases natural acids into the soil and neutralizes the excess amounts of bases present in the soil.
- **Beetle Leaves:** Addition of slaked lime to beetle leaves produces red colour due to neutralisation reaction.
- **Acidity in Stomach:** Secretion of hydrochloric acid in the stomach creates acidic medium required for the digestion of food. However, secretion of excess acid causes acidity or ulcer problems. This acidity can be subsided by taking antacid syrups which usually contain magnesium hydroxide which is a weak base.
- **Stinge of an Ant or Bee and Wasp Stinge:** Stinge of an ant or bee produces formic acid. Washing with baking soda solution gives relief from the burning sensation. Wasp stinge produces venom which is basic in nature and hence vinegar is applied to neutralise it and give relief.
- **Industrial waste:** The wastes released by the industries are acidic in nature. If these acidic effluents are directly let out in the water bodies then it causes great harm and can also be fatal for aquatic organisms. To counter this effect these industrial wastes are neutralized with the addition of bases.

Salt

Salt is a substance which contains positive and negative ions or radicals and ionises completely in its aqueous solution. These are formed by a neutralisation reaction.

Example:

$$\text{Acid} + \text{Base} \xrightarrow{\text{Neutralization}} \text{Salt} + \text{Water}$$

When a reaction between acids and bases happens in such a way that some of the replaceable hydrogen ions in acid or replaceable hydroxyl ions in the base are left unreplaced, then these reactions are called **partial neutralisation reactions**. During this process, acidic or basic salts are formed.

Info Bytes!

Sweet and Sour—One of India's most popular cuisines, Gujarati food, is known for its hint of sweetness in almost all dishes. This is achieved by balancing the acidic and basic ingredients perfectly!

Types of Salts

Given below is the description of major types of salts with their examples.

1. **Normal Salts:** When all the H^+ ions furnished by an acid molecule are replaced by the metal ions, then the salts formed are called **normal salts**. These salts are formed during complete neutralisation.

   Examples:

   $$2NaOH + H_2SO_4 \rightarrow Na_2SO_4 + 2H_2O$$

   $$2H_3PO_4 + 3Ca(OH)_2 \rightarrow Ca_3(PO_4)_2 + 6H_2O$$

2. **Acidic Salts**: When a dibasic or tribasic acid is treated with a base and less number of H^+ ions are replaced by the metal ions of the base, then the salt formed is still left with at least one hydrogen molecule. The salt can further undergo neutralisation and eventually forms a normal salt. Such a salt is called an **acidic salt**. These salts furnish hydrogen ions when dissolved in water. These salts are formed by partial neutralisation.

Examples: $NaOH + H_3PO_4 \rightarrow NaH_2PO_4 + H_2O$ (Sodium dihydrogen phosphate (acidic salt))

$NaOH + NaH_2PO_4 \rightarrow Na_2HPO_4 + H_2O$ (Disodium hydrogen phosphate (acidic salt))

$NaOH + Na_2HPO_4 \rightarrow Na_3PO_4 + H_2O$ (Sodium phosphate (normal salt))

3. **Basic Salts:** When a diacidic or triacidic base is treated with an acid and less number of OH^- ions are replaced by the negative ion of the acid, then the salt formed is still left with at least one OH^- ion. The salt can further undergo neutralisation to form a normal salt. Such salts are called **basic salts**. These salts furnish hydroxyl ions when dissolved in water. These salts are formed by partial neutralisation.

Examples: $Ca(OH)_2 + HCl \rightarrow Ca(OH)(Cl) + H_2O$ (Calcium hydroxychloride (basic salt))

$Ca(OH)Cl + HCl \rightarrow CaCl_2 + H_2O$ (Calcium chloride (normal salt))

The differences between an acidic and a basic salt are listed in Table 3.10.

Table 3.10 Comparitive Study of Acidic and Basic Salts

Acidic Salt	Basic Salt
It contains replaceable hydrogen ions.	It contains replaceable hydroxyl ions.
It ionises in water and gives hydrogen ions.	It ionises in water and gives hydroxyl ions.
It turns blue litmus to red.	It turns red litmus to blue.
It gives no colour with phenolphthalein.	It gives pink colour with phenolphthalein.

4. **Double Salts**: The salts which contain more than one simple salt are called **double salts**. These salts undergo complete dissociation in their aqueous solutions. They give reactions of all ions present in both the simple salts.

Examples: (i) Mohr's salt, $FeSO_4.(NH_4)_2SO_4.6H_2O$.
This dissociates into Fe^{2+}, NH_4^+, SO_4^{2-} ions and gives their individual chemical test.
(ii) Potash alum, $K_2SO_4.Al_2(SO_4)_3.24H_2O$.

5. **Mixed Salts**: The salts which contain more than one basic or acidic radical are called **mixed salts**. These salts undergo complete dissociation in aqueous solutions. They give the reactions of all the ions produced in aqueous solutions.

Examples: (i) Sodium potassium carbonate ($NaKCO_3$) (Na^+, K^+ and CO_3^{2-} radicals)
(ii) Bleaching powder ($CaOCl_2$) (Ca^{2+}, OCl^-, Cl^- radicals)

6. **Complex Salts:** The salt which contains one or more simple ions and one complex ion is called **complex salt**. A complex ion is made up of group of atoms which does not undergo further dissociation into individual atoms or ions and acts as a complete unit.

These salts undergo dissociation into a complex ion and a simple ion.

Examples: (i) Potassium ferrocyanide $K_4[Fe(CN)_6]$

$$K_4[Fe(CN)_6] \xrightarrow{\text{Dissociation}} \underset{\text{(Simple ion)}}{4K^+} + \underset{\text{(Complex ion)}}{[Fe(CN)_6]^{4-}}$$

(ii) Sodium argentocyanide $Na[Ag(CN)_2]$

Derivation of Names of Salts

The name of a salt is basically derived from the acid from which it is formed. The salts derived from the hydracids are given names ending with **'ide'** suffix. If the salt contains hydrogen, then hydrogen is added to the suffix (Table 3.11).

Table 3.11 Naming of Salts of Hydracids

Formula of Acids	Formula of Bases	Salts Formed	Name of the Salts
HCl	NaOH	NaCl	Sodium chloride
H_2S	NaOH	Na_2S	Sodium sulphide
H_2S	NaOH	NaHS	Sodium hydrogen sulphide

The salts derived from oxy acids are given names depending on the type of the oxy acid. The salts of **'ous'** acids are given **'ite'** suffix and the salts of **'ic'** acids are given **'ate'** suffix. If hydrogen is present in the salt, hydrogen or **'bi'** is added to the name of the radical, i.e., corresponding suffix (Table 3.12).

Table 3.12 Naming of Salts of Oxyacids

Formula of Acids	Formula of Bases	Formula of Salts	Name of the Salts
H_2SO_3	KOH	K_2SO_3	Potassium sulphite
		$KHSO_3$	Potassium hydrogen sulphite
H_2SO_4	NaOH	Na_2SO_4	Sodium sulphate
		$NaHSO_4$	Sodium hydrogen sulphate
H_3PO_4	NaOH	$NaPO_4$	Sodium phosphate
		Na_2HPO_4	Disodium hydrogen phosphate
		NaH_2PO_4	Sodium dihydrogen phosphate

In the same way, the salts of nitrous acid and nitric acid are called **nitrites** and **nitrates**, respectively. The salts of carbonic acid are called **carbonates** and **bicarbonates** or **hydrogen carbonates**. The positive ion part is called **basic radical** and the negative ion part is called **acidic radical**.

Preparation of Simple Salts

1. Sodium chloride is prepared by the neutralisation of sodium hydroxide with hydrochloric acid.

$$\underset{\text{Sodium hydroxide}}{NaOH} + HCl \rightarrow \underset{\text{Sodium chloride}}{NaCl} + H_2O$$

2. Potassium chloride is prepared by the neutralisation of potassium hydroxide with hydrochloric acid.

$$\underset{\text{Potassium hydroxide}}{KOH} + HCl \rightarrow \underset{\text{Potassium chloride}}{KCl} + H_2O$$

3. Calcium chloride is prepared by the neutralisation of calcium hydroxide with hydrochloric acid.

$$\underset{\text{Calcium hydroxide}}{Ca(OH)_2} + 2HCl \rightarrow \underset{\text{Calcium chloride}}{CaCl_2} + 2H_2O$$

4. Zinc sulphate is prepared by reacting zinc oxide with sulphuric acid.

$$\underset{\text{Zinc oxide}}{ZnO} + H_2SO_4 \rightarrow \underset{\text{Zinc sulphate}}{ZnSO_4} + H_2O$$

5. Copper sulphate is prepared by reacting copper oxide with sulphuric acid.

$$CuO + H_2SO_4 \rightarrow CuSO_4 + H_2O$$

Copper oxide — Copper sulphate

6. Ammonium chloride is prepared by the neutralisation of ammonium hydroxide with hydrochloric acid.

$$NH_4OH + HCl \rightarrow NH_4Cl + H_2O$$

Ammonium hydroxide — Ammonium chloride

Properties of Salts

1. Salts are solids at room temperature.
2. Salts of sodium and potassium are colourless, whereas salts of iron, copper, chromium, etc., are coloured.

   Examples: Ferrous sulphate is green, aqueous copper sulphate is blue and potassium dichromate is orange–red coloured.
3. Salts have high melting points.
4. Most of the salts are soluble in water. The only exceptions are carbonates, sulphides and sulphates of some metals.
5. The aqueous solutions of salts are good conductors of electricity. Hence, they are called **electrolytes**.
6. When a salt is dissolved in water, depending on the amount of salt dissolved in fixed amount of water, three types of solutions can be obtained.

   (a) **Unsaturated Solution**: If the solution is in a state in which it can still dissolve more amount of solute, the solution is said to be **unsaturated.**

   (b) **Saturated Solution**: If the solution is in a state in which it cannot dissolve any more amount of solute, the solution is said to be **saturated.**

   (c) **Supersaturated Solution**: If more amount of salt is made to dissolve in the saturated solution under some conditions, the solution is said to be **supersaturated.**

Hydrated Salts

In case of some salts, some water molecules are found to be attached to the crystals of salt. These are called **hydrated salts.** In these salts, a fixed number of water molecules gets attached to each molecule of the salt. This is known as **water of crystallisation**. A hydrated salt is represented by writing the number of water molecules along with the formula of the salt.

Examples: (i) $CuSO_4.5H_2O$

(ii) $FeSO_4.7H_2O$

(iii) $Na_2SO_4.10H_2O$

The salts which do not possess water of crystallisation are called **anhydrous salts.**

Examples: $CuSO_4$, $FeSO_4$, etc.

All hydrated salts lose water of crystallisation on heating and become anhydrous salts. In case of some salts, the colour of the salt is due to the presence of water of crystallisation. Those salts become colourless on heating. For example, $CuSO_4.5H_2O$ is blue in colour and on heating loses blue colour as it forms white coloured anhydrous $CuSO_4$. However, some salts lose water of crystallisation either completely or partially on exposure to atmospheric air. These are called **efflorescent substances**. For example, $Na_2CO_3.10H_2O$ loses nine water molecules on exposure to air and the remaining one water molecule on heating.

Similarly, there are some substances which absorb moisture from the atmosphere on exposure to air. By absorbing moisture, they may dissolve in the water absorbed and change into solution. Such substances are called **deliquescent substances**. For example, calcium chloride, magnesium chloride, mercuric nitrate, zinc chloride, etc.

However, some substances do not undergo any change in physical state on the absorption of moisture from the atmospheric air. These are called **hygroscopic substances**. For example, calcium oxide, sulphuric acid, cobalt chloride, etc.

Uses of Acids, Bases and Salts

Various uses of acids are listed in Table 3.13.

Table 3.13 Various Uses of Acids

Name of the Acids	Uses	Properties Used
Hydrochloric acid	Cleaning metal surfaces before tinning and galvanising Dyeing Preparation of glucose from starch	• Reaction of acids with metal oxide coating. • HCl reacts with complex organic compounds and forms coloured compounds. • HCl carries out hydrolysis of starch to glucose.
Sulphuric acid	Manufacture of fertilisers Car batteries Dyes, drugs, paints, plastics, detergents	• Reaction with bases to form soluble salts. • Electrolyte. • Complex organic reactions to form varied products.
Nitric acid	Fertilisers Explosives Purification of noble metals (Au, Pt, etc.)	• Highly soluble nature of nitrate salts. TNT, TNG. • Insoluble nature of Au and Pt in HNO_3.
Phosphoric acid	Fertilisers	Phosphorus is an essential nutrient for plants.
Carbonic acid	Soda water and soft drinks	Tangy taste imparted to water. CO_2 is dissolved in water at high pressure.
Acetic acid	Additive in food stuffs	Preservative action and sour taste.
Tartaric acid	Baking powder	Neutralising action.

Various uses of bases are listed in Table 3.14.

Table 3.14 Various Uses of Bases

Name of the Bases	Uses	Properties Exploited	Solubility in Water
Sodium hydroxide (caustic soda) and **potassium hydroxide.**	• Manufacture of soap • Paper pulp preparation • Synthetic fibres • Manufacture of medicines • Preparation of metallic sodium • Used as a laboratory reagent	• Reaction with oil • Reaction with hydrocarbons of wood	Soluble

(Continued)

Table 3.14 Continued

Name of the Bases	Uses	Properties Exploited	Solubility in Water
Calcium hydroxide	• Making mortar • Removal of hair from animal skin • Spread on beetle leaves • Preparation of bleaching powder • Used as a good disinfectant in white washing • To prepare Bordeaux mixture ($CuSO_4$ + lime)	• Hardening of mortar on exposure to air. • Neutralisation	Slightly soluble
Magnesium hydroxide	Antacid	Neutralising action on insoluble excess HCl produced in the stomach.	

Various uses of salts are listed in Table 3.15.

Table 3.15 Uses of salts

Chemical Names and Formulae	Common Names	Uses
Sodium chloride, NaCl	Common salt	Food additive Preservative for pickles Manufacture of chlorine and NaOH antacid tablets
Sodium bicarbonate, $NaHCO_3$	Baking soda	Leavening agent for cakes. Fire extinguisher Washing clothes
Sodium carbonate, $Na_2CO_3.10H_2O$	Washing soda	Manufacture of glass Detergents
Sodium nitrate, $NaNO_3$	Chile salt petre	Manufacture of nitric acid, gunpowder, and in fireworks Fertiliser
Potassium nitrate, KNO	Nitre	Manufacture of gunpowder, nitric acid Fireworks
Ammonium carbonate, $(NH_4)_2CO_3$	Smelling salt	Relief from common cold
Magnesium sulphate, $MgSO_4.7H_2O$	Epsom salt	Laxative
Ferrous sulphate, $FeSO_4.7H_2O$	Green vitriol	Making of ink, curing of leather
Copper sulphate, $CuSO_4.5H_2O$	Blue vitriol	Fungicide in agriculture, dyeing and printing, electroplating
Calcium sulphate hemihydrate, $CaSO_4.\frac{1}{2}H_2O$	Plaster of Paris	Making of statues, setting of broken bones

(Continued)

Table 3.15 Continued

Chemical Names and Formulae	Common Names	Uses
Potassium aluminium sulfate dodecahydrate, $K_2SO_4.Al_2(SO_4)_3.24H_2O$	Potash alum	Purification of water
Ammonium chloride, NH_4Cl	Salammoniac	Used as a laboratory reagent
Calcium oxychloride, $CaOCl_2$	Bleaching powder	Bleaching clothes and purification of water
Sodium nitrate, $NaNO_3$	Chile salt petre	As fertiliser, in glass and fireworks
Sodium thiosulphate, $Na_2S_2O_3$	Hypo	As an antichlor for removing excess of chlorine from the bleached articles in textile industries
Zinc sulphate, $ZnSO_4.7H_2O$	White vitriol	In medicine as an eye lotion and in making lithopone, a paint base

Indicators

During the process of neutralisation, a point called **neutralisation point** is reached when all the H^+ ions of an acidic solution are neutralised exactly by the OH^- ions of a basic solution. Further addition of a base to an acid or an acid to a base adds excess OH^- or H^+ ions which changes the nature of the solution from an acidic to a basic or the basic to the acidic, respectively. In order to identify the neutralisation point, during the experiment, certain substances are added which show different colours in acidic and basic solutions. Such substances undergo colour change at the neutralisation point which indicates complete neutralisation and hence are called **indicators**. Certain naturally occurring substances can act as indicators as they change colour based on the nature of a substance.

Konnect

Red cabbage, which can be found in Indian vegetable markets, can be used as a pH indicator It changes to various colours depending on whether the solution is acidic or basic.

Example: red cabbage juice.

The other indicators used are litmus, methyl orange and phenolphthalein.

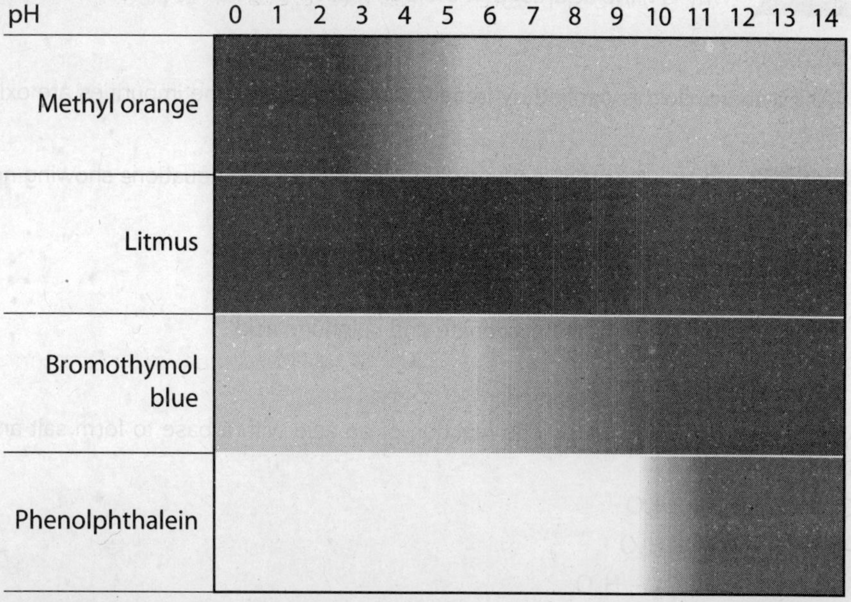

Figure 3.1 Colour change in indicators in the presence of acids and base

Natural indicators

Indicators are the substances which are used to identify the acidic or basic nature of a substance. The substances which are found naturally and can be used to determine the nature of the substances are called **natural indicators.**

Examples: Litmus; Red cabbage juice; Turmeric

Red Cabbage Juice: It can be prepared by chopping red cabbage, grinding it and filtering the extract.

Red cabbage juice when added to acidic solutions shows pink colour. When it is added to a neutral solution, it gives purple colour. In a basic or alkaline solution, it shows greenish yellow colour.

Litmus: It is a common indicator which is extracted from lichens. It shows red colour in acidic solution and blue colour in basic solution.

Turmeric: It shows yellow colour in acidic solutions and red colour in alkaline solutions.

Konnect

Natural Indicators and Beauty—Henna, often used in India for intricate body art and as a natural hair dye, can vary in colour based on the pH level of the skin or hair it's applied.

Action of Indicators on Acids and Bases

The action of indicators on acids and bases is shown in Table 3.16.

Table 3.16 Action of Indicators on Acids and Bases

Names of Indicator	Colours in Acidic Solution	Colours in Basic Solution
Litmus	Red	Blue
Methyl orange	Pink (orange red)	Yellow
Phenolphthalein	Colourless	Pink
Turmeric	Yellow	Red
Bromothymol	Yellow	Blue

EXAMPLE 3.3 Why is nitric acid used in the purification of gold?

SOLUTION

Nitric acid is a good oxidising agent. Gold is purified by treating it with HNO_3; all the impurities are oxidised by nitric acid.

EXAMPLE 3.4 What is meant by neutralisation? Give balanced equations showing neutralisation reactions of the following.

(a) Slaked lime and sulphuric acid

(b) Sodium bicarbonate and hydrochloric acid.

(c) Magnesium carbonate and sulphuric acid.

SOLUTION

All acids react with alkalies to form salt and water. The reaction of an acid with a base to form salt and water as the products is called neutralisation.

(a) $Ca(OH)_2 + H_2SO_4 \rightarrow CaSO_4 + 2H_2O$

(b) $NaHCO_3 + HCl \rightarrow NaCl + CO_2 + H_2O$

(c) $MgCO_3 + H_2SO_4 \rightarrow MgSO_4 + CO_2 + H_2O$

POINTS TO REMEMBER

- ✔ Many acids are obtained from the parts of plants and some acids are produced by animals also. These are called organic acids due to the fact that their primary sources of origin are living systems.
- ✔ The acids which are synthesised from the minerals obtained from the earth's crust are called mineral acids or inorganic acids.
- ✔ The acids which contain hydrogen, and another non-metal are called hydracids. The acids which contain oxygen along with hydrogen and non-metal are called oxyacids.
- ✔ An acid is defined as a substance which on dissolution in water furnishes H^+ ions as the only positively- charged ions. A base is defined as a substance which on dissolution in water furnishes OH^- ions as the only negatively-charged ions.
- ✔ The splitting up of a substance into ions when dissolved in water is called ionisation.
- ✔ The acids and bases which undergo complete ionisation when dissolved in water and furnish large concentration of H^+ or OH^- ions, respectively are called strong acids and strong bases.
- ✔ The acids and bases which ionise partially and furnish less concentration of H^+ and OH^- ions, respectively are called weak acids and weak bases.
- ✔ Concentrated acids or bases contain lesser proportion of water in contrast to the dilute acids or bases which contain larger proportion of water.
- ✔ The reaction of an acid with a base to form salt and water as the products is called neutralisation.
- ✔ Salt is a substance which contains positive and negative ions or radicals and ionises completely in its aqueous solution.
- ✔ In case of some salts, some water molecules are found to be attached to the crystals of salt. These are called hydrated salts.
- ✔ The salts which do not possess water of crystallisation are called anhydrous salts.
- ✔ Some salts lose water of crystallisation either completely or partially on exposure to atmospheric air. These are called efflorescent substances.
- ✔ By absorbing moisture, they may dissolve in the water absorbed and change into solution. Such substances are called deliquescent substances.
- ✔ Some substances do not undergo any change in physical state on the absorption of moisture from the atmospheric air. These are called hygroscopic substances.
- ✔ During the process of neutralisation, a point called neutralisation point is reached when all the H^+ ions of an acid solution are neutralised exactly by the OH^- ions of a basic solution.
- ✔ Some substances undergo colour change at the neutralisation point which indicates complete neutralisation and hence are called indicators.
- ✔ The substances which are found naturally and can be used to determine the nature of the substances are called natural indicators.

PRACTICE QUESTIONS CLASSROOM WING

Very Short Answer Type Questions

Directions for questions from 1 to 5:
Fill in the blanks.

1. Methyl orange turns lime water ________.
2. Chemical formula and chemical name of plaster of Paris are ________and ________ respectively.
3. The salt formed by removal of water of crystallisation from hydrated salt is called ________.
4. Hydrated zinc sulphate is ________ in colour.
5. ________ which is a hydrated salt is used as a fungicide in agriculture.

Directions for questions from 6 to 43:
For each of the questions, four choices have been provided. Select the correct alternative.

6. Which among the following acids is present in lemons?
(a) Acetic acid (b) Oleic acid
(c) Stearic acid (d) Ascorbic acid
7. Identify the weak mineral acid among the following.
(a) Palmitic acid (b) Acetic acid
(c) Carbonic acid (d) hydrochloric acid
8. For the formation of a normal salt from one molecule of H_2SO_4, how many molecules of NaOH are required?
(a) One (b) Two
(c) Four (d) Three
9. Which among the following pairs of bases do not decompose on heating?
(a) Calcium hydroxide, potassium hydroxide
(b) Sodium hydroxide, potassium hydroxide
(c) Copper hydroxide, calcium hydroxide
(d) Codium hydroxide, copper hydroxide
10. Which among the following is a strong acid?
(a) Acetic acid (b) Sulphurous acid
(c) Carbonic acid (d) Nitric acid
11. Among the following, which substance turns phenolphthalein to pink?
(a) Soda water (b) Lime water
(c) Common salt (d) Sugar solution
12. Washing soda is________
(a) hydrated sodium carbonate
(b) anhydrous sodium carbonate
(c) hydrated magnesium sulphate
(d) anhydrous magnesium sulphate
13. A salt formed by the partial neutralisation of hydroxyl ions of a base by an acid is called ________ salt.
(a) normal (b) acidic
(c) basic (d) none of these
14. Which among the following is a hydrated salt?
(a) Marble (b) Baking soda
(c) Green vitriol (d) All the above
15. Salt used in purification of water is:
(a) potash alum (b) epsom salt
(c) green vitriol (d) blue vitriol
16. Monobasic weak acid among the following is:
(a) carbonic acid (b) oxalic acid
(c) acetic acid (d) nitric acid
17. ________ on hydrolysis gives a strong acid.
(a) Sulphur dioxide (b) Carbon dioxide
(c) Sulphur trioxide (d) Nitrogen oxide
18. Which among the following is the application of neutralisation?
(a) Farmers add slaked lime to soil.
(b) Persons suffering from acidity are given antacid tablets.
(c) Usage of lithium hydroxide in submarines.
(d) All the above.
19. Salt solutions are good conductors of electricity. This is due to the presence of ________ in solution state.
(a) mobile electrons (b) mobile ions
(c) molecules (d) both (a) and (c)
20. Which among the following is used to remove moisture from the surroundings?
(a) Calcium chloride
(b) Magnesium chloride
(c) Zinc chloride
(d) Calcium oxide
21. X is a base which is soluble in water. Then, the metal present in X may be:
(a) aluminium (b) copper
(c) magnesium (d) manganese
22. Monobasic weak acid among the following is:
(a) carbonic acid (b) oxalic acid
(c) acetic acid (d) nitric acid

23. _______ on hydrolysis gives only strong acid.
(a) Sulphur dioxide (b) Carbon dioxide
(c) Sulphur trioxide (d) Nitrogen dioxide

24. Arrange the pairs in sequence in decreasing order of basicity of an acid and acidity of a base followed by the normal salts formed by the given acid–base pairs in the same order, respectively.
(1) Acetic acid and ammonium hydroxide
(2) Oxalic acid and barium hydroxide
(3) Phosphoric acid and aluminium hydroxide
(4) Barium oxalate
(5) Ammonium acetate
(6) Aluminium phosphate
(a) 14365 (b) 321645
(c) 143526 (d) 341526

25. Match the following

	Column A		Column B
A.	$CuSO_4$	a.	Hygroscopic
B.	$Na_2CO_3.10H_2O$	b.	Deliquescent
C.	Concentrated H_2SO_4	c.	Efflorescent
D.	$ZnCl_2$	d.	Anhydrous salt

(a) A→b, B→c, C→d, D→a
(b) A→d, B→c, C→a, D→b
(c) A→c, B→d, C→b, D→a
(d) A→c, B→d, C→a, D→b

26. Role of nitre in the manufacture of gunpowder is :
(a) to supply oxygen
(b) to supply nitrogen
(c) to decrease the rate of combustion
(d) to absorb temperature produced by combustion

27. Which among the following is a weak acid?
(a) Sulphuric acid (b) Hydrochloric acid
(c) Nitric acid (d) Carbonic acid

28. The salt formed by the complete neutralisation of aluminium hydroxide with sulphuric acid is:
(a) $Al_2(SO_3)_3$ (b) $Al_2(SO_4)_3$
(c) $Al(HSO_4)_3$ (d) $Al(HSO_3)_3$

29. Identify the common use(s) of both Chile salt petre and nitre.
(a) Manufacture of gunpowder
(b) Manufacture of fertiliser
(c) Manufacture of glass
(d) All the above

30. Acidic and double salts among the following are respectively:
(a) potash alum and sodium phosphate
(b) sodium dihydrogen phosphate and Mohr's salt
(c) Mohr's salt and calcium hydroxy chloride.
(d) sodium phosphate and Mohr's salt

31. Which of the following is a dibasic weak mineral acid?
(a) Acetic acid (b) Sulphuric acid
(c) Phosphoric acid (d) Sulphurous acid

32. If a non-metal forms only two oxides and one oxide on hydrolysis gives an acid, then the non-metal could be:
(a) sulphur (b) carbon
(c) phosphorus (d) nitrogen

33. Which among the following is/are poor conductor(s) of electricity?
(a) Pure H_2SO_4
(b) Pure HNO_3
(c) Liquefied hydrogen chloride
(d) All the above

34. Which among the following is an antacid pair?
(a) $Mg(OH)_2$, NaOH (b) $Mg(OH)_2$, $Al(OH)_3$
(c) KOH, NaOH (d) $Al(OH)_3$, NaOH

35. Match the following:

	Column A		Column B
A.	CaO	a.	Deliquescent
B.	$MgCl_2.6H_2O$	b.	Hydrated salt, but not deliquescent
C.	$FeSO_4.7H_2O$	c.	Anhydrous and deliquescent salt
D.	$MgSO_4$	d.	Hygroscopic

(a) A → d, B → a, C → b, D → c
(b) A → a, B → d, C → b, D → c
(c) A → b, B → c, C → d, D → a
(d) A → d, B → c, C → b, D → a

36. The gaseous products that are formed when gunpowder is subjected to heating are dissolved in water. Identify the products formed on dissolution.
(a) H_2CO_3, HNO_3 (b) H_2SO_3, H_2SO_4
(c) H_2SO_4, HNO_2 (d) H_2SO_3, H_2CO_3

37. Identify the pair of water-soluble bases.
(a) Copper oxide and potassium oxide
(b) Copper oxide and sodium oxide
(c) Sodium, oxide and potassium oxide
(d) Aluminium oxide and magnesium oxide

38. **Assertion (A)**: Generally pickles are stored in glass vessels and plastic vessels.

Reason (R): The components of pickles are highly reactive towards glass/plastic.

(a) Both A and R are true and R is the correct explanation for A.

(b) Both A and R are true and R is not the correct explanation for A.

(c) A is true and R is false.

(d) Both A and R are false.

39. Arrange the salts given below in the order of complex salt, basic salt, normal salt and mixed salts, respectively.

(1) $Ca_3(PO_4)_2$ (2) $Ca(OH)Cl$

(3) $CaOCl_2$ (4) $K_4[Fe(CN)_6]$

(a) 4231 (b) 2431

(c) 4213 (d) 1234

40. Arrange the following equations in the correct sequence to obtain a normal salt.

(1) $Al(OH)Cl_2 + HCl \rightarrow AlCl_3 + H_2O$

(2) $Al(OH)_3 + HCl \rightarrow Al(OH)_2Cl + H_2O$

(3) $Al(OH)_2Cl + HCl \rightarrow Al(OH)Cl_2 + H_2O$

(a) 321 (b) 231

(c) 123 (d) 312

41. **Assertion (A)**: Pure H_2SO_4 is colourless.

Reason (R): On long standing H_2SO_4 undergoes decomposition to form SO_2.

(a) Both A and R are true and R is the correct explanation for A.

(b) Both A and R are true and R is not the correct explanation for A.

(c) A is true and R is false.

(d) Both A and R are false.

42. A non-metallic element is converted into a compound X after a series of reactions. A little amount of X when tested with blue litmus turns to red. X on complete reaction with another compound Y gave the product which did not respond to litmus test. Identify the correct sequence of the reactions.

(1) $2SO_2 + O_2 \rightarrow 2SO_3$

(2) $H_2SO_4 + 2KOH \rightarrow K_2SO_4 + 2H_2O$

(3) $SO_3 + H_2O \rightarrow H_2SO_4$

(4) $S + O_2 \rightarrow SO_2$

(a) 1342 (b) 4132

(c) 2314 (d) 4321

43. Identify the application of neutralisation among the following.

(a) Addition of slaked lime to soil.

(b) Doctors giving antacid to patient suffering from acidity.

(c) Usage of lithium hydroxide in submarines.

(d) All the these

Directions for questions from 44 to 46:
Match the entries given in Column A with the appropriate ones in Column B. More than one suitable content of Column B can also be considered correct for an entry in Column A and some content given in Column B may not be the appropriate one for any entry in Column A.

44. Match the statements of Column A with those of Column B.

Column A	Column B
(i) Potash alum	(A) Leavening agent for cakes
(ii) Plaster of Paris	(B) Laxative
(iii) Sodium carbonate	(C) Purification of water
(iv) Sodium bicarbonate	(D) Manufacture of glass
(v) Epsom salt	(E) Making statues

45.

Column A	Column B
A. Sodium dihydrogen phosphate	(a) Basic salt
B. Calcium hydroxy chloride	(b) Gunpowder
C. Nitre	(c) Manufacture of glass
D. Ammonium carbonate	(d) Acidic salt
	(e) Normal salt
	(f) Smelling salt

46.

Column A	Column B
A. Efflorescent	(a) Cobalt chloride
B. Deliquescent	(b) Sodium chloride
C. Hygroscopic	(c) Zinc chloride
D. Food additive	(d) Mercuric nitrate
	(e) Washing soda

Directions for questions from 47 to 65:
Answer the following questions.

47. Name the acid present in

(a) curd (b) tamarind

48. Name the acid which is produced by the sting of an ant.

49. What is meant by an alkali? Give two examples.

50. Give common names of sodium hydroxide and potassium hydroxide.

51. Name the substances formed by the dissolution of following oxides in water.
(a) CO_2 (b) MgO

52. What is the action of litmus on an acid and a base?

53. Name a natural indicator.

54. Give the formulae of the following salts:
(a) blue vitriol (b) green vitriol
(c) potash alum

55. Name the salt used for the manufacture of glass. Give its formula.

56. Name the salts used for the following purposes:
(a) Purification of water
(b) Fire extinguisher

57. Name the acid present in:
(a) lemon (b) vinegar

59. What are neutral oxides? Give examples.

59. Name the acid and base from which the following salts are formed.
(a) Sodium chloride (b) Potassium sulphate
(c) Calcium nitrate

60. What are the suffixes of salts formed from the following acids?
(a) Carbonic acid (b) Nitrous acid
(c) Sulphuric acid (d) Nitric acid

61. Write the chemical formula of hypo.

62. Identify the basic and acidic radicals in sodium nitrate.

63. Give two examples of hydrated salts.

64. Define water of crystallisation.

65. What is the formula of Plaster of Paris?

Short Answer Type Questions

66. What is the similarity between Oxalic and Carbonic acid?

67. Why does iron become passive on treatment with concentrated nitric acid?

68. What is the distinguishing feature of a hygroscopic substance from a deli-quescent substance?

69. What are active metals? Give examples with equations.

70. Explain the corrosive action of acids and alkalies. Give examples.

71. Distinguish between an acid and base with respect to definitions.

72. Define the following and give an example for each.
(a) efflorescent substances
(b) deliquescent salts
(c) hygroscopic salts

73. What are mineral acids? How can they be further classified on the basis of nature of the constituents?

74. Distinguish between strong acids and weak acids. Give two examples of each.

75. Write a short note on naming of acids.

76. What is meant by neutralisation? Give balanced equations showing neutralisation reactions of the following:
(a) slaked lime and sulphuric acid
(b) sodium bicarbonate and hydrochloric acid
(c) magnesium carbonate and sulphuric acid

77. What is the action of heat on the following?
(a) Ammonium hydroxide
(b) Aluminium hydroxide
(c) Sodium hydroxide

78. What are indicators? Give examples.

79. Distinguish between acidic salts and basic salts.

80. What do we observe when solid zinc chloride and anhydrous cobalt chloride are taken in the two open containers ‘A’ and ‘B’ respectively? Give reasons.

81. Mention four important properties of salts.

82. Mention two uses of the salts given below:
(a) sodium chloride
(b) sodium bicarbonate
(c) calcium sulphate hemihydrate

83. Mention two important uses of the following acids and also mention the property exploited.
(a) hydrochloric acid (b) nitric acid

Essay Answer Type Questions

84. Arrange the following salts in the increasing order of the total number of ions produced on dissociation per molecule of the salt.
(a) $CaOCl_2$ (b) $K_2SO_4.Al_2(SO_4)_3$
(c) $Na[Ag(CN)_2]$ (d) $Fe_2(SO_4)_3$

85. Out of the following electronic configurations, which of these can form a neutral oxide?
(a) 2, 4 (b) 2, 8, 6
(c) 2, 5

86. Give the chemical properties of acids and bases by giving balanced chemical equations.

87. Sodium oxide on dissolution in water gives 'X' and sulphur trioxide on dissolution in water gives 'Y'. Identify the nature of products formed if one molecule of 'X' reacts with one molecule of 'Y' and two molecules of 'X' reacts with one molecule of 'Y'. Write all the required balanced chemical equations.

88. Describe the methods of preparation of acids and bases with the help of examples.

89. Give equations for the dissociation of the following compounds in their solutions and write the formulae of the salts formed from them.
(a) H_2SO_4 (b) $Mg(OH)_2$.

90. Explain the naming of salts with examples.

91. (1) By using moist blue litmus paper, classify the given compounds given below as acids and bases:
$Ca(OH)_2$, H_2SO_4, CH_3COOH, $NaOH$, KOH, $Mg(OH)_2$, HNO_3, NH_4OH

(2) Mention the acidic or basic or neutral nature of solutions by using
(a) litmus
(b) methyl orange
(c) phenolphthalein indicators

92. Mention the uses of the following bases and mention the property exploited in those uses.
(a) Sodium hydroxide
(b) Calcium hydroxide
(c) Magnesium hydroxide

PRACTICE QUESTIONS COMPETITION WING

Level 1: Apply your Concepts

Directions for questions from 1 to 15:
Fill in the blanks.

1. The acids which are obtained from the minerals are called ________.
2. The oxides of __________ on hydrolysis give bases.
3. Ammonium hydroxide on heating gives __________ and __________.
4. Zinc on reaction with dilute sulphuric acid liberates __________ gas.
5. Mineral acids react with metallic carbonate to form its respective metallic salt, ________ and ________.
6. Hydrochloric acid is a ________ acid. (monobasic/dibasic)
7. Carbonic acid is a ________ acid. (strong/weak)
8. Sulphur dioxide on hydrolysis gives ______.
9. Acid turns methyl orange solution to ______.
10. Ammonium hydroxide is an ______. (acid/alkali)
11. Sodium sulphate is a ________ salt.
12. Formula of washing soda is ________.
13. Nitre is the common name of ________.
14. Mercuric nitrate is a ________ salt. (deliquescent/efflorescent)
15. Chile salt petre is used in the manufacture of ________. (nitric acid/nitrous acid)

Directions for questions from 16 to 25:
State whether the following statements are true or false.

16. Hydrochloric acid is a monobasic acid.
17. Carbonic acid is a strong acid.
18. Sulphur dioxide on hydrolysis gives sulphuric acid.
19. Acids turn methyl orange solution to pink.
20. Ammonium hydroxide is an alkali.
21. Lead sulphide is a normal salt.
22. Formula of washing soda is $Na_2CO_3.7H_2O$.
23. Nitre is the common name of sodium nitrate.
24. Mercuric nitrate is a deliquescent salt.
25. Chile salt petre is used in the manufacture of nitric acid.

Directions for questions from 26 to 61:
For each of the questions, four choices have been provided. Select the correct alternative.

26. **Assertion (A):** All alkalis are bases but all bases are not alkalis.
    Reason (R): Some bases are insoluble in water.
    (a) Both A and R are true and R is the correct explanation of A.
    (b) Both A and R are true, but R is not the correct explanation of A.
    (c) A is true and R is false.
    (d) A is false and R is true.
27. **Assertion (A):** Nitric acid is used in the purification of gold.
    Reason (R): Nitric acid is a strong oxidizing agent.
    (a) Both A and R are true and R is the correct explanation of A.
    (b) Both A and R are true, but R is not the correct explanation of A.
    (c) A is true and R is false.
    (d) A is false and R is true.
28. H_3PO_4 is an example of:
    (a) monobasic acid
    (b) dibasic acid
    (c) tribasic acid
    (d) strong acid
29. $Ca(OH)_2$ in an example of:
    (a) monoacidic base
    (b) diacidic base
    (c) triacidic base
    (d) strong base

30. $CaCl_2$ is an example of:
(a) normal salt
(b) acidic salt
(c) basic salt
(d) complex salt

31. Among the following, identify an extremely corrosive alkali.
(a) Ammonium hydroxide
(b) Calcium hydroxide
(c) Potassium hydroxide
(d) Magnesium hydroxide

32. Generally, hydrolysis of metal oxides gives
(a) acids
(b) bases
(c) salts
(d) hydrogen gas

33. Name of the salt formed by treating calcium oxide solution with nitric acid is ________.
(a) calcium nitrate
(b) calcium nitrite
(c) calcium hydrogen nitrate
(d) calcium hydrogen nitrite

34. Formula of potassium hydrogen sulphite is:
(a) $KHSO_3$ (b) K_2SO_3
(c) K_2SO_4 (d) $KHSO_4$

35. Smelling salt is:
(a) sodium chloride
(b) calcium carbonate
(c) ammonium chloride
(d) ammonium carbonate

36. Dibasic weak mineral acid among the following is:
(a) acetic acid
(b) sulphuric acid
(c) phosphoric acid
(d) sulphurous acid

37. If a non-metal forms only two oxides and one oxide on hydrolysis gives an acid, then the non-metal could be:
(a) sulphur
(b) carbon
(c) phosphorus
(d) nitrogen

38. Antacid pair among the following is:
(a) $Mg(OH)_2$, NaOH
(b) $Mg(OH)_2$, $Al(OH)_3$
(c) KOH, NaOH
(d) $Al(OH)_3$, NaOH

39. Which among the given is/are poor conductors of electricity?
(a) Concentrated and pure H_2SO_4
(b) Concentrated and pure HNO_3
(c) Liquid hydrogen chloride
(d) All the above

40. Hygroscopic substance among the following is:
(a) calcium oxide (b) sodium oxide
(c) common salt (d) calcium chloride

41. Among the following, identify the pair of water-soluble bases.
(a) copper oxide and potassium oxide
(b) copper oxide and calcium oxide
(c) magnesium oxide and potassium oxide
(d) aluminium oxide and magnesium oxide

42. A metallic element is converted into a compound 'A' after a series of reactions. Compound A turns red litmus to blue. A on reaction with another compound B which turns blue litmus to red gave a compound C which responded to litmus test like compound B C on further reaction with A gave a compound D which did not respond to litmus test. Identify the correct sequence of steps for the formation of A, B, C and D.
(1) $NaOH + H_2SO_4 \rightarrow NaHSO_4 + H_2O$
(2) $4Na + O_2 \rightarrow 2Na_2O$
(3) $NaHSO_4 + NaOH \rightarrow Na_2SO_4 + H_2O$
(4) $Na_2O + H_2O \rightarrow 2NaOH$
(a) 1324 (b) 2314
(c) 2413 (d) 4213

43. Arrange the following pairs in a sequence of decreasing order of acidity of base and increasing order of basicity of an acid and the salts formed between an acid and base with equal basicity and acidity in their increasing order, respectively.
(1) Sodium chloride
(2) Barium hydroxide and sulphuric acid
(3) Ferric phosphate
(4) Ferric hydroxide and hydrochloric acid
(5) Barium sulphate
(6) Sodium hydroxide and phosphoric acid
(a) 426153 (b) 624153
(c) 426351 (d) 624351

44. Odd one among the following with respect to the strength of acids is:

(a) phosphoric acid (b) carbonic acid
(c) sulphuric acid (d) acetic acid

45. One molecule of an 'ic' acid of a non-metal having 5 electrons in valence shell reacts with a molecule of base to form a salt X. The base corresponds to the metal with one electron in valence shell. If the salt so formed can react with the same base in 1 : 2 ratio, predict the formula of the salt X.

(a) K_2SO_4 (b) Na_2HPO_4
(c) KH_2PO_4 (d) Na_3PO_4

46. Three elements form their respective oxides A, B and C. A and C are gases and B is a solid which on dissolution in water turns red litmus to blue. In presence of moisture, A turns blue litmus to red and C is neutral to litmus. Then, A, B and C may be, respectively:

(a) SO_3, MgO, NO
(b) SO_2, CaO, CO_2
(c) CO,Na_2O, SO_3
(d) SO_2, $Ca(OH)_2$, NO_2

47. Two salts X and Y are taken in two test tubes A and B, respectively, and subjected to heating. Water is added to two test tubes, in case of A salt regains its original colour and in case of B water starts boiling. Then, X and Y may be, respectively:

(a) blue vitriol and limestone
(b) blue vitriol and baking soda
(c) nitre and limestone
(d) nitre and washing soda

48. The salt formed by complete neutralisation of calcium hydroxide with oxy acid of sulphur having four oxygen atoms is:

(a) calcium sulphite
(b) calcium bisulphate
(c) calcium sulphate
(d) calcium bisulphite

49. Role of nitre in the manufacture of gunpowder is :

(a) to supply oxygen
(b) to supply nitrogen
(c) to decrease the rate of combustion
(d) absorb temperature produced by combustion

50. Generally, pickles are stored in:

(a) tin vessels or glass vessels
(b) tin vessels or plastic vessels
(c) glass vessels or plastic vessels
(d) aluminium vessels or tin vessels

51. Pure HNO_3 is colourless, however, it gradually becomes yellow on standing due to ______.

(a) the decomposition of HNO_3 and formation of NO
(b) the decomposition of HNO_3 and formation of NO_2
(c) oxidation by atmospheric O_2 and formation of NO
(d) oxidation by atmospheric O_2 and formation of NO_2

52. H_2SO_4 is used in the manufacture of fertilisers. The property exploited in H_2SO_4 is:

(a) formation of soluble salts
(b) strong acid
(c) good electrolyte
(d) good dehydrating agent

53. Weak acid among the following is:

(a) sulphuric acid (b) hydrochloric acid
(c) nitric acid (d) carbonic acid

54. A salt 'x' has a positive radical in which the metal has electronic configuration 2, 8, 8, 2. The negative radical is formed from an acid used in soft drinks. One molecule of the salt 'x' reacts with one molecule of a base. Predict the formula of the salt 'x.'

(a) $Mg(HCO_3)_2$ (b) $Ca(HCO_3)_2$
(c) $CaCO_3$ (d) $MgCO_3$

55. Which among the following is true regarding aqueous solution of sulphur trioxide and sodium oxide?

(a) both solutions turn blue litmus to red.
(b) Both solutions turn red litmus to blue.
(c) Aqueous solutions of SO_3 and Na_2O turn blue litmus to red and red litmus to blue, respectively.
(d) Aqueous solutions of SO_3 and Na_2O turn red litmus to blue and blue litmus to red, respectively.

56. Blue-coloured solid anhydrous cobalt chloride is exposed to atmosphere and forms a pink-coloured solid. From this, we can infer that cobalt chloride is:

(a) hygroscopic (b) deliquescent
(c) efflorescent (d) none of these

57. Name and formula of the salt formed by complete neutralisation of aluminium hydroxide with ic acid of sulphur having four oxygen atoms is:

(a) aluminium sulphite, $Al_2(SO_3)_3$
(b) aluminium sulphate, $Al_2(SO_4)_3$
(c) aluminium sulphate, $Al_2(SO_3)_3$
(d) aluminium sulphite, $Al_2(SO_4)_3$

58. Gaseous products formed when gunpowder is subjected to heating are dissolved in water. Identify the products formed on dissolution.
(a) H_2CO_3, HNO_3
(b) H_2SO_3, H_2SO_4
(c) H_2SO_4, HNO_2
(d) H_2SO_3, H_2CO_3

59. Generally, pickles are not stored in tin vessels because:
(a) tin is a costly metal.
(b) tin is having high reactivity towards food components.
(c) tin is a denser metal.
(d) tin shows corrosive action.

60. Pure nitric acid on longstanding turns yellow due to the formation of:
(a) O_2, NO and H_2O
(b) O_2, NO_2 and H_2O
(c) NO, NO_2 and H_2O
(d) N_2O, O_2 and H_2O

61. Identify the acid used in the purification of metals like gold and silver.
(a) Sulphuric acid
(b) Phosphoric acid
(c) Hydrochloric acid
(d) Nitric acid

Directions for questions from 62 to 64:
Match the entries given in Column A with the appropriate ones in Column B. More than one suitable content of Column B can also be considered correct for an entry in Column A and some content given in Column B may not be the appropriate one for any entry in Column A.

62.

	Column A		Column B
A.	Carbonic acid	(a)	Baking powder
B.	Tartaric acid	(b)	Antacid
C.	Caustic soda	(c)	Soft drinks
D.	Milk of magnesia	(d)	Additive in food stuffs
		(e)	Soap industry

63.

	Column A		Column B
A.	Green vitriol	(a)	$Na_2CO_3 \cdot 10H_2O$
B.	Blue vitriol	(b)	$MgSO_4 \cdot 7H_2O$
C.	Epsom salt	(c)	$FeSO_4 \cdot 7H_2O$
D.	Washing soda	(d)	$CuSO_4 \cdot 5H_2O$
		(e)	$CaSO_4 \cdot ½\ H_2O$

64.

	Column A (indicator)		Column B (colour in acidic solution)
A.	Methyl orange	(a)	Red
B.	Phenolphthalein	(b)	Yellow
C.	Turmeric	(c)	Colourless
D.	Litmus	(d)	Blue
		(e)	Pink

Level 2: Review Your Concepts

65. The names of some compounds are given below. Arrange them in the increasing order of replaceable H ions.
(a) Sodium dihydrogen phosphate
(b) Phosphoric acid
(c) Sodium acetate
(d) Potassium hydrogen sulphate

66. (a) Is baking soda the same as baking powder? Support your answer
(b) 'Phosphoric acid is an effective rust remover'. Justify.

67. Explain why HPO_3^{-2} can form a normal salt with a monovalent cation.

68. Explain how the reaction:
$NaOH + H_2SO_4 \rightarrow NaHSO_4 + H_2O$; corresponds to partial neutralisation?

69. A few drops of phenolphthalein are added to an aqueous solution of KOH. This is neutralized by sulphuric

acid. What observation is expected at the neutralisation point?

70. Why is nitric acid used in the purification of gold?

71. Hydrated sodium sulphate and hydrated copper sulphate are taken in two air-tight containers X and Y, respectively. When blue-coloured $CoCl_2$ is introduced into the two containers, there is colour change in one container. Identify the container and give reasons in support of your answer.

72. A teacher demonstrated action of acids on metals in a laboratory. After the activity was over, one naughty student took an aluminium rod. He dipped it in a bottle containing concentrated nitric acid. Later, he dipped it in a beaker containing dil H_2SO_4. But he did not find any bubbles coming out. He was surprised because he was able to see bubbles coming out when a metal rod is dipped in sulphuric acid when the teacher conducted the experiment. He then approached the teacher and asked what is wrong with his activity. Predict the answer given by the teacher.

73. In a chemistry practical examination, three friends DEAN, BEAN and SEAN were given test tubes A, B, and C, respectively filled with solutions. DEAN added blue litmus, BEAN added methyl orange and SEAN added the litmus solution to the given test tube, respectively. DEAN found the blue litmus turning to red, BEAN observed methyl orange turning to yellow but SEAN found no action in the solution provided to him in the test tube. Comment on the nature of the three solutions given.

74. One molecule of H_3PO_4 is treated with one molecule of NaOH, two molecules of NaOH and three molecules of NaOH separately. Comment on the nature of products formed and write their names.

75. An element X on treatment with oxygen gives Y which on hydrolysis produces Z. Z on treatment with higher oxide of carbon A gives a milky white precipitate B. Identify X, Y, Z, A and B?

76. Element X has fourth shell has valence shell and the number of electrons are in 1 : 1 ratio in the first, fourth and second, third shells respectively. Its corresponding oxide Y on hydrolysis gives Z. Explain the changes that take place when phenolphthalein and methyl orange are added to Z separately.

77. Calcium hydroxide on heating gives a solid product X and on treatment with hydrochloric acid gives another solid product Y. What do you observe when X and Y are exposed to atmosphere? Explain.

78. A non-metal X with electronic configuration 2, 8, 6 forms corresponding -ous and -ic acids. Identify both the acids and explain the method of dilution of the corresponding -ic acid.

79. Between H_2SO_4 and H_3PO_4, which solution possesses greater number of H^+ ions in the given volume assuming that the number of molecules of both acids is equal? Give reasons.

80. Sunny and Bunny are neighbours staying in the same apartment. In summer vacation, one day they wanted to prepare some snacks for eating. During that process, the food material fell on the floor and the beautiful marble flooring became dirty. Sunny was afraid that his mother would scold him and in a hurry, brought some acid to clean the floor. But Bunny stopped him and said that it will spoil the flooring permanently. Why did Bunny say so? Give reason.

Level 3: Assess Your Concepts

81. Arrange the following salts in the order of type of salt given below.

(i) Mixed salt (ii) Acidic salt
(iii) Double salt (iv) Normal salt
(v) Complex salt

(a) Disodium hydrogen phosphate
(b) Potassium ferrocyanide
(c) Mohr's salt
(d) Sodium potassium carbonate
(e) Ammonium oxalate

82. Calcium hydroxide is added to soils before applying fertilisers. Justify the purpose.

83. What is the role of calcium hydroxide used in making mortar and white washing?

84. Why is Chile salt petre used in the manufacture of gunpowder?

85. Write formulae and names of the various salts formed when magnesium hydroxide is treated with sulphurous acid.

86. X is a metal with eight and two electrons in M and N-shells respectively. X reacts with oxygen to form Y and reacts with hydrochloric acid to form Z that dissolves in water.

(a) Identify X, Y and Z.

(b) Between Y and Z which one can be used as a desiccant? Give reason.

ANSWER KEYS

Crossword

Across

3. Potash alum 7. Acidic salt 9. Organic acids 10. Neutralisation
11. Complex salts 15. Basic salt 17. Hygroscopic 18. Seven
19. Slaked lime

Down

1. Bleaching powder 2. Efflorescent 4. Hydrated salts 5. Oxalic acid
6. Hydracids 8. Ten 12. Tartaric acid 13. Oxyacids
14. Mixed salts 16. Partial

Classroom Wing

Very Short Answer Type Questions

1. yellow 2. $CaSO_4.\frac{1}{2}\ H_2O$, calcium sulphate hemihydrate 3. Anhydrous salt
4. white 5. Copper sulphate 6. (d) 7. (c) 8. (b)
9. (b) 10. (d) 11. (b) 12. (a) 13. (c)
14. (c) 15. (a) 16. (c) 17. (c) 18. (d)
19. (b) 20. (d) 21. (c) 22. (c) 23. (c)
24. (b) 25. (b) 26. (a) 27. (d) 28. (b)
29. (d) 30. (b) 31. (d) 32. (b) 33. (d)
34. (b) 35. (a) 36. (d) 37. (c) 38. (c)
39. (c) 40. (b) 41. (c) 42. (b) 43. (d)
44. (i) → (C); (ii) → (E); (iii) → (D); (iv) → (A); (v) → (B) 45. A → d, B → a, C → b, e, D → f
46. A → e, B → c, d, C → a, D → b

Competition Wing

Level 1: Apply your Concepts

1. Mineral acids 2. metal 3. ammonia water 4. hydrogen 5. CO_2, H_2O
6. monobasic 7. weak acid 8. sulphurous acid 9. pink 10. alkali
11. normal salt 12. $Na_2CO_3.10H_2O$ 13. potassium nitrate 14. deliquescent 15. Nitric acid
16. True 17. False 18. False 19. True 20. True
21. True 22. False 23. False 24. True 25. True
26. (a) 27. (b) 28. (c) 29. (b) 30. (a)
31. (c) 32. (b) 33. (a) 34. (a) 35. (d)
36. (d) 37. (b) 38. (b) 39. (d) 40. (a)
41. (c) 42. (c) 43. (a) 44. (c) 45. (c)
46. (a) 47. (a) 48. (c) 49. (a) 50. (c)
51. (b) 52. (a) 53. (d) 54. (b) 55. (c)
56. (a) 57. (b) 58. (d) 59. (b) 60. (b)
61. (d) 62. A → c, B → a, C → e, D → b 63. A → c, B → d, C → b, D → a
64. A → e, B → c, C → b, D → a

Hints and Explanations

CLASSROOM WING

Very Short Answer Type Questions

1. yellow
Methyl orange turns the colour of lime water to yellow.

2. $CaSO_4.\frac{1}{2}$ H_2O, calcium sulphate hemihydrate
Chemical name of Plaster of Paris is calcium sulphate hemihydrate and its formula is $CaSO_4.\frac{1}{2}$ H_2O.

3. anhydrous salt
The salt formed by removal of water of crystallization from hydrated salt is called anhydrous salt.

4. white
Hydrated zinc sulphate ($ZnSO_4.7\ H_2O$) is white in colour.

5. Copper sulphate
Blue vitriol ($CuSO_4$. $5H_2O$) is used as a fungicide in agriculture.

6. Ascorbic acid is present in lemons
Hence, the correct option is (d).

7. Carbonic acid is a weak mineral acid
Hence, the correct option is (c).

8. $H_2SO_4 + 2NaOH \rightarrow Na_2SO_4 + 2H_2O$
Hence, the correct option is (b).

9. Sodium hydroxide and potassium hydroxide do not decompose on heating.
Hence, the correct option is (b).

10. Nitric acid is strong acid and others are weak acids.
Hence, the correct option is (d).

11. Since lime water is basic in nature, it turns phenolphthalein to pink.
Hence, the correct option is (b).

12. Washing soda is hydrated sodium carbonate, i.e., Na_2CO_3. $10H_2O$.
Hence, the correct option is (a).

13. The salt formed by the partial neutralisation of hydroxyl ions of a base by an acid is called basic salt.
Hence, the correct option is (c).

14. Marble → $CaCO_3$
Green vitriol → $FeSO_4$. $7H_2O$
Baking soda → $NaHCO_3$
Hence, the correct option is (c).

15. Potash alum is used in purificawtion of water as it helps in hastening the sedimentation of suspended impurities
Hence, the correct option is (a).

16. Acetic acid on dissolution in water gives only one H^+ ion, it is a monobasic acid. In acetic acid, less than 30% of the molecules of it ionize in water to furnish H^+ ions and hence, it is a weak acid.
Hence, the correct option is (c).

17. SO_3 on hydrolysis gives H_2SO_4 which is a strong acid.
$SO_3 + H_2O \rightarrow H_2SO_4$
Hence, the correct option is (c).

18. The process due to which an acid completely reacts with a base to form salt and water as the only products is called neutralisation. Add slaked lime to soil to neutralize the acidity of the soil. People suffering from acidity are given antacid tablets like $Mg(OH)_2$ to neutralize acidity. Submariners in submarine and astronauts in spaceships, use lithium hydroxide to neutralize CO_2 which is exhaled.
Hence, the correct option is (d).

19. Salt solutions are good conductors of electricity due to the formation of mobile ions.
Hence, the correct option is (b).

20. Calcium oxide is a hygroscopic substance and hence, it is used to remove moisture from the surroundings.
Hence, the correct option is (d).

21. As X is soluble in water, X is alkaline. Generally, metals present in alkalies are Na, K, Mg and Ca.
Hence, the correct option is (c).

22. Acetic acid has only one replaceable H^+ ion, and hence, it is a monobasic acid and also it is a weak acid.
Hence, the correct option is (c).

23. SO_3 of hydrolysis gives H_2SO_4 which is a strong acid.

$SO_3 + H_2O \rightarrow H_2SO_4$

Hence, the correct option is (c).

24. Correct sequence is as follows:

(i) phosphoric acid, aluminium hydroxide

(ii) oxalic acid, barium hydroxide

(iii) acetic acid, ammonium hydroxide

(iv) ammonium acetate

(v) barium oxalate

(vi) aluminium phosphate

Hence, the correct option is (b).

25. A → d $CuSO_4$ is an example of anhydrous salt.

B → c $Na_2CO_3.10H_2O$ is an example of efflorescent substance.

C → a Conc. H_2SO_4 is an example of hygroscopic substance.

D → b $ZnCl_2$ is an example of deliquescent substance.

Hence, the correct option is (b).

26. Nitre is KNO_3, which on heating gives KNO_2 and O_2. The liberated oxygen is the source for the combustion of carbon and sulphur.

Hence, the correct option is (a).

27. Carbonic acid is a weak acid.

Hence, the correct option is (d).

28. $2Al(OH)_3 + 3H_2SO_4 \rightarrow \underset{\text{Aluminium sulphate}}{Al_2(SO_4)_3} + 6H_2O$

Hence, the correct option is (b).

29. Both Chile salt petre and nitre are used in the manufacture of gunpowder, fertiliser and glass.

Hence, the correct option is (d).

30. Acidic salt is sodium dihydrogen phosphate. Double salt is Mohr's salt.

Hence, the correct option is (b).

31. The acids which are obtained from the minerals present in the earth are called mineral acids. One molecule of a dibasic acid furnishes two H^+ ions, and hence, H_2SO_3 is a dibasic mineral acid which is also a weak acid.

Hence, the correct option is (d).

32. Carbon forms two oxides. CO_2 on hydrolysis gives carbonic acid and CO is neutral. Carbon is the non-metal.

$CO_2 + H_2O \rightarrow H_2CO_3$

Hence, the correct option is (b).

33. Acids act as good conductors of electricity when they are in the ionised state. Pure H_2SO_4, pure HNO_3 and liquefied HCl do not ionise, and hence are bad conductors of electricity.

Hence, the correct option is (d).

34. Antacid is a substance which is used to neutralise the acidity in stomach. Generally, antacids used are magnesium hydroxide and aluminium hydroxide.

Hence, the correct option is (b).

35. A → d CaO is an example of hygroscopic substance.

B → a $MgCl_2$ is an example of deliquescent substance.

C → b $FeSO_4.7H_2O$ is an example of hydrated salt.

D → c $MgSO_4$ is an example of anhydrous salt.

Hence, the correct option is (a).

36. The components present in gunpowder are KNO_3, C and S. KNO_3 on heating gives KNO_2 and O_2. The liberated O_2 is the source for the combustion of carbon and sulphur. The products formed are CO_2 and SO_2 which dissolve in water to form H_2CO_3 and H_2SO_3, respectively.

Hence, the correct option is (d).

37. Sodium oxide and potassium oxide are soluble in water and form alkalies namely sodium hydroxide and potassium hydroxide, respectively.

Hence, the correct option is (c).

38. Glass and plastic do not react with the components of pickle. Hence, pickles are stored in glass/plastic vessels.

Hence, the correct option is (c).

39. 4, 2, 1, 3

(i) $K_4[Fe(CN)_6]$ (ii) $Ca(OH)Cl$

(iii) $Ca_3(PO_4)_2$ (iv) $CaOCl_2$

Hence, the correct option is (c).

40. (i) $Al(OH)_3 + HCl \rightarrow Al(OH)_2Cl + H_2O$

(ii) $Al(OH)_2Cl + HCl \rightarrow Al(OH)Cl_2 + H_2O$

(iii) $Al(OH)Cl_2 + HCl \rightarrow AlCl_3 + H_2O$

Hence, the correct option is (b).

41. Pure H_2SO_4 is colourless.

H_2SO_4 is a stable acid. Hence, it does not undergo decomposition on long standing.

Hence, the correct option is (c).

42. Correct sequence of the reactions is:

(i) $S + O_2 \rightarrow SO_2$

(ii) $2SO_2 + O_2 \rightarrow 2SO_3$
(iii) $SO_3 + H_2SO_4$
(iv) $H_2SO_4 + 2KOH \rightarrow K_2SO_4 + 2H_2O$

Hence, the correct option is (b).

43. The process due to which an acid completely reacts with a base to form a salt and water products is called neutralisation. Slaked lime is added to soil to neutralise the acidity of the soil. Persons suffering from acidity is given antacid tablets containing $Mg(OH)_2$ to neutralise acidity. Submariners in a submarine and astronauts in spaceships use lithium hydroxide to neutralise CO_2 which is exhaled.

Hence, the correct option is (d).

44. Potash alum is used for the purification of water. Plaster of Paris is used for making statues. Sodium carbonate is used in the manufacture of glass. Sodium bicarbonate is used as a leavening agent for cakes. Epsom salt is used as a laxative.

(i) → (C); (ii) → (E); (iii) → (D); (iv) → (A); (v) → (B)

45. A → d Sodium dihydrogen phosphate is an acidic salt

B → a Calcium hydroxy chloride is a basic salt

C → b, e Nitre is one of the components present in gunpowder. It is a normal salt.

D → f Ammonium carbonate is called smelling salt.

46. A → e $Na_2CO_3.10H_2O$ loses nine water molecules on exposure to air and it is an example of efflorescent substance.

B → c, d Zinc chloride and mercuric nitrate are examples of deliquescent substances.

C → a Cobalt chloride is an example of hygroscopic substance.

D → b Sodium chloride is used as a food additive.

47. Lactic acid is present in curd and tartaric acid is present in tamarind.

48. Formic acid is produced by the sting of an ant.

49. All bases which are soluble in water are called alkalies. *Examples:* NaOH, NH_4OH.

50. Common names of NaOH and KOH are caustic soda and caustic potash, respectively.

51. (a) $CO_2 + H_2O \rightarrow H_2CO_3$ (carbonic acid)

(b) $MgO + H_2O \rightarrow Mg(OH)_2$ (magnesium hydroxide)

52. Acid turns blue litmus to red and base turns red litmus to blue.

53. Red cabbage juice is a natural indicator.

54. Blue vitriol, $CuSO_4.5H_2O$; Green vitriol, $FeSO_4.7H_2O$; Potash alum, $K_2SO_4.Al_2(SO_4)_3.24H_2O$.

55. Sodium carbonate is used for the manufacture of glass, $Na_2CO_3.10H_2O$.

56. (a) Potash alum is used for the purification of water.

(b) Sodium bicarbonate is used as a fire extinguisher.

57. Ascorbic acid is present in lemon and acetic acid is present in vinegar.

58. The oxides which are insoluble in water are called neutral oxides. *Examples:* NO, CO, etc.

59. (a) Sodium chloride
Acid — HCl, base — NaOH

(b) Potassium sulphate
Acid — H_2SO_4, base — KOH

(c) Calcium nitrate
Acid — HNO_3, base — $Ca(OH)_2$

60. (a) Carbonic acid → ate
(b) Nitrous acid → ite
(c) Sulphuric acid → ate
(d) Nitric acid → ate

61. Hypo is sodium thiosulphate and its formula is $Na_2S_2O_3$.

62. In sodium nitrate, Na^+ is the basic radical and NO_3^- is the acidic radical.

63. (i) $CuSO_4.5H_2O$ (copper sulphate)
(ii) $FeSO_4.7H_2O$ (ferrous sulphate)

64. In hydrated salts a fixed number of water molecules get attached to each molecule of the salt and these are known as water of crystallization.

65. Formula of plaster of Paris is $CaSO_4.\frac{1}{2}H_2O$

Short Answer Type Questions

66. Oxalic acid is a dibasic acid and forms two salts. Carbonic acid is also a dibasic acid and can form two salts.

67. Nitric acid is highly reactive and forms oxide of iron which acts as a protective layer. This prevents the further reaction of metal with acid.

68. Hygroscopic substance absorbs moisture and does not dissolve in it, in contrast to deliquescent sub-stance, which dissolves in the moisture absorbed.

69. Some metals displace hydrogen from strong acids such as HCl and H_2SO_4. These are called active metals.

Examples: $Zn + H_2SO_4 \rightarrow ZnSO_4 + H_2$

$Mg + 2HCl \rightarrow MgCl_2 + H_2$

70. All acids and some alkalies show corrosive action on skin as they form painful blisters when they come in contact with skin.

Examples: H_2SO_4 absorbs water from skin tissues and HNO_3 reacts with skin proteins to form a pulp-like mass.

NaOH and KOH are called caustic soda and caustic potash due to their causticizing action on skin.

71. An acid is defined as a substance which on dissolution in water furnishes H^+ ions as the only positively charged ions. A base is defined as a substance which on dissolution in water furnishes OH^- ions as the only negatively charged ions.

Examples of acids: $HCl \rightarrow H^+ + Cl^-$

$HNO_3 \rightarrow H^+ + NO_3^-$

Examples of bases: $NaOH \rightarrow Na^+ + OH^-$

$KOH \rightarrow K^+ + OH^-$

72. (a) Efflorescent Substances: The salts which lose water of crystallization either completely or partially on exposure to atmospheric air are called efflorescent substances.

$Na_2CO_3.10H_2O$ loses nine water molecules on exposure to air and the remaining one water molecule on heating.

(b) Deliquescent Substances: The substances which absorb moisture from the atmosphere on exposure to air. By absorbing moisture, they may dissolve in the water absorbed and change into solution. Such substances are called deliquescent substances.

Example: calcium chloride

(c) Hygroscopic Substances: The substances which do not undergo any change in physical state on the absorption of moisture from the atmospheric air. These are called hygroscopic substances.

Examples: calcium oxide, cobalt chloride, etc.

73. The acids which are synthesized from the minerals obtained from earth's crust are called mineral acids. These mineral acids can be further classified on the basis of various characteristics.

Based on the constituent elements in the acids, they are classified as hydracids and oxyacids. The acids which contain hydrogen and another non-metal are called hydracids. The acids which contain oxygen along with hydrogen and non-metal are called oxyacids.

74. **Strong acids**: The acids which undergo complete ionization when dissolved in water and furnish large concentration of H^+ ions are called strong acids.

Examples: strong acids

$HCl \rightarrow H^+ + Cl^-$

$H_2SO_4 \rightarrow 2H^+ + SO_4^{-2}$

Weak acids: The acids which ionize partially and furnish less concentration of H^+ ions are called weak acids. All organic acids are weak acids.

Examples: weak acids

$CH_3COOH \rightarrow CH_3COO^- + H^+$

$H_2CO_3 \rightarrow 2H^+ + CO_3^{-2}$

75. **Naming of acids**: Hydracids are named as hydro ….. ic acid by including the name of the non-metal.

Examples:

HCl	hydrochloric acid
HBr	hydrobromic acid
HI	hydroiodic acid
H_2S	hydrosulphuric acid

Oxyacids are named according to the number of oxygen atoms present in the acid. Generally, most of the non-metals form two types of oxyacids. The acid containing less number of oxygen atoms is called '**ous acid**.' The acid containing more number of oxygen atoms is called '**ic acid**.'

Examples:

Names of non-metal	Formulas of oxyacid	Names of oxyacid
Sulphur	H_2SO_3	Sulphurous acid
	H_2SO_4	Sulphuric acid
Nitrogen	HNO_2	Nitrous acid
	HNO_3	Nitric acid
Chlorine	$HClO_2$	Chlorous acid
	$HClO_3$	Chloric acid
Carbon	H_2CO_3	Carbonic acid
Phosphorus	H_3PO_3	Phosphorous acid
	H_3PO_4	Phosphoric acid

76. All acids react with alkalies to form salt and water. The reaction of an acid with a base to form salt and water as the products is called neutralisation.

(a) $Ca(OH)_2 + H_2SO_4 \rightarrow CaSO_4 + 2H_2O$

(b) $NaHCO_3 + HCl \rightarrow NaCl + CO_2 + H_2O$

(c) $MgCO_3 + H_2SO_4 \rightarrow MgSO_4 + CO_2 + H_2O$

77. (a) Ammonium hydroxide decomposes rapidly to give ammonia gas and water upon slight heating.

$$NH_4OH \xrightarrow{\Delta} NH_3 + H_2O$$

(b) On heating, aluminium hydroxide gives alumina and water.

$$2Al(OH)_3 \rightarrow Al_2O_3 + 3H_2O$$

(c) NaOH melts on strong heating but it does not undergo decomposition.

78. Certain substances when added show different colours in acidic and basic solutions. Such substances undergo colour change at the neutralisation point which indicates complete neutralisation and hence are called indicators. Certain naturally occurring substances can also act as indicators as they change colour according to the nature of the substance.

Example: red cabbage juice

The other indicators used are litmus, methyl orange and phenolphthalein.

Action of indicators on acids and bases

Name of indicators	Colours in acidic solution	Colours in basic solution
Litmus	Red	Blue
Methyl orange	Pink (orange red)	Yellow
Phenolphthalein	Colourless	Pink
Turmeric	Yellow	Red

79. Differences between acidic and basic salts

Acidic salt	Basic salt
It contains replaceable hydrogen ions	It contains replaceable hydroxyl ions.
It ionizes in water and gives hydrogen ions	It ionizes in water and gives hydroxyl ions.
It turns blue litmus to red	It turns red litmus to blue.
It gives no colour with phenolphthalein	It gives pink colour with phenolphthalein.

80. Zinc chloride is a deliquescent substance and cobalt chloride is a hygroscopic substance. Zinc chloride absorb moisture, and changes into solution state. In beaker 'B' solid anhydrous cobalt chloride absorb moisture from atmosphere and it does not undergo any change in physical state and it remains in the solid state. Its colour changes from blue to pink.

81. Properties of salts

(i) Salts are solids at room temperature.

(ii) Salts have high melting points.

(iii) Most of the salts are soluble in water. The only exceptions are carbonates, sulphides and sulphates of some metals.

(iv) The aqueous solutions of salts are good conductors of electricity.

82.

Chemical names and formulas	Uses
(a) Sodium chloride, NaCl	(i) Food additive (ii) Preservative for pickles (iii) Manufacture of chlorine and NaOH
(b) Sodium bicarbonate $NaHCO_3$	(i) Antacid tablets (ii) Leavening agent for cakes (iii) Fire extinguisher
(c) Calcium sulphate hemihydrate $CaSO_4 \cdot \frac{1}{2}H_2O$	Making of statues, setting of broken bones

83.

Name of the acids	Uses	Properties exploited
(a) Hydrochloric acid	(i) Cleaning metal surfaces before tinning and galvanizing	Reaction of acids with metal oxide coating.
	(ii) Dyeing	HCl reacts with complex organic compounds and forms coloured compounds.
	(iii) Preparation of glucose from starch	HCl carries out hydrolysis of starchto glucose.

Name of the acids	Uses	Properties exploited
(b) Nitric acid	(i) Fertilizers	Highly soluble nature of nitrate salts.
	(ii) Explosives	TNT, TNG, etc.
	(iii) Purification of noble metals (Au, Pt)	Insoluble nature of Au and Pt in HNO_3.

Essay Answer Type Questions

84. (c) $Na[Ag(CN)_2] \rightarrow Na^+ + [Ag(CN)_2]^- \rightarrow 2$

(a) $CaOCl_2 \rightarrow Ca^{+2} + Cl^- + OCl^- \rightarrow 3$

(d) $Fe_2(SO_4)_3 \rightarrow 2Fe^{+3} + 3SO_4^{-2} \rightarrow 5$

(b) $K_2SO_4.Al_2(SO_4)_3.24H_2O \rightarrow 2K^+ + 2Al^{+3} + 4SO_4^{-2} \rightarrow 8$

Hence, the correct order is CADB.

85. Electronic configurations 2, 4 and 2, 5 correspond to carbon and nitrogen, respectively, which form neutral oxides (CO and NO).

86. **Some important chemical properties of acids**

Reactions	Examples
Reaction with metals: Some metals displace hydrogen from the strong acids (HCl and H_2SO_4). These are called active metals.	$Zn + H_2SO_4 \rightarrow ZnSO_4 + H_2$ $Mg + 2HCl \rightarrow MgCl_2 + H_2$
Reaction with metal oxides: All dilute mineral acids react with metallic oxides to form their respective metallic salts and water.	$ZnO + H_2SO_4 \rightarrow ZnSO_4 + H_2O$ $CaO + 2HNO_3 \rightarrow Ca(NO_3)_2 + H_2O$
Reaction with metal carbonates: This reaction also comes under neutralisation but accompanied by the release of CO_2 gas along with the formation of salt and water.	$CaCO_3 + 2HCl \rightarrow CaCl_2 + H_2O + CO_2$ $MgCO_3 + H_2SO_4 \rightarrow MgSO_4 + CO_2 + H_2O$

Some important chemical properties of bases

Reactions	Examples
Action of heat	NaOH, KOH
1. Some hydroxides melt on strong heating. They do not undergo decomposition.	$Ca(OH)_2 \xrightarrow{\Delta} CaO + H_2O$
2. Other metal hydroxides undergo decomposition on strong heating.	$2Al(OH)_3 \xrightarrow{\Delta} Al_2O_3 + 3H_2O$
3. Ammonium hydroxide decomposes rapidly to give ammonia gas and water upon slight heating.	$NH_4OH \longrightarrow NH_4 + H_2O$

87. $Na_2O + H_2O \rightarrow 2NaOH$

$SO_3 + H_2O \rightarrow H_2SO_4$

'X' is sodium hydroxide and 'Y' is sulphuric acid. One molecule of sodium hydroxide reacts with one molecule of sulphuric acid gives one molecule of sodium bisulphate which is a acidic salt and one molecule of water. Similarly, two molecules of sodium hydroxide reacts with one molecule of sulphuric acid gives one molecule of sodium sulphate which is a normal salt and two molecules of water.

$NaOH + H_2SO_4 \rightarrow NaHSO_4 + H_2O$

$2NaOH + H_2SO_4 \rightarrow Na_2SO_4 + 2H_2O$

88. Methods of preparation of acids and bases

Acids

From non-metals: Non-metallic elements on heating with oxygen give corresponding oxides. Some oxides on dissolution in water give the corresponding acids and hence, such non-metallic oxides are called **acidic oxides**.

Examples: $C + O_2 \rightarrow CO_2$

$CO_2 + H_2O \rightarrow H_2CO_3$

$S + O_2 \rightarrow SO_2$

$SO_2 + H_2O \rightarrow H_2SO_3$

$2SO_2 + O_2 \rightarrow 2SO_3$

$SO_3 + H_2O \rightarrow H_2SO_4$

The oxides which are insoluble in water are called **neutral oxides**.

Examples: NO, CO

Bases

From metals: Metals on heating with oxygen give metal oxides which are basic in nature. These metal oxides on dissolution in water give corresponding **alkalies** (water-soluble bases).

Examples: $4Na + O_2 \rightarrow 2Na_2O$

$Na_2O + H_2O \rightarrow 2NaOH$

$2Mg + O_2 \rightarrow 2MgO;$

$MgO + H_2O \rightarrow Mg(OH)_2$

89. $H_2SO_4 \rightarrow 2H^+ + SO_4^{-2}$

$Mg(OH)_2 \rightarrow Mg^{+2} + 2OH^-$

$Mg(OH)_2 + H_2SO_4 \rightarrow MgSO_4 + 2H_2O$

$Mg(OH)_2 + H_2SO_4 \rightarrow Mg(HSO_4)_2 + H_2O$

$Mg\ HSO_4 + Mg(OH)_2 \rightarrow Mg\ SO_4 + H_2O$

$Mg\ (OH)_2 + H_2SO_4 \rightarrow Mg(OH)\ HSO_4 + H_2O$

$Mg\ (OH)(HSO_4) + H_2SO_4 \rightarrow Mg(HSO_4) + H_2O$

90. Derivation of names of salts: The name of a salt is basically derived from the acid from which it is formed. The salts derived from the hydracids are given names ending with '**ide**' suffix. If the salt contains hydrogen, then hydrogen is added to the suffix.

Formulae of acids	Formulae of bases	Salts formed	Names of the salts
HCl	NaOH	NaCl	Sodium chloride
H_2S	NaOH	Na_2S	Sodium sulphide
H_2S	NaOH	NaHS	Sodium hydrogen sulphide

The salts derived from oxy acids are given names depending on the type of oxy acid. The salts of '**ous**' acids are given '**ite**' suffix and the salts of 'ic' acids are given 'ate' suffix. If hydrogen is present in the salt, hydrogen or bi is added to the name of the radical.

Examples

Formulae of acids	Formulae of bases	Formulae of salts	Names of salts
H_2SO_3	KOH	K_2SO_3	Potassium sulphite
		$KHSO_3$	Potassium hydrogen sulphite
H_2SO_4	NaOH	Na_2SO_4	Sodium sulphate
		$NaHSO_4$	Sodium hydrogen sulphate
H_3PO_4	NaOH	Na_3PO_4	Sodium phosphate
		Na_2HPO_4	Disodium hydrogen phosphate
		NaH_2PO_4	Sodium dihydrogen phosphate

In the same way, the salts of nitrous acid and nitric acid are called nitrites and nitrates, respectively. The salts of carbonic acid are called carbonates and bicarbonates or hydrogen carbonates. The positive ion part is called basic radical and the negative ion part is called acidic radical.

91. (1)

Compounds	Colour of blue litmus	Nature of substance
$Ca(OH)_2$	No change	Basic
H_2SO_4	Changes to red	Acidic
CH_3COOH	Change to red	Acidic
NaOH	No change	Basic
KOH	No change	Basic
$Mg(OH)_2$	No change	Basic
HNO_3	Changes to red	Acidic
NH_4OH	No change	Basic

(2)

Indicators	Acidic	Basic	Neutral
Litmus	Red	Blue	No change in colour
Methyl orange	Yellow	Pink	No change
Phenolphthalein	Colourless	Pink	No change

92. Uses of bases

Name of the bases	Uses	Properties exploited
(a) Sodium hydroxide (caustic soda) and potassium hydroxide	(i) Manufacture of soap (ii) Paper pulp preparation (iii) Synthetic fibres (iv) Manufacture of medicines	Reaction with oil Reaction with hydrocarbons of wood
(b) Calcium hydroxide	(i) Making mortar (ii) Removal of hair from animal skin (iii) Spread on beetle leaves (iv) Preparation of bleaching powder (v) Preparation of metallic sodium (vi) Used as a laboratory reagent	Neutralisation of acidity of soils Hardening of mortar on exposure to air
(c) Magnesium hydroxide	Antacid	Neutralizing action on excess HCl produced in the stomach

Competition Wing

Level 1: Apply Your Concepts

1. mineral acids

The acids which are obtained from the minerals are called mineral acids.

2. metal

Metallic oxides on hydrolysis give bases.

3. ammonia, water

$$\underset{\text{Ammonium hydroxide}}{NH_4OH} \xrightarrow{\text{warm}} \underset{\text{Ammonia}}{NH_3} + \underset{\text{Water}}{H_2O}$$

4. hydrogen

$$Zn + \underset{\text{(dil)}}{H_2SO_4} \rightarrow ZnSO_4 + H_2\uparrow$$

5. CO_2, H_2O

Generally, mineral acids on reaction with metallic carbonates give metallic salts, carbon dioxide and water.

6. Hydrochloric acid is a monobasic acid.
7. Carbonic acid is a weak acid.
8. Sulphur dioxide on hydrolysis gives sulphurous acid.
9. Acids turn methyl orange solution to pink.
10. Ammonium hydroxide is an alkali.
11. Sodium sulphate is a normal salt.
12. Formula of washing soda is $Na_2CO_3.10H_2O$ (sodium carbonate decahydrate)
13. Nitre is the common name of potassium nitrate.
14. Mercuric nitrate is a deliquescent salt.
15. Chile salt petre is used in the manufacture of nitric acid.
16. The number of hydrogen ions furnished by one molecule of an acid, on dissolving in water, is called basicity of an acid. Hydrochloric acid (HCl) is a monobasic acid.
17. The acids which ionise completely in water to furnish large concentration of H^+ ions are called strong acids. The acids in which less number of molecules ionise in water to furnish H^+ less concentration of ions are called weak acids. Carbonic acid (H_2CO_3) is a weak acid.
18. $SO_2 + H_2O \rightarrow \underset{\text{Sulphurous acid}}{H_2SO_3}$
19. Acids turn methyl orange solution to pink.
20. As NH_4OH is soluble in water it is an alkali.
21. Normal salt is formed by complete replacement of the hydrogen ions of an acid with metal ions.

    Example: PbS
22. Washing soda is sodium carbonate decahydrate with the formula $Na_2CO_3.10H_2O$.
23. Nitre is the common name of potassium nitrate.
24. Deliquescent salts change into solution form due to the absorption of water from air. Mercuric nitrate is a deliquescent salt.
25. Chile salt petre is the common name of sodium nitrate which is used in manufacture of nitric acid.
26. The bases which are soluble in water are called alkalis. All bases are not soluble in water.

    Hence, the correct option is (a).
27. Nitric acid is a strong acid as well as a strong oxidising agent. However, it is used for the purification of gold as gold remains insoluble in it.

    Hence, the correct option is (b).
28. H_3PO_4 on dissociation furnishes $3H^+$ ions in aqueous solution, therefore, it is a tribasic acid.

    Hence, the correct option is (c).
29. $Ca(OH)_2$ furnishes $2OH^-$ ions in aqueous solution, therefore, it is a diacidic base.

    Hence, the correct option is (b).
30. $CaCl_2$ in an example of normal salt as it is formed by complete neutralisation of an acid and a base.

    Hence, the correct option is (a).
31. Potassium hydroxide is an extremely corrosive alkali

    Hence, the correct option is (c).
32. Generally, hydrolysis of metal oxides gives bases.

    Hence, the correct option is (b).

33. Calcium nitrate salt is formed by treating calcium oxide solutionwith nitric acid.
Hence, the correct option is (a).

34. Formula of potassium hydrogen sulphite is $KHSO_3$.
Hence, the correct option is (a).

35. Ammonium carbonate is a smelling salt.
Hence, the correct option is (d).

36. The acids which are obtained from the minerals present in earth are called mineral acids. A weak acid is the acid in which less than 30% of molecules ionise in water. A dibasic acid is the one which furnishes two H^+ ions by one molecule of an acid. Hence, H_2SO_3 is a dibasic weak mineral acid.
Hence, the correct option is (d).

37. Carbon forms two oxides. CO_2 on hydrolysis gives carbonic acid and CO is neutral. Carbon is the non-metal.

$$CO_2 + H_2O \rightarrow H_2CO_3$$

Hence, the correct option is (b).

38. Antacid is the substance which is used to neutralise the acidity in stomach. Generally used antacids are magnesium hydroxide and aluminium hydroxide.
Hence, the correct option is (b).

39. Acids act as good conductors of electricity when they are in ionised state. Concentrated and pure H_2SO_4, concentrated and pure HNO_3, liquid HCl do not ionise, and hence are bad conductors of electricity.
Hence, the correct option is (d).

40. Calcium oxide is a hygroscopic substance which absorbs moisture without undergoing any change in its physical state.
Hence, the correct option is (a).

41. Magnesium oxide and potassium oxide are soluble in water and forming alkalies namely magnesium hydroxide and potassium hydroxide, respectively.
Hence, the correct option is (c).

42. (i) $4Na + O_2 \rightarrow 2Na_2O$
(ii) $Na_2O + H_2O \rightarrow 2NaOH$
(iii) $NaOH + H_2SO_4 \rightarrow NaHSO_4 + H_2O$
(iv) $NaHSO_4 + NaOH \rightarrow Na_2SO_4 + H_2O$
Hence, the correct option is (c).

43. (i) Ferric hydroxide and hydrochloric acid
(ii) Barium hydroxide and sulpheric acid
(iii) Sodium hydroxide and phosphoric acid
(iv) Sodium chloride
(v) Barium sulphate
(vi) Ferric phosphate
Hence, the correct option is (a).

44. Sulphuric acid is a strong acid, as sulphuric acid ionises completely in water to furnish large concentration of H^+ ions.
Hence, the correct option is (c).

45. The non-metal with 5 valence electrons is phosphorus and 'ic' acid of phosphorus is phosphoric acid. Metal with one electron in valence shell forms a base with the formula MOH. Since the salt can react with two molecules of base, the salt contains two replaceable hydrogen molecules. The formula of salt X is KH_2PO_4.
Hence, the correct option is (c).

46. SO_3 in presence of moisture turns blue litmus to red. NO is a neutral oxide and does not respond to litmus test. MgO is basic and turns red litmus to blue.
Hence, the correct option is (a).

47. X is blue vitriol ($CuSO_4$. $5H_2O$) which is blue in colour. This on heating loses water of crystallisation and forms anhydrous salt which is colourless. When water is added to anhydrous salt, it forms copper sulphate pentahydrate which is blue in colour.

$$\underset{\text{Blue}}{CuSO_4.5H_2O} \xrightarrow{\text{heating}} \underset{\text{Colourless}}{CuSO_4} \xrightarrow{+H_2O} \underset{\text{blue}}{CuSO_4.5H_2O}$$

Y is limestone, $CaCO_3$ which on heating gives CaO. It is an exothermic reaction, and hence, water starts boiling.
Hence, the correct option is (a).

48. 'ic' acid of sulphur with four oxygen atoms is H_2SO_4

$$H_2SO_4 + Ca(OH)_2 \rightarrow \underset{\text{calcium sulphate}}{CaSO_4} + 2H_2O$$

Hence, the correct option is (c).

49. Nitre is KNO_3, which on heating gives KNO_2 and O_2. The liberated oxygen is the source for the combustion of carbon and sulphur.
Hence, the correct option is (a).

50. The components present in pickles are inert towards glass and plastics. Hence, generally, pickles are stored in glass vessels or plastic vessels.
Hence, the correct option is (c).

51. Pure HNO_3 is highly unstable which undergoes decomposition giving H_2O, O_2 and NO_2. NO_2 is a reddish brown gas, dissolves in HNO_3 and imparts yellow colour.

$4HNO_3 \rightarrow 2H_2O + 4NO_2 + O_2$

Hence, the correct option is (b).

52. Sulphuric acid can form various salts which are soluble in water. These salts can be used as fertilisers.

Hence, the correct option is (a).

53. Carbonic acid is a weak acid.

Hence, the correct option is (d).

54. The acid used in soft drinks is H_2CO_3. The metallic radical in salt should be Ca^{+2}. The formula of the acidic salt should be $Ca(HCO_3)_2$.

Hence, the correct option is (b).

55. Aqueous solution of sulphur trioxide is acidic in nature, and hence, it turns blue litmus to red. As aqueous solution of sodium oxide is basic in nature, it turns red litmus to blue.

Hence, the correct option is (c).

56. Cobalt chloride is a hygroscopic substance, and hence, absorbs moisture and forms pink-coloured hydrated cobalt chloride without undergoing any change in its state.

Hence, the correct option is (a).

57. $2Al(OH)_3 + 3H_2SO_4 \rightarrow Al_2(SO_4)_3 + 6H_2O$

Aluminium sulphate

Hence, the correct option is (b).

58. The components present in gunpowder are KNO_3, C and S. KNO_3 on heating gives KNO_2 and O_2. The liberated O_2 is the source for the combustion of carbon and sulphur. The products formed are CO_2 and SO_2 which dissolve in water to form H_2CO_3 and H_2SO_3.

Hence, the correct option is (d).

59. The components present in pickles (generally organic acids) are highly reactive towards tin and form harmful compounds.

Hence, the correct option is (b).

60. Pure nitric acid is highly unstable, and hence, undergoes decomposition forming NO_2, H_2O and O_2. NO_2 is a reddish brown gas. Dilute solution of NO_2 appears as yellow colour.

$4HNO_3 \rightarrow 4NO_2 + 2H_2O + O_2$

Hence, the correct option is (b).

61. Nitric acid is used in the purification of metals like gold and silver since it dissolves the impurities like various metal oxides present on the surface of gold (or) gold being insoluble in HNO_3 remains insoluble.

Hence, the correct option is (d).

62. A → c Carbonic acid is used in soda water and soft drinks.

B → a Tartaric acid is a component of baking powder. Tartaric acid is used in making cakes for baking process.

C → e Sodium hydroxide is used in soap industry.

D → b Magnesium hydroxide is used as an antacid to neutralise the acidity.

63. A → c Formula of green vitriol is $FeSO_4.7H_2O$

B → d Formula of blue vitriol is $CuSO_4.5H_2O$

C → b Formula of Epsom salt is $MgSO_4.7H_2O$

D → a Formula of washing soda is $Na_2CO_3.10H_2O$

64. A → e Methyl orange shows pink colour in an acidic solution.

B → c Phenolphthalein is colourless in an acidic solution.

C → b Turmeric shows yellow colour in an acidic solution.

D → a Litmus when added to an acidic solution gives red colour.

Level 2: Review Your Concepts

65 (c) Sodium acetate – CH_3COONa – No replaceable hydrogen

(d) Potassium hydrogen sulphate – $KHSO_4$ – One replaceable hydrogen

(a) Sodium dihydrogen phosphate – NaH_2PO_4 – Two replaceable hydrogens

(b) Phosphoric acid – H_3PO_4 – Three replaceable hydrogens

Hence, the correct order is CDAB.

66. (a) Baking powder is a mixture of baking soda and tartaric acid. Sodium bicarbonate on heating decomposes to give CO_2 which imparts puffiness to the foodstuff. However, during this reaction, sodium carbonate is formed as one of the products. This imparts alkalinity and slight yellow tinge to the foodstuff. Tartaric acid neutralises sodium carbonate and removes the yellow colour and alkalinity.

(b) Phosphoric acid reacts with rust and forms ferric phosphate and water.

$2H_3PO_4 + Fe_2O_3.xH_2O \rightarrow 2FePO_4 + (x + 3)H_2O.$

67. HPO_3^{-2} is the ion formed by the dissociation of H_3PO_3. H_3PO_3 is a dibasic acid and undergoes dissociation as follows:

$H_3PO_3 \rightarrow H_2PO_3^- + H^+$

$H_2PO3^- \rightarrow HPO_3^{-2} + H^-$

HPO_3^{-2} further cannot lose H^+ ion as hydrogen is not replaceable. Therefore, it can give a normal salt of formula M_2HPO_3 with a monovalent cation.

68. $NaHSO_4$ is an acidic salt which contains one replaceable hydrogen and can further undergo neutralisation. Therefore, the formation of $NaHSO_4$ corresponds to partial neutralisation.

69. Phenolphthalein shows a pink colour when added to the solution of KOH. On complete neutralisation, at the neutralisation point, it turns to colourless as it is colourless in an acidic medium.

70. Nitric acid is a good oxidising agent. Gold is purified when treated with HNO_3 as it is not soluble in HNO_3 and all the impurities are oxidised by nitric acid.

71. Hydrated sodium sulphate $\rightarrow Na_2SO_4.\ 10H_2O$

Hydrated copper sulphate $\rightarrow CuSO_4.5H_2O$

As hydrated sodium sulphate is efflorescent in nature, it loses water of crystallisation. Blue-coloured $CoCl_2$ present in container X absorbs moisture and turns to pink-coloured $CoCl_2.2H_2O$

$$\underset{\text{blue}}{CoCl_2} \xrightarrow{\text{moisture}} \underset{\text{pink}}{CoCl_2.2H_2O}$$

72. HNO_3 is highly corrosive in nature. As a result, it forms an oxide layer on Al rod which acts as a passive layer. This passive layer prevents the reaction between Al and H_2SO_4. Hence, no liberation of hydrogen gas.

73. As A turns blue litmus to red, it is acidic in nature. As B turns methyl orange to yellow, it is basic in nature. As C is neutral towards both the litmus, it is neutral in nature, i.e., a normal salt solution.

74. $H_3PO_4 + NaOH \rightarrow \underset{\text{acidic salt}}{NaH_2PO_4} + H_2O$

$H_3PO_4 + 2NaOH \rightarrow \underset{\text{acidic salt}}{Na_2HPO_4} + 2H_2O$

$H_3PO_4 + 3NaOH \rightarrow \underset{\text{neutral salt}}{Na_3PO_4} + 3H_2O$

$NaH_2PO_4 \rightarrow$ sodium dihydrogen phosphate

$Na_2HPO_4 \rightarrow$ disodium hydrogen phosphate

$Na_3PO_4 \rightarrow$ sodium phosphate

75. As, Z on treatment with oxide A of carbon, gives milky appearance to the solution by forming B, Z is $Ca(OH)_2$, A is CO_2, B is $CaCO_3$.

As Z is produced by hydrolysis of Y. Y is CaO. As Y is prepared by treating X with oxygen, X is Ca.

$$\underset{(X)}{Ca} + O_2 \rightarrow \underset{(Y)}{CaO}$$

$$\underset{Y}{CaO} + H_2O \rightarrow \underset{Z}{Ca(OH)_2}$$

$$\underset{Z}{Ca(OH)_2} + \underset{A}{CO_2} \rightarrow \underset{B}{CaCO_3} + H_2O$$

76. As the element burns with a brick red flame, it is calcium with electronic configuration 2, 8, 8, 2.

$$\underset{(X)}{Ca} + O_2 \rightarrow \underset{(Y)}{CaO}$$

$$\underset{(Y)}{CaO} + H_2O \rightarrow \underset{(Z)}{Ca(OH)_2}$$

As $Ca(OH)_2$ is basic in nature, it turns phenolphthalein to pink and methyl orange to yellow.

77. $Ca(OH)_2 \rightarrow \underset{(X)}{CaO} + H_2O$

$Ca(OH)_2 + HCl \rightarrow \underset{(Y)}{CaCl_2} + H_2O$

CaO is hygroscopic in nature, absorbs moisture and remains in solid state.

$CaCl_2$ is deliquescent in nature, absorbs moisture and is converted into solution state.

78. Non-metal with electronic configuration 2, 8, 6 is sulphur. Corresponding ous and ic acids of sulphur are H_2SO_3 and H_2SO_4, respectively.

H_2SO_4 is diluted by adding acid to water with continuous stirring because addition of water to acid is associated with liberation of large amount of heat at a time which may lead to violent and explosive reaction.

79. As H_2SO_4 is a strong acid, it produces greater number of H^+ ions, i.e., complete ionisation.

$$H_2SO_4 \rightarrow 2H^+ + SO_4^{-2}$$

As H_3PO_4 is a weak acid, it produces less number of H^+ ions, i.e., partial ionisation.

$$H_3PO_4 \rightarrow 3H^+ + PO_4^{-3}$$

80. The major component of marble is $CaCO_3$. It being basic in nature, reacts with an acid to form salt and water (neutralisation reaction). Hence, acids being reactive with marble, they cannot be used for cleaning marble flooring.

Level 3: Assess Your Concepts

81. (d) $NaKCO_3$ – Mixed salt

(a) Na_2HPO_4 – Acidic salt

(c) $FeSO_4(NH_4)_2\ SO_4.6H_2O$ – Double salt

(e) $(NH_4)_2C_2O_4$ – Normal salt

(b) $K_4[Fe(CN)_6]$ – Complex salt

Hence, the correct order is DACEB.

82. Generally soils are slightly acidic in nature. As calcium hydroxide is basic in nature, it neutralises the acidity of soils. Calcium hydroxide is prepared from naturally occurring limestone.

83. Mortar is a mixture of calcium hydroxide, sand and water. On exposure to atmosphere calcium hydroxide reacts with CO_2 forming $CaCO_3$ which is a hard substance, and hence, strengthens the construction. $Ca(OH)_2$ is used for white washing because of the formation of white-coloured $CaCO_3$ substance.

84. Gunpowder is a heterogeneous mixture of C, S and KNO_3. On heating KNO_3 undergoes decomposition and liberates oxygen which supports combustion of carbon and sulphur. During combustion a huge amount of heat is liberated and pressure increases inside the small area. As a result, explosion takes place.

85. $Mg(OH)_2$ is a diacidic base and H_2SO_3 is a dibasic acid. Hence, there is possibility of three different salts.

$$Mg(OH)_2 + H_2SO_3 \rightarrow \underset{\text{magnesium hydroxy bisulphite}}{Mg(OH)\ HSO_3} + H_2O$$

$$Mg(OH)\ HSO_3 + H_2SO_3 \rightarrow \underset{\text{magnesium bisulphite}}{Mg(HSO_3)_2} + H_2O$$

$$Mg(OH)_2 + H_2SO_3 \rightarrow \underset{\text{magnesium bisulphite}}{Mg(HSO_3)_2} + H_2O$$

$$Mg(HSO_3)_2 + Mg(OH)_2 \rightarrow \underset{\text{magnesium sulphite}}{2MgSO_3} + 2H_2O$$

86. (a) Electronic configuration of X is 2, 8, 8, 2 X is calcium, Y is calcium oxide and Z is calcium chloride.

(b) CaO is hygroscopic in nature, absorbs moisture and remains in solid state. $CaCl_2$ is deliquescent in nature, absorbs moisture and gets converted into solution. Hence, CaO can be used as a desiccant.

CHAPTER

4

Air and Oxygen

Remember

Before beginning this chapter, you should be able to:

- know the concept of atmosphere.
- prove presence of gases in our surrounding.
- have basic concept of states of matter.

Key Ideas

After completing this chapter, you should be able to:

- have knowledge of different layers of atmosphere and their importance.
- describe composition and characteristics of air.
- understand methods of preparation and properties of important gases like oxygen, carbon dioxide, nitrogen and hydrogen.
- study the importance of these gases in nature and their uses.
- learn the cause, effect and different measures to curb air pollution.

Scientific Crypt

A Tribute to Joseph Priestley (1733 – 1804)

Joseph Priestley, an english chemist and a natural philosopher discovered the active ingredient of air without which the existence of life is not possible. He described air as a composition of a mixture of gases and dethrone the age old idea about air as an elementary substance. He called the highly reactive ingredient of air as "dephlogisticated air" and the great French chemist Antoine Lavoisier named it as "oxygen".

He invented carbonated water, the rubber eraser and a dozen of key chemical compounds. He was also a maveric theologian. He was forced to flee his homeland, England in 1794 because of his unorthodox religious writings and vocal support for the American and French revolution. Priestley's home in Pennsylyania was designated as National Historic Chemical society, the world's largest scientfic society.

FUN TIME

CROSSWORD

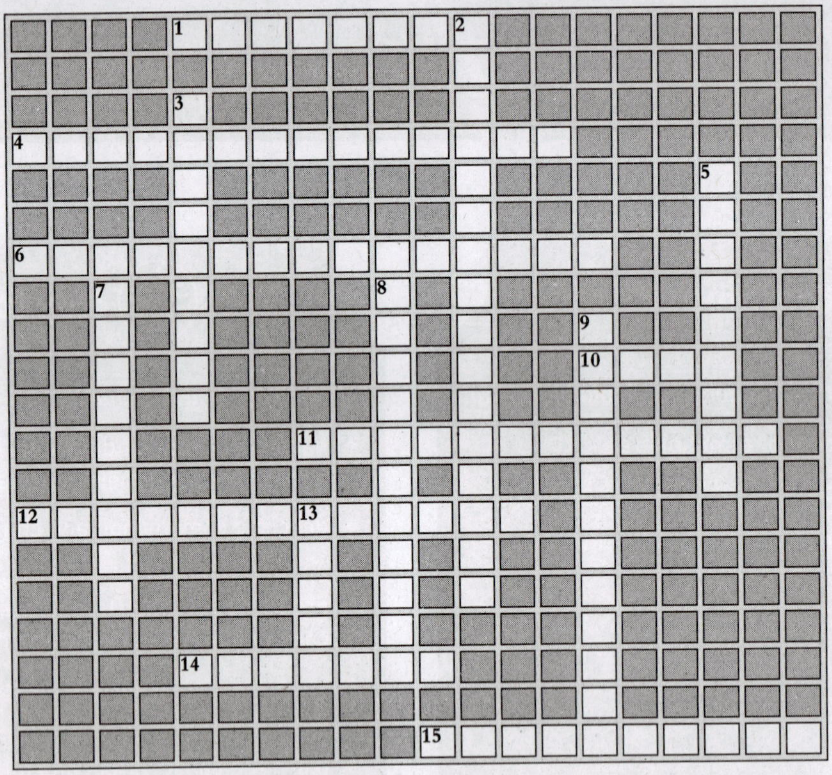

Across

1. A mixture of 95% oxygen and 5% carbon dioxide.
4. Name given to the iron coated with zinc.
6. The space beyond the ionosphere.
10. The hydrated form of iron oxide
11. The layer of atmosphere in which aeroplanes fly
12. Catalytic addition of hydrogen to some carbon compounds
14. The process of coating of tin on the iron
15. The process of coating of mixture of silicates on the iron at high temperature

Down

2. The process of conversion of atmospheric nitrogen into nitrates
3. The fall in temperature with increase in height at the rate of 6°C/Km
5. Instrument used to measure the atmospheric pressure
7. A mixture of liquid oxygen, coal and petroleum jelly
8. The accumulation of molecules of one substance over the surface of another substance
9. The layer of atmosphere that holds the maximum percentage of the total mass of the atmosphere
13. Inert gas used in advertisement glow tubes

INTRODUCTION

The planet earth has endowed us with the basic necessities of life like air, water, food, etc. Out of all the necessities, air is the most vital for life as we cannot live with out it for more than a minute. Earlier, we have learnt that air is a homogeneous mixture of gases which surrounds the planet Earth and is known as **atmosphere**. Atmosphere becomes thinner with distance from the Earth and the region above the atmosphere which is absolutely free of air is called **outer space**. The atmosphere holds the air, moisture and dust particles which are associated with natural processes like formation of clouds, precipitation, etc. It also protects us from harmful radiations. Hence, is considered as a protective cover which is further divided into five distinct layers.

Layers of Atmosphere

Our atmosphere is divided into five layers on the basis of variations in chemical composition, density and temperature at different heights from the surface of the earth.

Troposphere

Key features of this layer are listed below.

(a) The layer of atmosphere which begins at the earth's surface and extends up to 20-km height is called **troposphere**.

(b) It holds the maximum percentage of the total mass of the atmosphere.

(c) The density of the air and temperature gradually decrease with height. As we move to the upper layers, the temperature drops from about 17°C to 51°C.The fall in temperature with increase in height at the rate of 6°C/km is called **lapse rate**.

(d) Most of the weather phenomena occur in this layer due to rapid variations in temperature.

(e) The height and thickness of this layer vary from the equator to the poles.

Stratosphere

Key features of this layer are listed below.

(a) The layer of atmosphere above the troposphere which extends up to 50 km above the earth's surface is called **stratosphere**.

(b) It holds 19% of the atmospheric gases.

(c) Up to a height of 25 km from the earth's surface, the temperature does not change much. But as the height increases from 25 km, the temperature starts to increase due to the absorption of highly energetic UV radiations. Here, the temperature rises from −60°C to −15°C. This region of increase in temperature with height is called **inversion layer**. The region that extends from 25 km to 40 km above the earth's surface is called **ozonosphere** or **ozone layer**. This layer absorbs harmful UV radiations, and thus, protects life on the earth.

(d) Aeroplanes fly in this layer.

> **Info Bytes!**
>
> The Mesosphere, one of the atmospheric layers, is the coldest region in the Earth's atmosphere with temperatures going as low as −90°C. This is where most meteors burn up, creating "shooting stars"!

Mesosphere

(a) The layer above the stratosphere which extends to about 8590 km above the earth's surface is called **mesosphere**.

(b) Temperature decreases from about −15°C to −120°C.

(c) Meteorites burn up in this layer.

Thermosphere or Ionosphere

(a) This layer is also called **upper atmosphere** which extends up to 690–950 km above the earth's surface.

(b) The density of air is lesser than the mesosphere. The molecules in this layer absorb highly energetic radiations and get ionised. Hence, this layer consists of ions and free electrons.

(c) The temperature in this layer increases with height due to the absorption of high energetic radiations. The temperature can reach a maximum of 2000°C at the top of this layer.

(d) Radio waves get reflected in this layer which, thus, helps in long-distance radio communications. However, TV waves do not get reflected. Hence, artificial satellites are used for TV transmission.

(e) Auroras appear in this layer of atmosphere.

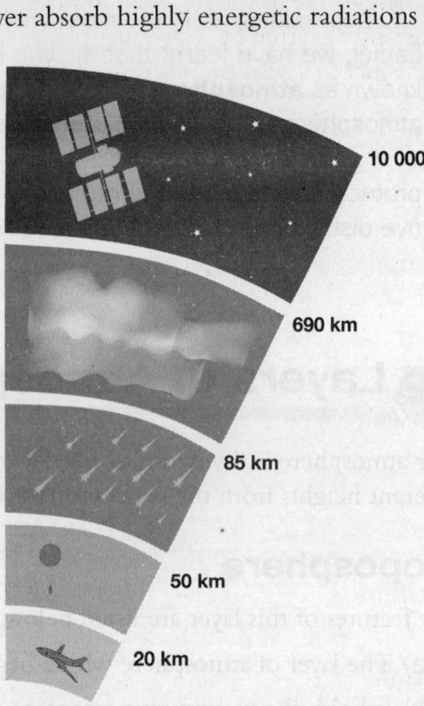

Figure 4.1 Layers of atmosphere

Auroras

The auroras (northern and southern lights) appear as luminous bands or streams, which extend to altitudes of 320 km and are visible from the surface of the earth at the higher northern or southern latitudes.

Cause of Auroras

When the high energetic electrons from the sun interact with earth's magnetic field, they cause auroras. These high energetic electrons from the sun collide with the molecules like N_2 and O_2 present in the atmosphere. The electrons of O_2 or N_2 atoms get excited to higher energy levels and when they return to their lower energy levels, they emit beautiful colours of light.

Info Bytes!

Even though the Exosphere is the outermost layer of our atmosphere, it doesn't have a definitive end. It just gradually fades into the vacuum of space!

Exosphere

(a) It is the outermost layer of the atmosphere which extends up to 10,000 km above the earth's surface.

(b) This layer absorbs harmful ionising radiations.

Air and its Composition

The atmosphere that is made up of different layers holds various components of air. Before and during the 15th century, air was regarded as an element. However, in 1674, Mayow predicted that air consists of two components, an active component and an inactive component. In the year 1789, Lavoisier gave the ratio of these two components, that is oxygen and nitrogen in air, as 1 : 4 by volume. Later, it was experimentally proved that O_2 and N_2 are the major components of air.

Nitrogen and oxygen are the two major components of air by volume which make up approximately 99 per cent of the dry atmosphere. The other gases found in the earth's atmosphere include water vapour, carbon dioxide, nitrous oxide, methane, ozone, hydrogen and inert gases like neon, helium, argon which are present in trace amounts.

The composition of air does not remain uniform throughout the atmosphere. It varies from place to place. Table 4.1 gives the average atmospheric composition.

Table 4.1 Percentage composition of air

Components of air	Percentage by volume
Nitrogen	78.084
Oxygen	20.947
Argon	0.934
Carbon dioxide	0.033
Water vapour	Variable (0 – 4)

The atmospheric layers composed of air possess weight and they exert pressure. The downward pressure exerted by air due to its weight on surroundings is called **atmospheric pressure.** The SI unit of atmospheric pressure is Pascal or kilo Pascal. The instrument used to measure the atmospheric pressure is called **barometer**. The atmospheric pressure decreases with height due to the decrease in density of air with increase in altitude. As the density of air is more in the troposphere, the pressure exerted by molecules of air is also more. Hence, the atmospheric pressure is maximum at sea level and is found to be equal to 1 atm or 760 mm of Hg.

Significance of Oxygen and Nitrogen

Nitrogen and oxygen which are major components of the atmosphere have very important associations with life. Nitrogen being an inactive component of atmosphere dilutes the activity of oxygen. Oxygen, an active component, is considered to be a supporter of life on earth as it is responsible for carrying out the important processes like respiration and combustion.

Significance of Inert Gases and Water Vapour

The significance of inert gases and water vapour is described in Table 4.2.

Table 4.2 Significance of inert gases and water vapour

Inert Gas	Significance
Helium	To fill weather-observation balloons
Argon	To fill electric bulbs at low pressure
Neon	Used in advertisement glow tubes
Water vapour along with dust particles	Help in the formation of fog, mist, clouds, etc.

Info Bytes!

Argon, an inert gas in the atmosphere, is used to protect historical documents like the Magna Carta and the U.S. Declaration of Independence by preserving them in argon-filled cases.

EXAMPLE 4.1 What is the role of water vapour in the formation of fog?

SOLUTION

The presence of water vapour in atmosphere influences the climatic conditions. Water vapour present in atmosphere gets condensed on dust particles during night time (winter nights) because of low temperature. Depending up on the temperature, the water vapour produces snow, fog, mist, etc. When water vapour condenses on dust particles and remains suspended in atmosphere, it is called fog.

EXAMPLE 4.2 Mention any three importances of atmosphere.

SOLUTION

(I) The air present in atmosphere is used for breathing.
(II) The moisture and dust particles present in air help in formation of clouds.
(III) The atmosphere protects us from harmful radiations.

EXAMPLE 4.3 Name the different layers of atmosphere.

SOLUTION

The different layers of atmosphere are:

(I) Troposphere (II) Stratosphere (III) Mesosphere
(IV) Thermosphere (V) Exosphere

Oxygen

Carl Scheele, a Swedish chemist, prepared oxygen by the decomposition of nitre and mercuric oxide. This oxygen was found to support combustion, hence, he named it as **fire air** or **vital life**. Joseph Priestly, an English chemist, prepared oxygen by focusing sun rays with the help of convex lens on mercuric oxide taken in a test tube. Antoine Lavoisier proved that oxygen is an element and by assuming it as an essential constituent of an acid he named it as **oxygen** which means *acid former*.

Occurrence

It occurs both in free and combined states. It is the most abundant element in the earth's crust.

1. **Free State:** Oxygen is present in atmospheric air in free elemental state up to about 21% by volume and 23% by mass of the total air. Oxygen is found in dissolved state in water bodies, due to which aquatic species are able to survive.
2. **Combined State:** Oxygen is found in combined state in the most vital component of life that is water. It is also found in combined state in plants and animals. However, 50% of oxygen is present in the form of minerals, such as, silicates, carbonates and oxides of various metals.

Info Bytes!

Ancient Indian scriptures and Ayurveda texts laud the healing and invigorating properties of fresh air. Modern science later identified the key component of this rejuvenating mix as oxygen. In Indian culture, Pranayama, a yogic practice, focuses on controlled breathing techniques, harnessing the power of oxygen.

Preparation of Oxygen

Oxygen can be prepared as a by product of various reaction and it can be prepared in the laboratory. Some of those methods are discussed below.

General Methods of Preparation

General methods of preparation are shown in Table 4.3.

Table 4.3 General methods of preparation of oxygen

Method	Chemical equation	Observation	Test
(i) **Thermal decomposition of metal oxides.** Mercuric oxide upon heating undergoes decomposition to produce a corresponding metal and oxygen gas.	$2HgO \xrightarrow{\Delta} 2Hg + O_2\uparrow$	Mercury vapour condenses on the cooler parts of the test tube to form a mirror-like surface.	The glowing splinter rekindles into flame.
(ii) **Thermal decomposition of metal nitrates:** Highly active metal nitrates on heating decompose to give metal nitrite and oxygen.	$2KNO_3 \xrightarrow{\Delta} 2KNO_2 + O_2\uparrow$	Crystals of potassium nitrate melt and decompose to give a colourless gas.	The glowing splinter rekindles into flame.

Laboratory Method of Preparation

Decomposition of Hydrogen Peroxide

Principle: Hydrogen peroxide in the presence of a catalyst, i.e., manganese dioxide (MnO_2) undergoes decomposition to give water and oxygen at room temperature. The role of MnO_2 is to speed up the reaction and also to make the reaction take place at room temperature.

$$2H_2O_2 \xrightarrow{MnO_2} 2H_2O + O_2 \uparrow$$

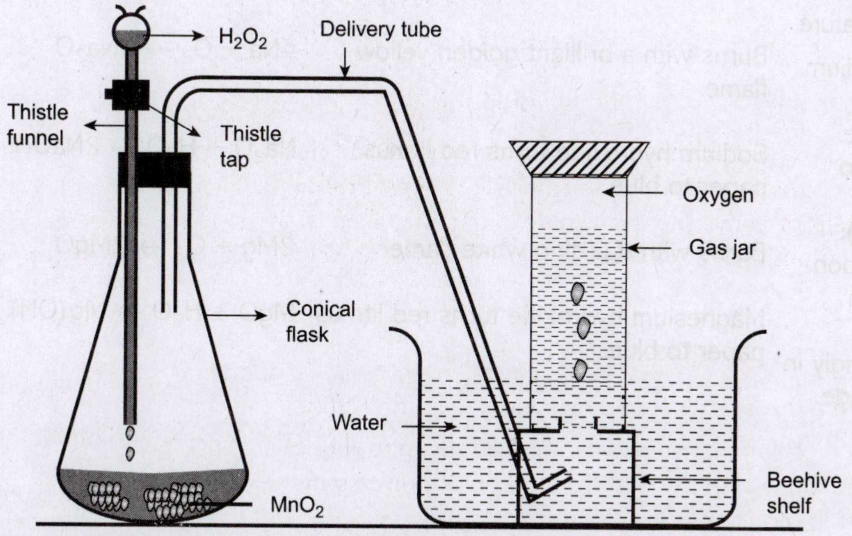

Figure 4.2 Laboratory preparation of oxygen from H_2O_2

Experiment: MnO_2 is taken in a clean and dry conical flask. H_2O_2 solution is added dropwise through the thistle funnel which is fitted to a conical flask with the help of a rubber stopper.

Observation: The oxygen gas evolved passes through a delivery tube and then into the beehive shelf which is placed in a trough of water. The oxygen gas, evolved, appears in the form of bubbles and is collected in the gas jar inverted over the beehive shelf. The gas rekindles a glowing splinter.

Method of Collection of Oxygen Gas: O_2 gas evolved is collected by downward displacement of water.

Precautions:

1. Heating of reaction mixture should be avoided.
2. MnO_2 used should be devoid of impurities.

Physical Properties of Oxygen

Physical properties of oxygen are shown in Table 4.4.

Table 4.4 Physical properties of oxygen

Physical properties	Characteristics
Colour, odour and taste	Colourless, odourless and tasteless
Solubility in water	Fairly soluble in water
Vapour density	It is slightly heavier than air
Liquefaction	Can be liquefied at high pressures and low temperatures

Konnect

Thermal decomposition of metal oxides is not employed for laboratory preparation because Hg vapours are poisonous and HgO is very expensive. Moreover, it produces a very small amount of O_2. **Thermal decomposition of metal nitrates** is not used for laboratory preparation because the rate of evolution of O_2 is slow and strong heating is required.

Konnect

The substance which alters the rate of reaction but does not take part in that chemical reaction is called **catalyst**.

Konnect

Vapour density of a gas or vapour at a certain temperature and pressure can be defined as the ratio of mass of the certain volume of gas or vapour to the mass of the same volume of hydrogen gas at the same temperature and pressure. Hence, vapour density is a relative term.

Chemical Properties of Oxygen

Chemical properties of oxygen are listed in Table 4.5.

Table 4.5 Chemical properties of oxygen

Chemical properties	Observations	Chemical equations
I. Reaction with metals: Metals react with oxygen to form corresponding metallic oxides which are generally basic in nature.		
(a) **Reaction with sodium (Na):** Sodium reacts vigorously with O_2 at room temperature to form sodium oxide.	Burns with a brilliant golden yellow flame.	$4Na + O_2 \rightarrow 2Na_2O$
Sodium oxide dissolves in water to form sodium hydroxide.	Sodium hydroxide turns red litmus paper to blue.	$Na_2O + H_2O \rightarrow 2NaOH$
(b) **Reaction with magnesium (Mg):** Magnesium reacts with oxygen upon slight heating to form magnesium oxide.	Burns with dazzling white flame	$2Mg + O_2 \rightarrow 2MgO$
Magnesium oxide dissolves sparingly in water to form magnesium hydroxide.	Magnesium hydroxide turns red litmus paper to blue.	$MgO + H_2O \rightarrow Mg(OH)_2$
II. Reaction with non-metals: Non-metals react with oxygen to form corresponding non-metallic oxides which are generally acidic in nature.		
(a) **Reaction with carbon:** When red hot charcoal or carbon is heated in an atmosphere of oxygen, it forms carbon dioxide (a colourless gas).	Sparkles and crackling sound are observed. Huge amount of heat is also liberated.	$C + O_2 \rightarrow CO_2\uparrow$
CO_2 gas gets dissolved in water to form carbonic acid (H_2CO_3).	H_2CO_3 turns blue litmus paper to red. Hence, CO_2 is acidic in nature.	$CO_2 + H_2O \rightarrow H_2CO_3$
Test for CO_2: When CO_2 gas is passed through lime water, a milky white precipitate of calcium carbonate ($CaCO_3$) is formed.	Lime water turns milky due to the formation of $CaCO_3$.	$Ca(OH)_2 + CO_2 \rightarrow CaCO_3\downarrow + H_2O$
(b) **Reaction with sulphur:** Sulphur when heated in an atmosphere of oxygen burns to form sulphur dioxide.	Burns with a brilliant blue flame, SO_2 has a suffocating smell.	$S + O_2 \xrightarrow{\Delta} SO_2\uparrow$
SO_2 when dissolved in water forms sulphurous acid (H_2SO_3)	H_2SO_3 turns blue litmus paper to red. Hence, SO_2 is acidic in nature.	$SO_2 + H_2O \xrightarrow{\Delta} H_2SO_3$
Test for SO_2: When SO_2 gas is exposed to acidified potassium dichromate paper, the paper turns green.	Paper turns green due to the formation of $Cr_2(SO_4)_3$ chromic sulphate.	$3SO_2 + K_2Cr_2O_7 + H_2SO_4 \xrightarrow{\Delta} K_2SO_4 + Cr_2(SO_4)_3 + H_2O$ green
(c) **Reaction with phosphorus:** When phosphorus is heated in an atmosphere of oxygen, it burns to produce phosphorus pentoxide.	Burns with dazzling, dense white fumes	$4P + 5O_2 \rightarrow 2P_2O_5$
P_2O_5 when dissolved in water forms phosphoric acid (H_3PO_4).	H_3PO_4 turns blue litmus paper to red. Hence, P_2O_5 is acidic in nature.	$P_2O_5 + 3H_2O \rightarrow 2H_3PO_4$

Combustion

The most important property of oxygen is combustion. The combustible materials react with oxygen to release certain amount of energy which can be utilised for various domestic or industrial purposes. This reaction is called **burning** or **combustion** and those combustible substances are called **fuels**.

$$C_6H_{12}O_6 + 6O_2 \rightarrow 6CO_2 + 6H_2O + \text{Energy}$$

Respiration taking place in living organisms also is one type of combustion reaction as it involves the reaction of glucose with oxygen to form carbon dioxide and water along with the release of energy.

$$C_6H_{12}O_6 + 6O_2 \rightarrow 6CO_2 + 6H_2O + \text{Energy}$$

Despite the close similarity of respiration with combustion, there are some striking differences between combustion and respiration.

Table 4.6 Difference between combustion and respiration

Combustion	Respiration
Fast process	Slow process
Takes place at high temperature	Takes place at body temperature
Catalysts are not essential	Enzymes are essential
Energy is released in the form of heat and light.	Energy is released in the form of heat only.

Change in Mass During Combustion

The mass of the substances appears to increase during the reaction with oxygen. That is because of the addition of mass of oxygen.

$$2Mg + O_2 \rightarrow 2MgO$$

If the burning of magnesium ribbon is considered, when 24 g of magnesium is subjected to combustion, 40 g of magnesium oxide is formed. This is because 16 g of oxygen is added to it.

Burning of a Candle: Candle is made up of wax which is a mixture of hydrocarbons. When a hydrocarbon is subjected to combustion, carbon dioxide and water are formed. If we consider the combustion of the simplest hydrocarbon that is methane, the reaction can be written as

$$CH_4 + 2O_2 \rightarrow CO_2 + 2H_2O$$

The molecular mass of methane is 16g. 16 g of methane on combustion gives 44 g of carbon dioxide and 36 g of water vapour. The total mass of the products formed would be 80 g. This is because of the addition of 64 g of oxygen.

1. **Flame:** Flame is the visible light energy emitted due to the combustion of gas or vapour.
   Examples: Combustion of candle, kerosene, camphor etc gives rise to flames.

   Some fuels directly undergo combustion without getting vapourised. The substances which do not vapourise do not produce any flame during burning.
   Example: Coal

2. **Zones of a Candle Flame:** A candle is made up of wax which is a mixture of various hydrocarbons. When it is lighted, wax melts and then vaporises which subsequently gives rise to a flame. The structure of flame is composed of three distinct zones as shown in the figure.
   - **Zone A:** It is the innermost zone which appears dark. It is the coldest part of the flame and is known as **zone of unburnt wax vapours.** It consists of unburnt carbon particles.
   - **Zone B:** It is the middle zone called **'luminous zone'**. It consists of partially or incompletely burnt gases which leaves carbon particles and the heated carbon particles burn and make the flame luminous. This flame is orange to yellow in colour. It produces soot due to incomplete combustion.

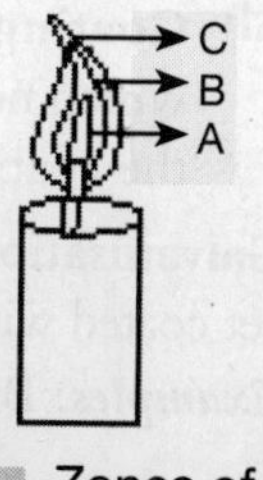

Figure 4.3 Zones of a flame

- **Zone C:** It is the outermost zone called **non-luminous zone.** This flame is blue in colour indicating that complete combustion takes place in this zone and hence it is the hottest zone. It does not produce any soot.

Other Chemical Properties

Combustibility

As oxygen does not burn on its own, it is a non-combustible gas. However, it is a supporter of combustion as it allows burning of other substances.

Example: A glowing wooden splint bursts into flame in an atmosphere of oxygen.

Action with Litmus

Oxygen is neither acidic nor basic in nature. It is neutral, hence, it does not respond to either blue litmus or red litmus paper.

Rusting

The process of conversion of iron into its hydrated form of oxide in a humid atmosphere is called **rusting**. The hydrated form of its oxide is called **rust**.

$$4Fe(s) + 3O_2 \rightarrow 2Fe_2O_3\ (s)$$

$$Fe_2O_3\ (s) + xH_2O\ (l) \rightarrow \underset{\text{rust}}{Fe_2O_3.xH_2O\ (s)}$$

(x indicates the number of water molecules which is variable)

Iron gets corroded due to the formation of rust. The rust is a brownish flaky substance which easily crumbles from the surface of a metal. Hence, it weakens the iron structures.

Prevention of Rusting

Prevention of rusting of iron is done to make different structures for varied purposes like the manufacture of machinery and tools for industrial purposes, construction of bridges, railway tracks and manufacture of furniture, bodies of cooking stoves, refrigerators, buckets, suitcases and other household goods. To prevent rusting of iron, different methods and processes are employed which are discussed below.

Info Bytes!

Iron does not get rusted in dry atmosphere.

1. The metal iron is coated with other substances which prevent the exposure of iron to humid air thereby preventing rusting.
   (a) **Coating with Red Lead Oxide or Tar:** The bridges, electric poles, etc., are coated with red lead oxide paint or tar which protects iron from rusting.
   (b) **Coating with Enamel Paint:** Doors and windows, bodies of cars, buses and other automobiles, etc., are first given coat of red lead oxide paint followed by enamelled paint so as to enhance the appearance of the structure.
   (c) **By Enamelling:** The process of coating of mixture of silicates on the surface of iron, at high temperatures is called enamelling. It also gives good appearance for the articles. Articles like bodies of cooking stoves, refrigerators, plates, wash basins, ovens, etc., are given this type of coating.
   (d) **Coating with Oil or Grease:** The movable machine or engine parts are coated with a layer of oil or grease which not only prevents rusting but also lubricates them. They cannot be coated with other substances because the coating wears off as these parts keep on moving.
2. **Galvanisation:** Iron sheets which are dipped in molten zinc are passed through heavy rollers. As a result, the iron sheets get coated with zinc metal. This process is called **galvanisation** and iron coated with zinc is called **galvanised iron.**
   Examples: Buckets, tubs, iron trunks, etc.

3. **Tinning:** The process in which a protective layer of tin is coated on iron sheets is called **tinning**. The process is similar to galvanisation.
   Example: Containers or tins used to preserve edible food materials like oil, meat, vegetables, etc.
4. **Electroplating:** The metal iron is coated with another metal by the process called **electroplating**. The metals used for coating are chromium or nickel.
   Examples: Bicycle handles, rims, bumpers of car, etc.
5. **Alloying:** The process of mixing uniformly small quantities of different metals with a particular metal in their molten state in order to improve the mechanical properties of the metal is called **alloying**. Substances like carbon and chromium are added to iron to form a homogeneous mixture called **stainless steel**, an alloy by which it is made corrosion resistant.
   Percentage composition: Chromium — From 12 to 20 per cent
   Carbon — From 0.07 to 0.1 per cent
   Examples: Surgical instruments, tools, utensils, cutlery, etc.

Laboratory Tests to Detect Oxygen

Following are the tests performed in laboratories to detect the presence of oxygen:

1. It does not respond to litmus paper as it is neutral in nature.
2. It rekindles a glowing splinter.
3. It reacts with colourless nitric oxide to form reddish brown fumes of nitrogen dioxide.
4. It turns alkaline pyrogallol solution brown.

Uses of Oxygen

Following are some of the vital roles of oxygen:

1. **Respiration:** Oxygen is necessary for respiration of living beings. Oxygen inhaled during respiration is utilised in oxidising the glucose to carbon dioxide and water, which is accompanied with evolution of energy.

$$C_6H_{12}O_6 + 6O_2 \rightarrow 6CO_2 + 6H_2O + \text{energy}$$

2. **Fuels:** Oxygen is essential for burning or combustion of fuels.
3. **Artificial respiration:** It is used for artificial respiration in the places where there is no sufficient supply of oxygen. It is used by deep-sea divers, submariners, mountaineers, astronauts, aviators, etc.
4. **Medical:** A mixture of 95% oxygen and 5% CO_2 is called **carbogen**. It is given to the patients suffering from breathing problems.
5. **Cutting and Welding:** A mixture of hydrogen and oxygen on burning gives oxyhydrogen flame of 2800°C temperature, whereas a mixture of hydrogen and acetylene produces oxyacetylene flame which has 3300°C temperature. These flames easily melt the metals, and hence, used for cutting or welding them.
6. **Space Ships:** Liquid oxygen is used for burning fuel in the rockets and space ships.
7. **Explosive:** A mixture of coal, petroleum jelly and liquid oxygen is called **cartridge** and is used for blasting rocks.
8. **Chemical Industry:** It is used in the preparation of H_2SO_4 and HNO_3.

> **Konnect**
>
> The Taj Mahal, India's iconic white marble mausoleum, is showing signs of yellowing due to pollution, including carbon dioxide emissions. Efforts are being made to limit emissions in the vicinity to protect this world heritage site.

Carbon Dioxide

Jan Baptist van Helmont predicted the formation of this gas when charcoal is burnt in air and he called this gas **carbonium**. He predicted the occurrence of this gas in coal mines and found that it can extinguish candle flame. Later, Joseph Black prepared this gas by heating magnesium carbonate and he named the gas as fixed air.

Lavoisier named this gas as *acid carbonique* and he established it as an oxide of carbon. According to the IUPAC system, the gas was named carbon dioxide.

Occurrence

Carbon dioxide is a gas which occupies about 0.003% of the total volume of air. It is the fifth abundant gas in the atmosphere.

1. **Free State:** It is found in the free state in the atmosphere and also found in water bodies like oceans, lakes, rivers, etc., in the dissolved form.
2. **Combined State:** It is generally found in combined state in the form of carbonate minerals such as limestone, magnesite, dolomite, etc.

Preparation of Carbon Dioxide

Carbon dioxide can be prepared as a byproduct of various reaction and it can be prepared in the laboratory. Some of those methods are discussed below.

General Methods of Preparation

(a) Combustion: CO_2 is released into the atmosphere when carbon-containing fuels like coal, natural gas, etc., are burnt.

Examples: $C + O_2 \rightarrow CO_2\uparrow + \text{heat}$

$CH_4 + 2O_2 \rightarrow CO_2\uparrow + 2H_2O + \text{heat}$

(b) Decomposition of Metal Carbonates: Metal carbonates on strong heating decompose to produce CO_2 gas and corresponding metal oxides.

Exceptions: Sodium carbonate and potassium carbonate.

Examples: $CaCO_3 \xrightarrow{\Delta} CaO + CO_2\uparrow$

$CuCO_3 \xrightarrow{\Delta} CuO + CO_2\uparrow$

$ZnCO_3 \xrightarrow{\Delta} ZnO + CO_2\uparrow$

(c) Decomposition of Metal Hydrogen Carbonates: Active metal hydrogen carbonate like sodium hydrogen carbonate, commonly called baking soda, on heating produces CO_2 gas along with the formation of corresponding metal carbonate and water.

$$\underset{\text{Sodium bicarbonate or sodium hydrogen carbonate}}{2NaHCO_3} \xrightarrow{\Delta} \underset{\text{sodium carbonate}}{Na_2CO_3} + H_2O + CO_2\uparrow$$

(d) Action of Dilute Acids on Metal Carbonates and Hydrogen Carbonates: Metal carbonates and hydrogen carbonates when treated with dilute acids liberate CO_2 gas with the formation of corresponding salts.

$$Na_2CO_3 + H_2SO_4 \rightarrow Na_2SO_4 + H_2O + CO_2\uparrow$$

$$Ca(HCO_3)_2 + 2HNO_3 \rightarrow Ca(NO_3)_2 + 2H_2O + 2CO_2$$

Laboratory Method of Preparation

Principle: Dilute HCl is made to react with marble chips which contain calcium carbonate to evolve carbon dioxide gas.

$$CaCO_3 + 2HCl \rightarrow CaCl_2 + H_2O + CO_2\uparrow$$

Process: A conical flask fitted with a two-holed rubber cork is taken. Dilute HCl is added dropwise through thistle funnel which is inserted into the conical flask through one hole of rubber cork. CO_2 gas evolved passes through a delivery tube, which is inserted into the conical flask through another hole of rubber cork into the gas cylinder.

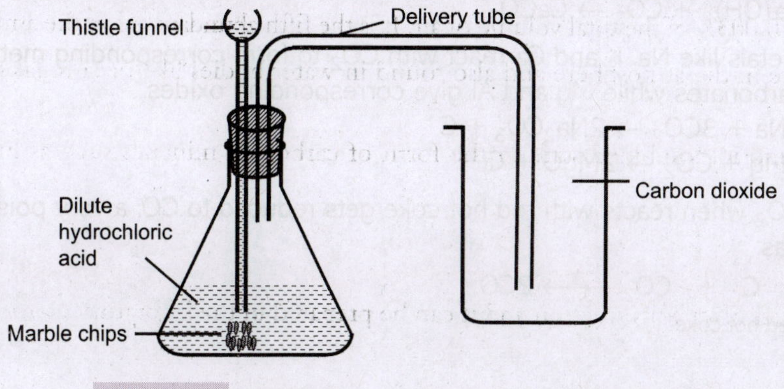

Figure 4.4 Laboratory preparation of carbon dioxide

Konnect

Diluted H_2SO_4 is not used for the preparation of CO_2 because the calcium sulphate formed being insoluble in water forms a layer over marble chips, and thus, marble chips do not come in contact with dil H_2SO_4 further.

$$CaCO_3 + H_2SO_4(dil) \rightarrow CaSO_4\downarrow + H_2O + CO_2\uparrow$$

Method of Collection of Gas: CO_2 being heavier than air is collected by upward displacement of air.

Physical Properties of Carbon Dioxide

Physical properties of CO_2 are shown in Table 4.7.

Table 4.7 Physical Properties of carbon dioxide

Parameters	Characteristics
Colour	To fill weather-observation balloons
Odour	To fill electric bulbs at low pressure
Solubility in water	Used in advertisement glow tubes
Vapour density	Heavier than air, vapour density = 22
Nature	Acidic. Hence, changes blue litmus to red
Formation of dry ice	At very high pressures when it is allowed to expand suddenly through a small nozzle it forms solid carbon dioxide which is known as **dry ice.**

Table 4.8 Chemical Properties of carbon dioxide

Properties	Observation and inference
(i) **Combustibility**	It does not burn and it does not support burning of other substances in its atmosphere. Hence, it is neither combustible nor a supporter of combustion
(ii) **Reaction with water**	CO_2 reacts with water to form carbonic acid. Hence, CO_2 is acidic in nature. $CO_2 + H_2O \rightarrow H_2CO_3$
(iii) **Acidic properties of CO_2** (a) Reaction with alkali	It reacts with alkali (base) to form salt and water. This reaction is called **neutralisation**. *Examples:* $CO_2 + 2NaOH \rightarrow Na_2CO_3 + H_2O$

(Continued)

Table 4.8 Continue

Properties	Observation and inference
(b) Reaction with lime water	CO_2 reacts with lime water to form a milky white precipitate, i.e., $CaCO_3$ $Ca(OH)_2 + CO_2 \rightarrow CaCO_3$
(c) Reaction with metals	Metals like Na, K and Ca react with CO_2 to form corresponding metal carbonates while Mg and Al give corresponding oxides. $4Na + 3CO_2 \rightarrow 2Na_2CO_3 + C$ $2Mg + CO_2 \rightarrow 2MgO + C$
(iv) **Reaction with non-metals**	CO_2 when reacts with red hot coke gets reduced to CO, a very poisonous gas. $C + CO_2 \xrightarrow{\Delta} 2CO$ Red hot coke

Chemical Properties of Carbon Dioxide

Chemical properties of CO_2 are shown in Table 4.8.

Laboratory Tests for Carbon Dioxide

Following are the tests performed in laboratories to detect the presence of carbon dioxide:

1. When a lightened candle is exposed to the atmosphere of CO_2, it gets extinguished.
2. It turns lime water milky and when excess CO_2 is passed through the solution, precipitate formed disappears.

Konnect

When excess CO_2 is passed through the above solution, the precipitate dissolves due to the formation of $Ca(HCO_3)_2$

$CaCO_3 + H_2O + CO_2 \rightarrow Ca(HCO_3)_2$

Uses of Carbon Dioxide

Carbon Dioxide finds many applications in various fields like industry, medicine, agriculture, etc. It is a natural raw material available for the plants to synthesise the food material by the process called **photosynthesis**. Moreover, it maintains the temperature of the earth. The various other uses of CO_2 are given below.

1. **Manufacture of Useful Chemicals:** It is extensively used in the production of industrial chemicals such as washing soda, baking soda ($NaHCO_3$), white lead ($Pb(OH)_2.PbCO_3$), etc.
2. **Soft Drinks:** It is dissolved in soft drinks under high pressure so as to impart tangy taste.
3. **Medical Purpose:** Carbogen, which consists of 5% CO_2 and 95% O_2 stimulates breathing (artificial respiration), and hence, it is used by patients suffering from asthma, pneumonia, etc.

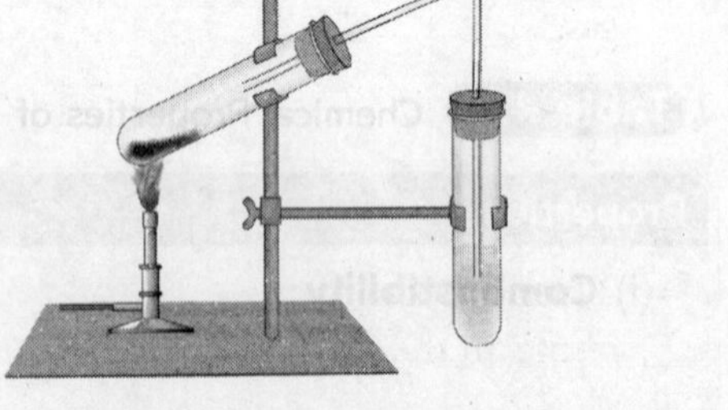

Figure 4.5 Laboratory test of Carbon dioxide

4. **Refrigeration:** Dry ice is used as a refrigerant to preserve perishable foods like meat, fish, fruits, vegetables, etc., for longer time.
5. **Preservation of Foodstuffs:** It is used to preserve food grains.
6. **Regeneration of Oxygen:** CO_2 present in the atmosphere is used by the plants to prepare their food by the process called **photosynthesis**. In this process, CO_2 and H_2O combine in the presence of sunlight to form glucose

and O_2 which is added to the atmosphere.

$$6CO_2 + 6H_2O \xrightarrow{\text{Sunlight}} \underset{\text{(Glucose)}}{C_6H_{12}O_6} + 6O_2 \uparrow$$

7. **Fire extinguisher:** CO_2 is a non-supporter of combustion, non-combustible and being heavier than air it can be used to put off fires. The device used to put off fires is called **fire extinguisher.**

Nitrogen

Nitrogen is one of the constituent elements in most of the materials present in the cells and tissues of the living organisms. Hence, nitrogen is also considered as one of the building blocks of life along with carbon. Most of it is present in the form of amino acids and proteins. It is very much required for the survival of plants and animals.

Nitrogen makes up 80% of the atmospheric air and hence abundantly available. However, this nitrogen is not directly accessible to the living organisms. This nitrogen has to be converted to usable form. This is known as nitrogen fixation.

Occurrence

1. Nitrogen exists in a free state in the atmosphere. It is the major component of air which is present up to about 78% by volume.
2. It is also found in a combined state in the form of salts like KNO_3, $NaNO_3$ and also in organic matter such as proteins, etc.

Preparation of Nitrogen

General Methods of Preparation

- **Thermal Decomposition of Ammonium Dichromate:** Red crystals of ammonium dichromate are subjected to strong heating, it decomposes to give nitrogen gas. This is a violent reaction and is associated with flashes of light.

$$(NH_4)_2 Cr_2O_7 \xrightarrow{\Delta} N_2 + 4H_2O + Cr_2O_3$$

- **Oxidation of Ammonia:** Ammonia on oxidation with red hot copper oxide or chlorine gas produces nitrogen gas.

$$2NH_3 + 3CuO \rightarrow N_2 + 3H_2O + 3Cu$$
$$8NH_3 + 3Cl_2 \rightarrow N_2 + 6NH_4Cl$$

- **Thermal Decomposition of Sodium Azide:** Decomposition of sodium or barium azide at high temperature results in the formation of pure nitrogen.

$$2NaN_3 \rightarrow 2Na + 3N_2$$
$$Ba(N_3)_2 \rightarrow Ba + 3N_2$$

Laboratory Method of Preparation

Principle: Gentle heating of an aqueous solution of ammonium chloride with an aqueous solution of sodium nitrite gives nitrogen gas as the final product. This reaction is assumed to take place in two steps. In the first step, ammonium nitrite is produced which being unstable further decomposes to give nitrogen gas in the second step of the reaction.

$$NH_4Cl(aq) + NaNO_2(aq) \rightarrow NaCl(aq) + 2H_2O(l) + N_2(g)$$

$$\text{(i) } NH_4Cl + NaNO_2 \xrightarrow{\Delta} NH_4NO_2 + NaCl$$

$$\text{(ii) } NH_4NO_2 \xrightarrow{\Delta} N_2 + 2H_2O$$

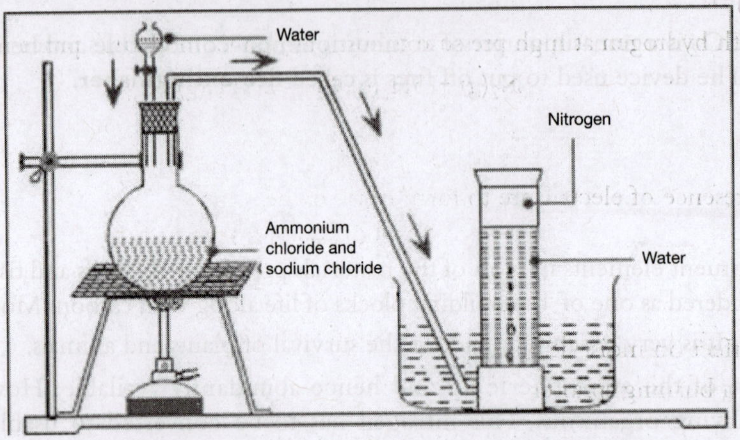

Figure 4.6 Laboratory Preparation of Nitrogen

Experiment: A mixture of ammonium chloride and sodium nitrite is taken in a round-bottomed flask. Water is added into the flask by means of a thistle funnel. The mixture is subjected to heating.

Observation: The nitrogen gas evolved passes through a delivery tube and then into the beehive shelf which is placed in a trough of water. The nitrogen gas, evolved, appears in the form of bubbles and is collected in the gas jar inverted over the beehive shelf.

Method of Collection: Nitrogen gas is collected by downward displacement of water.

Precautions

1. The impurities such as nitric oxide and nitric acid formed during the process are removed by passing the gas through sulphuric acid containing potassium dichromate.
2. Solid sodium nitrite should not be taken for the reaction.

Physical Properties of Nitrogen

- It is a colourless, odourless, and tasteless gas.
- It is non-toxic but animals die in an atmosphere of nitrogen due to the lack of oxygen.
- It is sparingly soluble in water
- It is melting and boiling points are 63.2K and 77.2K respectively.

Konnect

When divers ascend too quickly from deep waters, nitrogen bubbles can form in their bloodstream causing joint pain, a condition known as decompression sickness or 'the bends'.

Chemical Properties of Nitrogen

- N_2 is almost non-reactive at ordinary temperatures. It neither burns nor supports combustion.

Reaction with Metals

- However, at high temperatures, it combines with highly reactive metals and to form nitrides.

$$6Li + N_2 \rightarrow 2Li_3N_2$$

$$3Mg + N_2 \rightarrow Mg_3N_2$$

$$2Al + N_2 \rightarrow 2AlN$$

$$3Ca + N_2 \rightarrow Ca_3N_2$$

Reaction with Non-metals

Under suitable conditions of temperature and pressure, nitrogen reacts with some non-metals forming the corresponding binary compounds.

Reaction with Hydrogen

At about 773 K it reacts with hydrogen at high pressure to form ammonia in Haber's process.

$$N_2(g) + 3H_2(g) \rightleftharpoons 2NH_3(g)$$

Reaction with Oxygen

N_2 combines with O_2 in presence of electric are to form nitric oxide.

$$N_2 + O_2 \rightarrow 2NO$$

Tests for Nitrogen

- Nitrogen gas has no effect on moist litmus paper.
- Nitrogen gas puts out a burning splinter.

Uses of Nitrogen

Following are the important uses of nitrogen gas:

1. It dilutes the activity of oxygen, and thus, prevents rapid burning.
2. It is used in the manufacture of ammonia. Compounds of ammonia are used as fertilisers.
3. Nitrogen is required for plants and animals to synthesise proteins. The free nitrogen cannot be assimilated by plants. Hence, nitrogen present in the atmosphere is converted into compounds by which it can be assimilated by plants. The process of conversion of atmospheric nitrogen into nitrates is called **nitrogen fixation**.

   During lightening, N_2 combines with O_2 to form NO which further reacts with O_2 to form NO_2. This gas dissolves in the water droplets of clouds and form HNO_3. During precipitation, it reaches soil and reacts with metal carbonates to form corresponding nitrates, and these nitrates are assimilated by plants.

$$N_2 + O_2 \rightarrow 2NO$$

$$2NO + O_2 \rightarrow 2NO_2$$

$$4NO_2 + 2H_2O + O_2 \rightarrow 4HNO_3$$

$$4HNO_3 + MCO_3 \rightarrow M(NO_3)_2 + CO_2 + H_2O$$

   Leguminous plants contain symbiotic bacteria in their root nodules which absorb atmospheric nitrogen and convert nitrogen into various compounds of nitrogen. The plants can easily assimilate and also the soil becomes enriched with nitrogen compounds.

4. Nitrogen being chemically less reactive (inert in nature), is used in the preservation of foods.

Konnect

India is a major producer of nitrogenous fertilizers. The green revolution in India, which increased crop yield and made the country self-sufficient in food grains in the 1970s, was heavily dependent on the use of such fertilizers.

Hydrogen

Hydrogen is the lightest among all elements. Atmospheric air is found to contain only trace amounts of hydrogen. Hydrogen gas was first prepared by the action of H_2SO_4 on iron. In 1762, Henry Cavendish for the first time established the elemental nature of hydrogen. He prepared this gas by the action of H_2SO_4 on zinc. Lavoisier named it **hydrogen** which means *water-former* (Hydro-water, gen-producing).

Occurrence

Availability of hydrogen gas in a free state is very rare. Although it is present in trace amounts in the atmosphere, hydrogen is present in the sun's atmosphere up to 1.1%. Very minute quantities of hydrogen are present in volcanic gases.

Most of the hydrogen is present in a combined state in nature. Hydrogen is present in various carbon compounds in the form of proteins, nucleic acids, vitamins, hormones, enzymes, etc., in plants and animals. Most of the naturally occurring substances such as wood, cotton, paper pulp, rubber, etc., contain hydrogen. Water is the most important source of hydrogen as hydrogen is present up to 11.1% by weight in water.

Preparation of Hydrogen

Hydrogen can be prepared as a byproduct of various reaction and it can be prepared in the laboratory. Since, Hydrogen is abundantly used in various purposes, it is also industrially prepared on a large scale. Some of those methods are discussed below.

General Methods of Preparation

General methods of preparation of hydrogen are shown in Table 4.9.

Table 4.9 General methods of Preparation of hydrogen

Method	Equation	Observation
Reaction of active metals with water	$2Na + 2H_2O \rightarrow 2NaOH + H_2\uparrow$	Na and K → Reaction is violent. They float on the surface of water. Ca → Brisk reaction and metal sinks in water.
Action of steam on hot metals	$Mg + H_2O \rightarrow MgO + H_2\uparrow$ $Fe + H_2O \rightleftharpoons Fe_3O_4 + H_2\uparrow$	Reaction is fast for Mg and slow for Al, Zn and Fe.
Action of dilute acids on metals	$Zn + 2HCl \rightarrow ZnCl_2 + H_2\uparrow$	
Action of concentrated alkali on metals	$2NaOH + 2Al + 2H_2O \rightarrow 2NaAlO_2 + 3H_2\uparrow$	Reaction takes place only on boiling.

Laboratory Method of Preparation

Principle: All the metals present above hydrogen in the reactivity series on reaction with dil. HCl or dil. H_2SO_4 liberate hydrogen gas. Zinc metal is preferred for this reaction.

$$Zn + 2HCl \rightarrow ZnCl_2 + H_2\uparrow$$
$$Zn + H_2SO_4 \rightarrow ZnSO_4 + H_2\uparrow$$

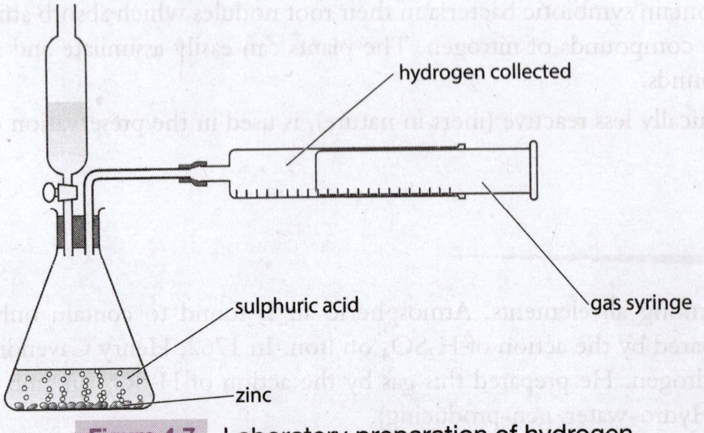

Figure 4.7 Laboratory preparation of hydrogen

Experiment: Some granulated zinc pieces are taken in a flat-bottom flask fitted with a two-holed air-tight cork. In one hole, a thistle funnel is inserted and in another hole, a long delivery tube is inserted. Dil. H_2SO_4 is added to the flask dropwise through the thistle funnel.

Observation: Effervescence is observed during the initial stages of the reaction. Then, a colourless and odourless gas evolves.

Collection of Gas: Hydrogen is collected by the downward displacement of water.

Purification of Hydrogen Gas: Since impure zinc is used for hydrogen gas preparation, the hydrogen gas collected is found to contain some impurities such as H_2S, SO_2, PH_3, AsH_3 and CO_2.These impurities are removed in stages.

Table 4.10 Removal of impurities associated with hydrogen gas

Impurities	Substances used for removal
AsH_3, PH_3	Silver nitrate solution
H_2S	Lead nitrate solution
CO_2, SO_2, NO_2	Caustic potash
H_2O (water vapour)	$CaCl_2$ or P_2O_5 (drying agent)

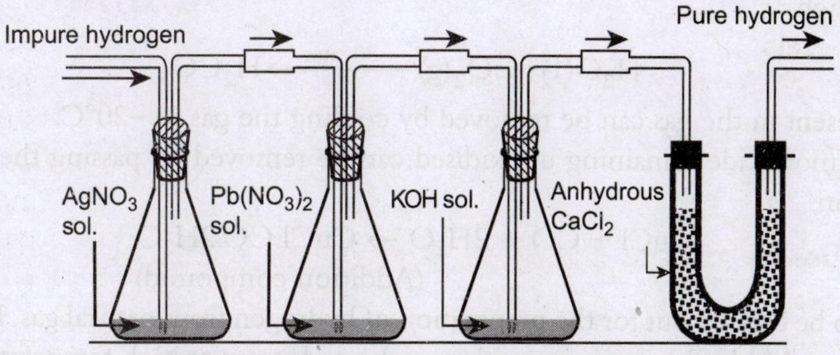

Figure 4.8 Purification of hydrogen gas

Collection of Purified Hydrogen Gas: To obtain pure and dry hydrogen, pure hydrogen gas is collected over mercury.

Precautions:

1. The entire apparatus should be kept air tight.
2. Contact with flame should be avoided.
3. Collection of the gas should be done only after the expulsion of air.
4. The end of the thistle funnel should almost touch the bottom.

Although all active metals liberate hydrogen gas, zinc is the preferred metal and the other metals are not used for this preparation method.

Table 4.11 Reasons for not using other metals for the preparation of hydrogen gas

Metals	Reason for not using
Sodium and potassium	Violent reaction with explosion
Calcium and magnesium	Expensive metals
Aluminium	Formation of protective coating of Al_2O_3 that renders the metal passive
Iron	Reversible reaction
Lead	Formation of insoluble $PbCl_2$ or $PbSO_4$ stops the further reaction

Industrial Methods of Preparation

1. **Electrolysis of Water:** Electrolysis of acidulated water liberates oxygen at the anode and hydrogen at the cathode. In fact, this method is employed for the preparation of oxygen gas where hydrogen is obtained as a by-product.

$$2H_2O \rightarrow 2H_2 + O_2$$

2. **Bosch Process:** Water gas is a mixture of carbon monoxide and hydrogen. Water gas can be prepared by passing steam over red hot coke.

$$\underset{\text{steam}}{C + H_2O} \rightarrow \underset{\text{water gas}}{CO + H_2}$$

Catalytic oxidation of water gas gives hydrogen gas.

$$CO + H_2 + H_2O \xrightarrow[450°C\text{-}500°C]{Fe_2O_3} CO_2 + 2H_2$$

Process:

(a) Superheated steam at 170°C, when passed through red hot coke or charcoal, gives a mixture of CO gas and hydrogen known as water gas.

(b) Water gas obtained is made to pass over Fe_2O_3 or Cr_2O_3 along with superheated steam at 500°C. Carbon monoxide present in water gas gets oxidised to CO_2 leaving hydrogen gas.

(c) The CO_2 gas is removed by compressing the gas at 30 atm pressure and passing it through water. Hydrogen being insoluble remains as such.

$$H_2O(1) + CO_2(g) \xrightarrow{30\ \text{atm}} H_2CO_3$$

(d) The water vapour present in the gas can be removed by cooling the gas to –20°C.

(e) The traces of carbon monoxide remaining unoxidised can be removed by passing the gas through ammonical cuprous chloride solution.

$$CuCl + CO + 2H_2O \rightarrow \underset{\text{(Addition compound)}}{CuCl.CO.2H_2O}$$

Bosch process can also be carried out for the preparation of hydrogen from natural gas. Natural gas contains methane as the major constituent. Methane on mixing with superheated steam at high temperature followed by compression to 30 atm pressure gives water gas. This is subjected to Bosch process for getting pure hydrogen gas.

Physical Properties of Hydrogen

Physical properties of hydrogen are discussed in Table 4.12.

Table 4.12 Physical properties of hydrogen

Parameters	Description
Odour	No characteristic odour for pure hydrogen. However, fishy odour of hydrogen gas is attributed to the presence of impurities
Solubility	Negligible
Density	Least density
Action on litmus	Neutral
Liquefaction	Difficult due to very low critical temperature and not possible at room temperature
Diffusion	Rate of diffusion is very high

Adsorption or Occlusion

In addition to the normal physical properties, hydrogen shows a specific property called adsorption or occlusion. The accumulation of molecules of one compound over the surface of another substance is called **adsorption**. Hydrogen gas gets adsorbed on the surface of some metals like palladium, platinum, nickel, etc. This phenomenon is called **occlusion**.

Chemical Properties of Hydrogen

1. **Reaction with Air:** Hydrogen burns in air, i.e., it reacts with oxygen of air forming water. A blue flame is also observed.

$$2H_2 + O_2 \rightarrow 2H_2O$$

2. **Reaction with Non-metals:** Hydrogen reacts with most of the non-metals forming corresponding hydrides.

   (a) **Reaction with Chlorine:** Hydrogen reacts with chlorine in the presence of sunlight to give hydrogen chloride. This is a photochemical reaction.

   $$H_2 + C_2 \xrightarrow{\text{light}} 2HCl$$

   (b) **Reaction with Nitrogen:** Nitrogen and hydrogen react in 1 : 3 ratio at high temperature and high pressure to form ammonia.

   $$N_2 + 3H_2 \rightleftharpoons 2NH_3 + \text{heat}$$

   (c) **Reaction with Sulphur:** On reaction with molten sulphur, hydrogen gas gives hydrogen sulphide.

   $$H_2 + S \rightarrow H_2S$$

3. **Reaction with Metals:** Hydrogen reacts with highly electropositive metals to form metallic hydrides.

   Examples:

   $$2K + H_2 \xrightarrow{\Delta} 2KH$$

   $$2Na + H_2 \xrightarrow{\Delta} 2NaH$$

   $$Ca + H_2 \rightarrow CaH_2$$

4. **Reaction with Metal Oxides:** Oxides of less reactive metals react with hydrogen to form the corresponding metal and water. This is due to the reduction of metallic oxide.

   Examples:

   $$\underset{\text{white}}{ZnO} + H_2 \rightarrow \underset{\text{bluish white}}{Zn} + H_2O$$

   $$\underset{\text{brown}}{2Fe_2O_3} + 6H_2 \rightarrow \underset{\text{grey}}{4Fe} + 6H_2O$$

   $$\underset{\text{yellow}}{PbO} + H_2 \rightarrow \underset{\text{grey}}{Pb} + H_2O$$

   $$\underset{\text{black}}{CuO} + H_2 \rightarrow \underset{\text{red}}{Cu} + H_2O$$

5. **Hydrogenation:** Catalytic addition of hydrogen to some carbon compounds is called **hydrogenation**.

   $$\underset{\text{Ethylene}}{H_2C = CH_2} + H_2 \rightarrow \underset{\text{Ethane}}{H_3C - CH_3}$$

   This principle is used in the process of hydrogenation of oils or hardening of oils.

Hydrogenation of Oils

Vegetable oil, which contains carbon and oxygen in greater percentage and less amount of hydrogen, cannot be solidified easily due to less percentage of hydrogen.

Examples: Groundnut oil and sunflower oil

Animal oils, such as ghee, which contain hydrogen in greater percentage get solidified easily under normal conditions. Vegetable oils also get solidified when hydrogen gas is passed through them at high pressure and high temperature in the presence of nickel catalyst.

Examples: Palm oil, Vanaspati and soap

Uses of Hydrogen

Important uses of hydrogen are listed below.

1. **In the Synthesis of Industrial Chemicals**

   (a) Manufacture of ammonia (Haber's process)

   $$N_2 + 3H_2 \underset{}{\overset{\text{Fe}}{\rightleftharpoons}} 2NH_3 + \text{heat}$$

(b) Manufacture of hydrogen chloride

$$H_2+Cl_2 \xrightarrow{\text{sunlight}} 2HCl$$

(c) Manufacture of methyl alcohol

$$[CO+H_2]+H_2 \xrightarrow[\text{Catalyst}]{\Delta} CH_3OH$$

(d) Manufacture of Dalda/Vanaspati and soap by the process of hydrogenation

(e) Manufacture of petrol/gasoline from coal

2. In Fuels and Torches

(a) **Fuel:** Many fuel gases contain hydrogen as a major constituent. This is because of high heat of combustion of hydrogen.

Examples: Water gas, coal gas, semi-water gas, etc.

(b) Electrical cells called fuel cells are also designed in which hydrogen gas is used.

(c) **Oxyhydrogen Blow Torch:** A mixture of hydrogen and oxygen is burnt to give a high temperature of 2800°C. This is used for welding of metals and for melting platinum and quartz.

(d) Liquid hydrogen is used as a rocket fuel.

(e) **Atomic Hydrogen Torch:** When an electric arc is generated in a stream of hydrogen between tungsten electrodes, the hydrogen molecules dissociate to give hydrogen atoms by absorbing large amount of energy. The atoms recombine to form hydrogen molecules by evolving the absorbed heat energy. As a result, high temperature is generated. This can be made use of in welding metals and alloys.

3. **Metallurgy:** Hydrogen is used as a good reducing agent in the extraction of some metals from their oxides.

Examples: Tungsten and molybdenum

$$WO_3 + 3H_2 \rightarrow W + 3H_2O$$

Nascent Hydrogen

It is also called newly born hydrogen. It is denoted by [H]. Nascent hydrogen can reduce compounds that do not readily react with normal hydrogen. Nascent hydrogen is usually produced by the reaction of metals with acids, e.g., zinc and sulphuric acid.

Applications of Nascent Hydrogen

1. Nascent hydrogen can be used as a rocket propellant. It could be stored in liquid helium to prevent it from recombining into molecular hydrogen.
2. Nascent hydrogen is claimed to reduce nitrites to ammonia or arsenic to arsine even under normal conditions.
3. It has temporary bleaching action.

Air Pollution

The composition of atmospheric gases changes due to the addition of other gases and suspended particles mainly by human-induced activities. This built up of other gases and suspended particulate matter is toxic to organisms living on the earth's surface. The variation in the composition of atmospheric air due to the release of harmful gases is called **air pollution.**

A substance when added to atmosphere producing adverse effects to human kind and surroundings is called **air pollutant.**

Examples: CO, chlorofluorocarbons (CFCs), O_3 in troposphere, etc.

Major Factors That Contribute to Air Pollution

Following eight are some of the major factors that cause air pollution.

1. Burning of fossil fuels
2. Deforestation
3. Volcanic eruption
4. Emissions from industries and vehicles
5. Agricultural activities
6. Lack of civic sense by the people
7. Pollination
8. Forest fires

Among the above-mentioned factors volcanic eruptions, forest fires and pollination are natural ways of contributing to air pollution.

Table 4.13 Pollutants that are released into the atmosphere due to various processes and their effects on environment

Pollutants	Sources	Processes	Effect on environment
Carbon monoxide	Automobiles	Incomplete combustion of fuels	Respiratory problems (reduction in intake of oxygen)
Sulphur dioxide	(i) Automobiles (ii) Industries (iii) Thermal power plants	(i) Incomplete combustion of fuels (ii) Metals extraction (iii) Paper making	(i) Causes acid rain (ii) Respiratory disorders
Nitrogen oxides	(i) Automobiles (ii) Industries	Incomplete combustion of fuels	(i) Formation of smog (ii) Causes acid rain
Carbon dioxide	(i) Automobiles (ii) High density of population (iii) Decrease in forest area	Combustion of fuels and deforestation	Global warming
Ozone	Industries		Global warming
CFCs	(i) Air conditioners, organic chemicals (ii) Refrigeration systems		Depletion of ozone layer
Metals	(i) Automobiles (Pb) (ii) Thermal power plants (Pb, Hg, As, Co, Cu)	(i) Present in petrol as anti-knock agents (ii) Chemical reactions	(i) Nervous disorders (ii) Problems of digestion (iii) Cancer
Hydrocarbons	(i) Automobiles (ii) Degradation of organic wastes	Exhaust gas	(i) Carcinogenic
Fly ash	Thermal power plants	Combustion of coal	(i) Metal oxides and toxic metals of fly ash cause health problems (ii) Silica causes bronchitis and lung cancer (iii) Contamination of ground water and clogging of drainage

(Continued)

Table 4.13 Continued

Pollutants	Sources	Processes	Effect on environment
Suspended particulate matter (SPM)	(i) Automobiles (ii) Industries (iii) Formation of smog	Exhaust gas	(i) Lung and respiratory disorders

Hazards of Air Pollution and Their Prevention

As the pollutants increase in atmospheric air, they affect both plant and animal life, cause respiratory problems, result in damage to monuments and so on. Particularly, the lead particles from smoke of motor engines cause damage to the nervous system. Some of the air pollution hazards along with their preventions are discussed below:

Acid Rain

The gases such as NO_2 and SO_2 that are released from factory chimneys, burning of fossil fuels, eruption of volcanoes, etc., dissolve in rain water forming HNO_3 and H_2SO_4, respectively. This is called **acid rain.**

$$2SO_2 + O_2 \rightarrow 2SO_3$$

$$SO_3 + H_2O \rightarrow H_2SO_4$$

$$2NO_2 + H_2O \rightarrow HNO_3 + HNO_2$$

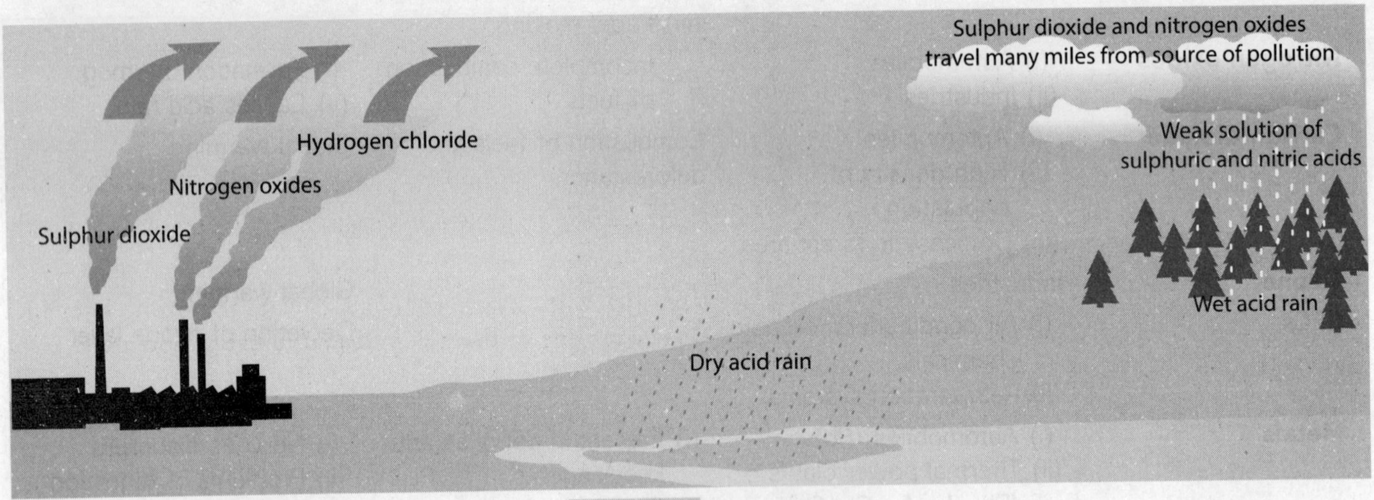

Figure 4.9 Acid Rain

Effects of Acid Rain:

(a) The fertility of the soil is lost or reduced.

(b) Damage to the crops.

(c) Pollutes water bodies like river, seas, etc.

(d) Corrodes 1the marble statues or monuments or buildings.

Prevention:

(a) Minimise the usage of fossil fuels. Fossil fuels such as petrol, diesel are replaced by CNG in some metropolitan cities.

(b) Use non-conventional sources of energy.

(c) Dispose industrial wastes safely.

Greenhouse Effect and Global Warming

The solar radiation is absorbed by the surface of oceans and vegetation on land. This absorbed radiation is transformed into heat and is re-radiated back into the atmosphere. Certain gaseous molecules present in the atmosphere absorb the infrared radiation (IR) and re-radiate the heat in all directions. Hence, these gases maintain the temperature of the earth's surface. The gases which absorb these IR are called **greenhouse gases** and the process is called **greenhouse effect**. This process supports life on earth. The greenhouse gases are CO_2, H_2O, N_2O, CH_4, O_3, CFCs, etc.

Increase in the levels of these gases results in gradual increase of temperature of earth's surface. This increased effect caused due to increase in the air pollutants is called **global warming**.

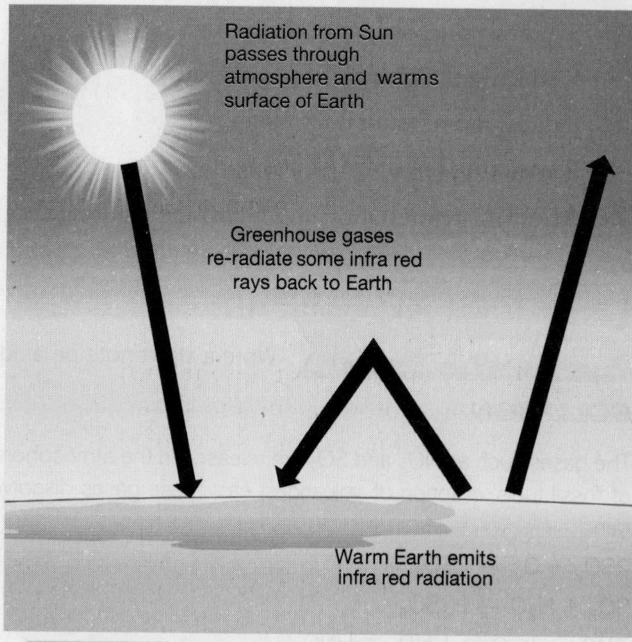

Figure 4.10 Greenhouse effect and global warming

Effects of Global Warming:

(a) Melting of ice caps and glaciers.

(b) Increase in frequency of floods, soil erosion unseasonal rains, etc.

Prevention:

(a) Reduction in the use of fossil fuels.

(b) Controlling deforestation.

(c) Restricting the use of CFCs.

Ozone Depletion

Ozone present in the troposphere contributes to the greenhouse effect. Ozone present in the stratosphere plays a vital role in protecting the life on earth's surface from harmful UV radiations. Ozone layer acts as a shield as it absorbs highly energetic harmful UV radiations.

Pollutants, such as CFCs, upon reaching the stratosphere react with ozone, and thus, deplete the ozone layer in a period of time. Hence, UV radiations reach the tropospheric layer due to the holes created in ozone and affect plant and animal life.

Prevention: Discovery of alternative substance for CFCs used in refrigeration and aerosols.

Hazards Caused by Carbon Monoxide

As the percentage of CO increases in the atmosphere, it affects the respiratory system. CO has 200 times more affinity for haemoglobin over oxygen and forms a stable compound called **carboxyhaemoglobin** which causes suffocation and sometimes it is even fatal to human life.

Prevention: Reduction in the burning of fossil fuels, cigarettes, etc.

Ways of Minimising Air Pollution

The following safe measures can be adopted so as to minimise air pollution.

1. Safe disposal of waste products.
2. Equipment like scrubbers and precipitators are to be used in industries to prevent the emissions of harmful gases.

3. Synthesis of ecofriendly chemicals.
4. Reducing the growth of population.
5. Judicial use of natural resources.
6. Restricting the usage of plastic.
7. Arresting deforestation and increasing planting or greenery.

EXAMPLE 4.4 Write a short note on acid rain.

SOLUTION

The gases such as NO_2 and SO_2 are released in the atmosphere through factory chimneys. They are also generated during the burning of fossil fuels, eruption of volcanoes, etc. These gases dissolve in rain water forming HNO_3 and H_2SO_4, respectively and cause acid rain.

$2SO_2 + O_2 \rightarrow 2SO_3$

$SO_3 + H_2O \rightarrow H_2SO_4$

$2NO_2 + H_2O \rightarrow HNO_3 + HNO_2$

EXAMPLE 4.5 Explain Greenhouse gas and global warming.

SOLUTION

Greenhouse gases are specific gases present in the Earth's atmosphere that have the ability to absorb and re-radiate infrared radiation (IR). These gases include carbon dioxide (CO_2), water vapour (H_2O), nitrous oxide (N_2O), methane (CH_4), ozone (O_3), and chlorofluorocarbons (CFCs), among others. The presence of these gases in the atmosphere leads to the greenhouse effect, a natural process wherein the gases trap heat, thereby maintaining the Earth's average temperature and making it habitable.

Global warming, on the other hand, refers to the long-term increase in Earth's average surface temperature due to human activities, primarily the emission of greenhouse gases from burning fossil fuels, deforestation, and other industrial processes. As the concentration of these greenhouse gases increases in the atmosphere, more heat gets trapped, leading to a rise in global temperatures. This rise in temperature can have several adverse effects, such as the melting of polar ice caps, rising sea levels, and extreme weather events. It's crucial to address global warming to ensure a sustainable environment for future generations.

EXAMPLE 4.6 A combines with B to form C and D. A and D are major contributors to global warming and both are carbon compounds. B is a supporter of combustion. Magnesium burns in the presence of B with a dazzling white flame and forms a product X which is basic in nature. With C, X forms a compound which turns red litmus paper blue. Give the respective chemical reactions involved.

SOLUTION

A is methane, B is oxygen, C is water vapour and D is carbon dioxide. Methane and CO_2 contribute to greenhouse effect and both are carbon compounds. Oxygen combines with magnesium to produce magnesium oxide with dazzling white flame.

$2Mg + O_2 \rightarrow 2MgO$, MgO is basic in nature.

$MgO + H_2O \rightarrow Mg(OH)_2$.

Magnesium hydroxide is the base which turns red litmus blue.

POINTS TO REMEMBER

- ✔ Most of the weather phenomena like the formation of clouds, rain, etc., take place in the troposphere, while the stratosphere protects the earth from harmful UV radiation and also aeroplanes fly in this region.
- ✔ The density of air is maximum near the earth's surface, i.e., in the troposphere.
- ✔ Nitrogen is an inactive component while oxygen is an active component. Nitrogen is used to preserve food materials while oxygen is required for burning and respiration.
- ✔ Nitrogen dilutes the activity of oxygen, and its compounds are used as fertilisers which are helpful for the growth of plants.
- ✔ Oxygen is prepared in the laboratory by the decomposition of H_2O_2 while CO_2 is prepared by the reaction of dil acid on marble chips. The O_2 gas obtained is collected by the downward displacement of water while CO_2 is collected by the upward displacement of air.
- ✔ CO_2 is essential for photosynthesis. Being a non-supporter of combustion, non-combustible and heavier than air, it can be used to extinguish fires. It is a greenhouse gas but leads to global warming if the amounts of CO_2 increase due to human-induced activities such as deforestation, excess usage of petrol, diesel, etc.
- ✔ Water vapour along with dust particles is responsible for the formation of clouds, fog, mist, etc.
- ✔ Rust is formed when iron articles get exposed to humid air. The formula of rust is $Fe_2O_3.xH_2O$. The formation of rust can be prevented by galvanisation, tinning, alloying, coating with enamel paint, etc.
- ✔ NO_2 particles, SO_2, excess CO_2, N_2O, CO, excess dust and other impurities are major pollutants in air which cause hazards like acid rain, global warming, ozone depletion, respiratory problems, etc.
- ✔ Afforestation, using CNG as a substitute for petrol and diesel, installation of catalytic converters in automobiles, electric precipitators and scrubbers in industries, etc., minimise pollution

DW

PRACTICE QUESTIONS CLASSROOM WING

Very Short Answer Type Questions

Directions for questions from 1 to 5:
Fill in the blanks.

1. The outermost layer of the atmosphere that absorbs ionizing radiations is _______.

2. The process where tin is used to preserve edible food materials is called _______.

3. _______, an inert gas is used to fill weather observation balloons.

4. The chemical formula of rust is _______.

5. The trapping of solar heat energy by certain gaseous molecules present in the earth's atmosphere is called _______.

Directions for questions from 6 to 40:
For each of the questions, four choices have been provided. Select the correct alternative.

6. With the increase in altitude, the atmospheric pressure:
   (a) increases
   (b) decreases
   (c) remains the same
   (d) first increases then decreases

7. In _______, the temperature decreases with the increase in altitude.
   (a) ionosphere (b) troposphere
   (c) ozonosphere (d) stratosphere

8. Which among the following gases present in atmosphere does not contribute to global warming?
   (a) Nitrogen oxides like N_2O
   (b) Carbon dioxide
   (c) Sulphur dioxide
   (d) Water vapour

9. _______ is the most abundant element in earth's crust.
   (a) Si (b) Al
   (c) O_2 (d) Fe

10. _______ is the process of mixing of a metal with metal or non-metal to form a homogeneous mixture.
   (a) Alloying (b) Electroplating
   (c) Tinning (d) Galvanisation

11. Which compound among the given is used for the laboratory preparation of oxygen?
   (a) KNO_3 (b) $Pb(NO_3)_2$
   (c) H_2O_2 (d) HgO

12. _______ is used as a supporter of combustion in rockets and space ships.
   (a) Liquid hydrogen (b) Liquid oxygen
   (c) Coke (d) Liquid carbon dioxide

13. A burning splinter gets extinguished in an atmosphere of CO_2. Identify the substance which continues to burn in an atmosphere of CO_2.
   (a) Coke (b) Magnesium
   (c) Sulphur (d) Phosphorus

14. Soda water contains excess _______ in dissolved state.
   (a) H_2 (b) CO_2
   (c) N_2 (d) O_2

15. _______ is used in the refrigeration of sea food.
   (a) Chlorofluorocarbons
   (b) Dry ice
   (c) Carbon dioxide gas
   (d) Inert gases

16. Excess intake of O_2 by a person results in several ill-effects. Which of the following activities leads to excess intake of O_2?
   (a) Deep-sea diving
   (b) Mountaineering
   (c) Travelling in an aeroplane
   (d) Walking on the moon

17. Identify the component which when present in the troposphere is a pollutant and when present in upper layers of atmosphere is a protector of life.
   (a) Chlorofluorocarbons (b) Ozone
   (c) Nitrous oxide (d) Water vapour

18. O_2 and CO_2 prepared in the laboratory can be collected by _______.
   (a) downward displacement of water and downward displacement of air, respectively
   (b) downward displacement of water and upward displacement of air, respectively
   (c) upward displacement of water in both the cases
   (d) downward displacement of water in both the cases

19. Which of the following processes is not associated with the formation of metal nitrates in soil?

(a) Acid rain
(b) Nitrogen fixation by leguminous plants
(c) Lightening followed by precipitation
(d) Formation of auroras

20. Arrange the following layers of the atmosphere in the decreasing order of their altitudes.

(1) Stratosphere (2) Troposphere
(3) Mesophere (4) Exosphere
(5) Ionosphere

(a) 34512 (b) 21354
(c) 42531 (d) 45312

21. Arrange the components of air in the increasing order of their percentage by volume.

(1) Nitrogen (2) Carbon dioxide
(3) Oxygen (4) Argon

(a) 2431 (b) 1342
(c) 4321 (d) 2134

22. _____ burns in oxygen with a brilliant golden yellow flame.

(a) Na (b) Ca
(c) Mg (d) K

23. Y is obtained by the decomposition of a substance X. Oxygen present in X is univalent. Y reacts with a neutral oxide and evolves Z which is composed of reddish brown fumes which turns moist blue litmus red. Identify X, Y and Z.

(a) H_2O_2, H_2 and CO_2
(b) H_2O_2, O_2 and NO_2
(c) $KClO_3$, Cl_2 and O_2
(d) HgO, O_2 and NO

24. Identify the four layers of atmosphere as per the temperature range mentioned and arrange them in a sequence. −60°C to −15°C, 17°C to −51°C, −15°C to −120°C and maximizing up to 2000°C

(1) Troposphere (2) Stratosphere
(3) Mesosphere (4) Exosphere
(5) thermosphere

(a) 2 1 3 5 (b) 1 2 3 5
(c) 2 1 3 4 (d) 3 1 2 5

25. Air is a homogeneous mixture of gases which also contains argon and nitrogen which are used for filling electric bulbs. But air is not filled in electric bulbs because:

(a) the active component of air oxidises the filament.
(b) the boiling point of air is greater than that of argon or nitrogen.
(c) air has impurities like dust particles.
(d) air exerts more pressure.

26. A list of four different substances is given below. The methods of preparation of the substances are also given. Arrange the methods of preparation in the order of the substances given.

(i) O_2 (ii) CO_2
(iii) SO_2 (iv) P_2O_5

(1) burning of a non-metal produces dense white fumes.
(2) burning of a non-metal with sparkles and crackling sound.
(3) heating of one of the binary compound of hydrogen.
(4) burning of a non-metal with a brilliant blue flame.

(a) 3 2 4 1 (b) 2 3 4 1
(c) 1 4 3 2 (d) 3 4 1 2

27. The holes in the ozonosphere is due to the attack of a pollutant that is released from:

(a) automobiles (b) air conditioners
(c) industries (d) volcanic eruptions

28. A gas X when passed through blue litmus solution turns it to red. Another gas Y when passed through either blue litmus or red litmus does not change the colour of the litmus. Identify the true statement regarding X and Y.

(a) X is basic while Y is neutral
(b) Y is neutral while X is acidic
(c) Y is basic while X is acidic
(d) Y is acidic while X is neutral

29. Identify the layers of atmosphere as per activities mentioned and arrange them in a sequence. Burning up of meteorites, flying of aeroplanes, reflection of radio waves, absorption of harmful ionising radiations and occurrence of most of the weather phenomena.

(1) Troposphere (2) Stratosphere
(3) Mesosphere (4) Ionosphere
(5) Magnetosphere

(a) 2 3 4 5 1 (b) 3 2 4 5 1
(c) 3 4 5 1 2 (d) 2 4 1 5 3

30.

Column A	Column B
(A) Tinning	(a) Iron trunks, sanitary
(B) Enamelling	(b) Engine parts
(C) Coating with oil, grease	(c) Wash basins, ovens
(D) Galvanisation	(d) Articles used to preserve edible food materials

(a) A → c, B → a, C → b, D → d
(b) A → d, B → c, C → b, D → a
(c) A → d, B → c, C → a, D → b
(d) A → b, B → d, C → a, D → c

31. Identify the substance which continues to burn in an atmosphere of N_2.
(a) Fe (b) Mg
(c) Cu (d) W

32. Fountain ink pen leaks at higher altitudes. It is due to:
(a) low atmospheric pressure
(b) high temperatures
(c) high atmospheric pressure
(d) Both (a) and (b)

33. Generally, a metal gets corroded due to oxidation. Name a metal which becomes chemically resistant due to oxidation.
(a) Zinc (b) Copper
(c) Aluminium (d) Iron

34. Which of the following processes does not contribute to the increase of suspended particulate matter in the atmosphere?
(a) Emissions from industries
(b) Burning of coal
(c) Burning of wood
(d) Usage of refrigerators and air conditioners

35. Which of the following pairs is a major contributor to global warming?
(a) Carbon dioxide and oxides of nitrogen
(b) Methane and water vapour
(c) Carbon dioxide and ozone
(d) Carbon dioxide and water vapour

36. The increase in the proportion of ______ in air leads to global warming.
(a) CO (b) CO_2
(c) SO_2 (d) N_2

37. Characteristic reactions for four different substances are given below. Arrange the tests in the order of the substances given below.
(i) P_2O_5 (ii) CO_2
(iii) O_2 (iv) SO_2
(1) Passage through potassium dichromate turns green.
(2) Dissolution in water gives a tribasic acid.
(3) Non-supporter of combustion but allows active metals continue to burn.
(4) Turns alkaline pyrogallol brown.
(a) 2 4 3 1 (b) 2 3 4 1
(c) 4 1 3 2 (d) 4 3 1 2

38. **Assertion (A)**: Many fuel gases contain hydrogen as a major constituent.
Reason (R): Liquid hydrogen is a very light fuel.
(a) Both (A) and (R) are true and (R) is the correct explanation for (A).
(b) Both (A) and (R) are true but (R) is not the correct explanation for (A).
(c) (A) is correct but (R) is false.
(d) (A) is false but (R) is true.

39. An element X burns with a brilliant blue flame in the presence of oxygen to form Y. Y turns acidified potassium dichromate paper green. Identify X and Y.
(a) nitrogen, nitrogen dioxide
(b) sulphur, sulphur dioxide
(c) phosphorus, phosphorus pentoxide
(d) sodium, sodium oxide

40. **Assertion (A)**: When carbon dioxide gas is passed through lie water, lime water is turned milky.
Reason (R): Calcium carbonate is soluble in water.
(a) Both (A) and (R) are true and (R) is correct explanation for (A).
(b) Both (A) and (R) are true but (R) is not the correct explanation for (A).
(c) (A) is correct but (R) is false.
(d) (A) is false but (R) is true.

Directions for questions from 41 to 43:
Match the entries given in Column A with the appropriate ones in Column B. More than one suitable content of Column B can also be considered correct for an entry in Column A and some content given in Column B may not be the appropriate one for any entry in Column A.

41. Match the statements of Column A with those of Column B.

	Column A (Pollutant)		Column B (Effect on Environment)
(i)	Carbon monoxide	(a)	Ozone depletion
(ii)	Increased levels of CH_4, CO_2, O_3	(b)	Formation of smog
(iii)	CFC's	(c)	Acid rain
(iv)	SO_2, NO_2	(d)	Reduction of O_2 intake
(v)	SPM	(e)	Global warming

43.

	Column A		Column B
(A)	Zinc	(a)	Bridges
(B)	Silicates	(b)	Galvanisation
(C)	Tar	(c)	Surgical instruments
(D)	Red lead oxide	(d)	Enamelling
		(e)	Electric poles

43.

	Column A Reactants		Column B Gaseous products
(A)	Hydrogen peroxide	(a)	Nitrogen
(B)	Calcium carbonate	(b)	Oxygen
(C)	Zinc granules	(c)	Hydrogen
(D)	Nitre	(d)	Carbon dioxide
		(e)	Nascent hydrogen

Directions for questions from 44 to 63:

Answer the following questions.

44. Which component of air is collected by the upward displacement of air?

45. What is atmosphere?

46. Name any two inert gases present in atmosphere.

47. Mention the percentage by volume of inactive and active components of atmosphere.

48. Name the device used to measure the atmospheric pressure.

49. How are the delicate colours of auroras caused?

50. Name the gas which absorbs ultraviolet rays.

51. Name the principal products of combustion of glucose.

52. Mention the significance of water vapour in atmosphere.

53. In which way is greenhouse effect useful to us?

54. Name the gases which are responsible for acid rain.

55. What happens when potassium nitrate is subjected to heating?

56. Define a catalyst.

57. Given the balanced chemical equation for the laboratory preparation of oxygen gas.

58. What is the action of litmus on oxygen?

59. What happens when a paper soaked in acidified potassium dichromate is exposed to SO_2 gas?

60. Mention the factors which influence rusting of iron.

61. What is alloying?

62. Name two metal carbonates from which carbon dioxide cannot be prepared by heating.

63. What is carbogen?

Short Answer Type Questions

64. Nitrogen, oxygen, helium, carbon dioxide and water vapour are the components of air. Arrange the properties given below in the order of gases given above.

(a) Colourless, odourless gas, acidic in nature, and neither combustible nor a supporter of combustion

(b) Colourless, odourless gas, inert in nature, and dilutes the activity of active compo-nents of air

(c) Colourless gas and forms acidic and basic compounds with non-metals and metals, respectively

(D) Colourless gas, inert in nature, and present in trace amounts

(E) Gaseous form, present in variable amounts, and chemically active along with the active component of air

65. What is greenhouse effect?

66. Mention various methods of minimising air pollution.

67. Explain the role of oxygen in the following:
(a) respiration (b) cutting and welding
(c) explosion

68. List out the important uses of CO_2.

69. Mention the ways of minimising global warming.

70. (A) Mention the advantage of existence of atmosphere.
(B) In stratosphere, temperature increases with altitude. Give reason. The stratosphere is more favourable for long distance flights than the troposphere. Justify it.

71. Explain ozone depletion.

72. Mention the effects of acid rain.

73. Mention various constituents of air and write their percentage by weight.

74. Mention any four physical properties of CO_2.

75. (A) Write a short note on nascent hydrogen.
(B) Platinum catalytic converter is used in motor vehicles to reduce air pollution. Explain how it can reduce air pollution from the motor vehicles?

76. Explain hydrogenation of oils.

77. Mention any four important uses of hydrogen.

78. Explain the process of nitrogen fixation.

79. What is the composition of water gas and how is it formed?

80. Mention the action of oxygen with the elements sulphur, phosphorus, sodium and magnesium.

81. Mention the methods for preventing acid rain.

82. What are the human activities that contribute to air pollution?

Essay Answer Type Questions

83. Describe the laboratory preparation of oxygen gas from hydrogen peroxide with a neat diagram.

84. Mention the general methods of preparation of CO_2 along with the chemical reactions.

85. Write a short note on rusting. What are the causes and effects of it? Explain different methods adopted to prevent rusting.

86. Explain the significance of nitrogen, oxygen and water vapour present in the atmosphere.

87. Describe the laboratory method of preparation of hydrogen gas.

88. Describe the chemical reaction of CO_2 with:
(a) lime water
(b) metals like sodium, potassium and calcium
(c) non-metals like carbon

89. Write a short note on the following layers of atmosphere.
(a) Troposphere (b) Stratosphere

90. (a) What is air pollution?
(b) Write a short note on the following:
(i) ozone depletion
(ii) hazards of carbon monoxide

91. Fill in the blanks given in the following table.

Impurities	Substances used for removal
(a) AsH_3, PH_3	________
(b) ________	Lead nitrate solution
(c) ________	Caustic potash
(d) H_2O (water vapour)	________

92. Name the pollutants responsible for the following effects.
(a) Reduction in intake of oxygen
(b) Cause of acid rain
(c) Greenhouse effect
(d) Formation of smog
(e) Depletion of ozone layer
(f) Problems of digestion
(g) Contamination of ground water
(h) Respiratory disorders

93. One molecule each of 'X' and oxygen react to form 'Y' which further reacts with one molecule of water to give 'Z'. The number of electrons present in the dinegative ion of 'X' is equal to atomic the number of Argon. Identify X, Y and Z. How does 'Y' contribute to acid rain? Justify.

PRACTICE QUESTIONS COMPETITION WING

Level 1: Apply your Concepts

Directions for questions from 1 to 15:
State whether the following statements are true or false.

1. Corrosion of marble statues and monuments is neither directly nor indirectly an effect of global warming.
2. Auroras appear in the layer of atmosphere which is known as stratosphere.
3. Chlorofluorocarbons depletes the ozone layer.
4. The catalyst alters the rate of reaction.
5. In the laboratory preparation of oxygen from hydrogen peroxide, SnO_2 is used as a catalyst.
6. Aeroplanes usually fly in the zone of mesosphere.
7. Meteorites burn up in thermosphere.
8. The percentage of noble gases present in air is more than that of CO_2.
9. Oxygen is neutral towards litmus.
10. Gases like nitrogen dioxide, sulphur dioxide present in atmosphere contribute to acid rain.
11. CO_2 can be used to preserve food grains from destruction by insects.
12. CO_2 can be collected by the downward displacement of air.
13. The electric spark produced during lightening helps nitrogen to combine with oxygen to form nitric oxide.
14. Carbogen is a mixture of 94 per cent oxygen, 4 per cent carbon dioxide and 2 per cent nitrogen dioxide.
15. Dust particles along with water vapour present in the atmosphere help in the formation of clouds.

Directions for questions from 16 to 25:
Fill in the blanks.

16. The pollutant that is not released into the air because of combustion of coal is ____________.
17. Ammonia (NH3), an important raw material for the manufacture of fertilizers, is manufactured at an industrial scale by a process called __________.
18. Water gas, an industrially important fuel, is a mixture of ____________ gases.
19. __________ is used as a rocket fuel.
20. Oxygen is _______ towards litmus.
21. Chemical formula of white lead is _______.
22. The atmospheric pressure is maximum at _____ and is found to be equal to ________.
23. In ________ layer of atmosphere TV waves do not get reflected. Hence, artificial satellites are used for television transmission.
24. Nascent hydrogen is a strong _______ agent. (reducing/oxidising)
25. ________ is used for burning fuel in rockets and space ships.

Directions for questions from 26 to 60:
For each of the questions, four choices have been provided. Select the correct alternative.

26. **Assertion (A):** The thermosphere consists of ions and free electrons because of the absorption of high energetic radiations.

    Reason (R): Temperature in the thermosphere can reach a maximum of 2000°C because of the absorption of high-energy radiations.

    (a) Both A and R are true and R is the correct explanation of A.
    (b) Both A and R are true, but R is not the correct explanation of A.
    (c) A is true and R is false.
    (d) A is false and R is true.

27. **Assertion (A):** O_2, SO_2 and NO_2 are called greenhouse gases.

    Reason (R): The gases that absorb infrared radiation are called greenhouse gases.

    (a) Both A and R are true and R is the correct explanation of A.
    (b) Both A and R are true, but R is not the correct explanation of A.
    (c) A is true and R is false.
    (d) A is false and R is true.

28. The component which when present in the troposphere is a pollutant and when present in upper layers of atmosphere is a protector of life among the following is ______.
(a) Chloroflurocarbons (b) Ozone
(c) Nitrous oxide (d) Water vapour

29. Arrange the following layers of atmosphere in the sequence as per the activity mentioned.
Burning up of meteorites, flying of aeroplanes, reflection of radio waves, absorption of harmful ionising radiations and occurrence of most of the weather phenomena.
(1) Troposphere (2) Stratosphere
(3) Mesosphere (4) Ionosphere
(5) Magnetosphere
(a) 2 3 4 5 1 (b) 3 2 4 5 1
(c) 3 4 5 1 2 (d) 2 4 1 5 3

30. The reaction of which of the following metals with steam is reversible?
(a) Calcium (b) Aluminium
(c) Iron (d) Lead

31. ______ is used in advertisement glow tubes.
(a) Neon (b) Helium
(c) Argon (d) Nitrogen

32. SI unit of atmospheric pressure is:
(a) Newton (b) Pascal
(c) Joule (d) kg/m

33. Which among the following gas was called acid formerly?
(a) Nitrogen (b) Hydrogen
(c) Carbon dioxide (d) Oxygen

34. Ozone present in ______ plays a vital role in protecting the life on earth surface from harmful UV rays.
(a) troposphere (b) stratosphere
(c) mesosphere (d) ionosphere

35. Which among the following metals is used in alloying of iron to prevent corrosion?
(a) Zinc (b) Tin
(c) Aluminium (d) Chromium

36. Fountain ink pen leaks at higher altitudes. It is due to:
(a) low atmospheric pressure
(b) high temperature
(c) high atmospheric pressure
(d) Both (a) and (b)

37. The holes in the ozonosphere is due to the attack of a pollutant that is released from:
(a) automobiles
(b) air conditioners
(c) industries
(d) volcanic eruptions

38. Which of the following phenomenon is an effect of acid rain?
(a) An increase in frequency of floods
(b) Unseasonal rainfalls
(c) Harmful effects by UV rays
(d) Death of aquatic animals

39. Identify the substance which does not continue to burn in an atmosphere of N_2.
(a) Na (b) Mg
(c) K (d) W

40. A gas is collected by the upward displacement of air but cannot be collected either downward or upward displacement of water. Identify the probable characteristics of the gas.
(a) It is heavier than air and insoluble in water.
(b) Its vapour density is equal to air and is highly soluble in water.
(c) It is heavier than air and is highly soluble in water.
(d) It is lighter than air and water.

41. Arrange the layers of the atmosphere as per the following terms related in a sequence, respectively. Inversion layer, convection currents, auroras, absorbs harmful ionising radiations and burning up of meteorites
(1) Troposphere (2) Stratosphere
(3) Exosphere (4) Mesosphere
(5) Ionosphere
(a) 45312 (b) 12354
(c) 21534 (d) 12435

42. Arrange the following given reactions in a sequence for the process of nitrogen fixation.
(1) Formation of metal nitrates
(2) Formation of nitrogen dioxide
(3) Formation of nitric oxide
(4) Formation of nitric acid
(a) 3214 (b) 3241
(c) 2143 (d) 4213

43. Meteorites burn up in the mesosphere but not in the thermosphere. It is due to:
(a) relatively thicker atmosphere in the mesosphere.
(b) relatively thicker atmosphere in the thermosphere.
(c) very low temperatures in the mesosphere.
(d) very low temperatures in the thermosphere.

44. Aeroplanes usually fly in the stratosphere because:
(a) of the presence of ozone layer.
(b) of the atmosphere being turbulent.
(c) of the decrease in temperature with altitude.
(d) of the absence of convection current.

45. Two non-metallic oxides A and B are produced by burning of fossil fuels. A pollutes both air and water. B does not cause water pollution and its presence in water is essential. It causes air pollution. Identify A and B.
(a) NO_2, SO_2 (b) SO_2, CO
(c) SO_2, CO_2 (d) CO_2, NO_2

46. Though zinc coating is cheaper than tin coating on iron, only tin coating is used for iron containers for storing food materials. Identify the correct reason.
(a) Zinc is less reactive than tin.
(b) Zinc acts as a preservative.
(c) Tin does not react with the components of food material.
(d) Tin lowers the ambient temperature, and thus, prevents spoilage of food.

47. A metal carbonate X when treated with dil HCl gives Y. 'Y' when used in mines area reduces suspended particulate matter in atmosphere. Identify Y.
(a) NaCl (b) H_2CO_3
(c) $CaCl_2$ (d) CO_2

48. The sculptures and monuments get damaged due to acid rains. Usage of scrubbers, containing lime, in industries decreases the percentage content of the major air pollutants that contribute to acid rain. The characteristic reaction involved in the scrubber is:
(a) neutralisation
(b) oxidation
(c) reduction
(d) combination followed by decomposition

49. Air is a homogeneous mixture of gases which also contains argon and nitrogen which are used for filling electric bulbs. But air is not filled in electric bulbs because:
(a) the active component of air oxidises the filament.
(b) the boiling point of air is greater than that of argon or nitrogen.
(c) air has impurities like dust particles.
(d) air exerts more pressure.

50. Both the formation of mist and clouds involve the condensation of water vapour. In which aspect do they differ from each other?
(a) The process of cloud formation takes place in summer, whereas the process of mist formation takes place in winter.
(b) The process of cloud formation takes place throughout the year while the formation of mist takes place only at certain times at particular temperatures.
(c) Clouds are suspended in the atmosphere while mist settles down on leaves, walls, etc., on earth's surface.
(d) The water droplets of a cloud have a much lower temperature than that of water droplets of mist.

51. The CO that is added up to the atmosphere due to the incomplete combustion of fuels can be decreased by the:
(a) usage of scrubber.
(b) usage of electric precipitator.
(c) usage of catalytic convertor.
(d) increasing greenery.

52. Y is obtained by the decomposition of a substance X. Oxygen present in X is univalent. Y reacts with a neutral oxide and evolves Z which is composed of reddish brown fumes which turns moist blue litmus to red. Identify X, Y and Z.
(a) H_2O_2, H_2 and CO_2
(b) H_2O_2, O_2 and NO_2
(c) $KClO_3$, Cl_2 and O_2
(d) HgO, O_2 and NO

53. Assume that temperature is recorded in the thermosphere with the help of a thermometer. You will be amazed to find that the temperature recorded in it will be extremely low. This is because:
(a) of the complete absorption of high energetic radiations by molecules.
(b) of the absence of atmosphere.
(c) of the presence of very few molecules or ions.
(d) it is at very high altitudes.

54. Cloud formation almost does not take place in the stratosphere because:

(a) the high temperature of this layer does not allow the water vapour to reach this layer.

(b) of the absence of convection current.

(c) of the absence of dust particles and convection current.

(d) All of the above

55. Which of the following pairs is a major contributor to global warming?

(a) Carbon dioxide, nitrogen oxide

(b) Methane, water vapour

(c) Carbon dioxide, ozone

(d) Carbon dioxide, water vapour

56. Generally, a metal gets corroded due to oxidation. Name a metal which becomes chemically resistant due to oxidation.

(a) Zinc (b) Copper

(c) Aluminium (d) Iron

57. Which of the following processes does not contribute to the increase of suspended particulate matter in the atmosphere?

(a) Emissions from industries

(b) Burning of coal

(c) Burning of wood

(d) Usage of refrigerators and air conditioners

58. Incomplete combustion of fuels does not contribute to:

(a) photochemical smog (b) acid rain

(c) global warming (d) Both (a) and (b)

59. Leguminous plants do not require the addition of nitrogenous fertilisers because:

(a) they can fix up atmospheric nitrogen.

(b) of the presence of Rhizobium bacteria in their root nodules.

(c) they possess nitrogen in roots, and hence, do not require external intake.

(d) Both (a) and (b)

60. A gas X when passed through blue litmus solution turns it to red. Another gas Y when passed through either blue litmus or red litmus does not change the colour of the litmus. Identify the true statement regarding X and Y.

(a) X is basic while Y is neutral.

(b) Y is neutral while X is acidic.

(c) Y is basic while X is acidic.

(d) Y is acidic while X is neutral.

Directions for questions from 61 to 63:
Match the entries given in Column A with the appropriate ones in Column B. More than one suitable content of Column B can also be considered correct for an entry in Column A and some content given in Column B may not be the appropriate one for any entry in Column A.

61.

	Column A		Column B
(A)	Oxides of nitrogen	(a)	Clogging drainage
(B)	Chloroflouro carbons	(b)	Causes acid rain
(C)	Fly ash	(c)	Formation of smog
(D)	Suspended particulate matter	(d)	Depletion of ozone layer
		(e)	Global warming

62.

	Column A		Column B
(A)	$SO_2 + H_2O \rightarrow$	(a)	H_2SO_4
(B)	$NO_2 + H_2O \rightarrow$	(b)	H_2SO_3
(C)	$P_2O_5 + H_2O \rightarrow$	(c)	H_3PO_4
(D)	$H_2O + CO_2$	(d)	H_3PO_3
		(e)	H_2CO_3
		(f)	$CO + H_2$ (water gas)
		(g)	HNO_3
		(h)	HNO_2

63.

Column A		Column B	
(A)	Oxygen	(a)	Preservation of food items
(B)	Nitrogen	(b)	Good reducing agent
(C)	Carbon dioxide	(c)	Kipps apparatus
(D)	Nascent hydrogen	(d)	Dilutes the activity of oxygen
		(e)	Major constituent of carbogen
		(f)	Making of white lead

Level 2: Review Your Concepts

64. While a teacher was teaching her class about air and oxygen she emphasised the importance of nitrogen in the atmosphere. A student named Vivek asked the teacher, 'What would happen if the percentages of nitrogen and oxygen were interchanged in the atmosphere?' The teacher praised him for the question and explained it. What was the teacher's explanation?

65. Given below is the change of temperature in different layers of the atmosphere.
   (a) The temperature increases with height and can reach to maximum of 2000°C at the top of this layer.
   (b) The temperature decreases from −15°C to −120°C.
   (c) The temperature increases from −60°C to −15°C with an increase in height and is called the inversion layer.
   (d) The temperature decreases with an increase in height at a rate of 6°C/km.
   (e) High temperature is because of the absorption of harmful ionizing radiations.

   Arrange the above statements in the order of the layers of the atmosphere from above the earth's surface.

66. Vidya went to her grandfather Rajaram's house to spend her summer vacation. Rajaram has coconut fields near his house. In the evening she went to the coconut field along with her grandfather. There the workers offered her coconut water. Her grandfather told the workers to provide a straw to facilitate drinking the coconut water comfortably. Can you explain the principle behind using straw for the above purpose?

67. Shakti along with his parents was going to the railway station by an auto to catch a train. Shakti's father was recollecting his childhood days and said that in those days, autos were run with petrol only. His mother added that diesel was used to run autos in later days. Shakti said that nowadays autos are preferably run with CNG. Shakti questioned his father regarding the advantage of CNG over petrol and diesel. What was his father's explanation?

68. Arjun's family stays in an area which is in the heart of the city for the sake of convenience. During the summer vacation, Arjun's family stays in their farm house which has all amenities. As the farm house is located in the city outskirts, they could escape from the hot sun in summer. Why is the temperature in the peripheral area relatively lower than that in the heart of the city?

69. Calculate the volume of nitrogen, oxygen and carbon dioxide in 750 L of air.

70. Troposphere is extended up to 6–20 km altitude from the earth's surface but the amount of oxygen is less at higher altitudes, i.e., on mountains or hill tops. Justify.

71. X and Y are gases at room temperature. X is less reactive and is used to preserve food material, while Y is required for combustion. Metal M gets corroded when it combines with Y in the presence of Z. An atom of M possesses 14 electrons in the second last shell and N is the last shell. Identify X, Y, Z and M.

72. Both galvanising and tinning are adopted for preventing rusting of iron but only tinned iron containers are used to preserve food material. Justify.

73. Why are people advised not to sleep in a closed room where coal is burnt in chulhas?

74. (A) The compounds X and Y combine to form a compound Z. 'Z' which is used for construction of monuments gets affected by acid rain. The compound X is used in white washing. Identify X, Y and Z and write the corresponding balanced chemical equations.

(B) When superheated steam is passed through an element X in hot condition, a mixture of A and B in 1:1 volume ratio is obtained. This mixture is a good fuel. This mixture is made to pass over Fe_2O_3 along with superheated steam at 500°C. A is oxidized to C and B is left behind. When C is passed through water at high pressure, D is formed which on the addition of red litmus turns to blue.

(a) Identify X, A, B, C and D.

(b) Name the process-what is it used for?

(c) How is the unreacted 'A' removed from the mixture at the end?

(d) Write the balanced chemical equations involved in the process.

75. What is the role of water vapour in the formation of fog?

76. An inverted glass jar is placed over a burning candle. After a while, the candle is removed and the inverted glass jar is placed in a trough of water. What do you observe and justify your observations.

77. Acid formed as a result of lightning reaches the earth's surface through precipitation, thus contributing to the acid rain as well as to the growth of plants. Justify.

Level 3: Assess Your Concepts

78. A, B, C and D are four layers of atmosphere. A helps in long-distance radio communications. In layer B, most of weather phenomena take place. The pollutants released from air conditioners and aerosols deplete layer D which also gets depleted by nitrous oxide. Meteorites burn up in layer C. Identify the layers A, B, C and D and arrange them in an increasing order of height from the surface of earth.

79. The element 'X' has only three shells in which the difference in number of electrons between the last shell and the second-last shell is equal to the number of electrons in the first shell. This element 'X' burns in oxygen to produce compound Y, which turns acidified potassium dichromate paper to green. Y turns moist blue litmus paper to red due to the formation of compound Z. Identify X, Y and Z.

80. (A) Ozone present in the troposphere is a major pollutant. However, ozone formation in aqua purifiers makes drinking water pure and safe. Explain.

(B) A metal has electron in 1:1 ratio in K and N shells and also in L and M shells. It forms a normal salt with the oxyacid of non-metal with Z = 6. Identify the salt. A natural material which contains this salt as the major component is treated with the binary acid of chlorine.

(a) Identify the gas evolved and write the balanced chemical equation.

(b) What happens if the above acid in the experiment is replaced by the higher oxyacid of a non-metal which has 6 electrons in its valance M shell?

(c) How is the gas formed collected? Justify the method of collection.

81. Carbon dioxide is used for extinguishing fires caused by petroleum products but not fires caused by metals like Na or Mg. Explain.

82. Explain the principle behind the usage of electric precipitators in industries and catalytic converters in automobiles for controlling air pollution.

AT

ANSWER KEYS

Crossword

Across

1. Carbogen
4. Galvanized iron
6. Valley of silence
10. Rust
11. Stratosphere
12. Hydrogenation
14. Tinning
15. Enamelling

Down

2. Nitrogen fixation
3. Lapse rate
5. Barometer
7. Cartridge
8. Adsorption
9. Troposphere
13. Neon

Classroom Wing

Very Short Answer Type Questions

1. Exosphere effect
2. Tinning
3. Helium
4. $Fe_2O_3.xH_2O$
5. greenhouse
6. (b)
7. (b)
8. (c)
9. (c)
10. (a)
11. (c)
12. (b)
13. (b)
14. (b)
15. (b)
16. (a)
17. (b)
18. (b)
19. (d)
20. (d)
21. (a)
22. (a)
23. (b)
24. (a)
25. (a)
26. (a)
27. (b)
28. (b)
29. (b)
30. (b)
31. (b)
32. (a)
33. (c)
34. (d)
35. (d)
36. (b)
37. (b)
38. (b)
39. (b)
40. (c)
41. (i) → (D), (ii) → (E), (iii) → (A), (iv) → (C), (v) → (B)
42. A → b, B → d, C → a, e, D → a, e
43. A → b, B → d, C → c, D → b

Competition Wing

Level 1: Apply your Concepts

1. False
2. False
3. True
4. True
5. False
6. False
7. False
8. True
9. True
10. True
11. True
12. False
13. True
14. False
15. True
16. CFCs
17. Haber's process
18. CO and H_2
19. Liquid hydrogen
20. neutral
21. $Pb(OH)_2.PbCO_3$
22. sea level, 760 mm of Hg
23. Ionosphere
24. reducing
25. liquid oxygen
26. (a)
27. (d)
28. (b)
29. (b)
30. (c)
31. (a)
32. (b)
33. (d)
34. (b)
35. (d)
36. (a)
37. (b)
38. (d)
39. (d)
40. (c)
41. (c)
42. (b)
43. (a)
44. (d)
45. (c)
46. (c)
47. (c)
48. (a)
49. (a)
50. (b)
51. (c)
52. (b)
53. (c)
54. (d)
55. (d)
56. (c)
57. (d)
58. (c)
59. (d)
60. (b)
61. A → b, c, e, B → d, e, C → a, D → c
62. A → b, B → g, h, C → c, D → e
63. A → e, B → d, a, C → f, a, D → b, c

Hints and Explanations

CLASSROOM WING

Very Short Answer Type Questions

1. The outermost layer of the atmosphere that absorbs harmful ionising radiations is the exosphere or magnetosphere.

2. The process where tin used to preserve edible food materials is coated is called tinning.

3. Helium

   Helium, an inert gas, is used to fill weather observation balloons.

4. $Fe_2O_3.xH_2O$

   The chemical formula of rust is $Fe_2O_3.xH_2O$.

5. greenhouse effect

   The trapping of solar heat energy by certain gaseous molecules present in the earth's atmosphere is called greenhouse effect.

6. With increase in altitude, the atmospheric pressure decreases.

   Hence, the correct option is (b)

7. In troposphere, the temperature decreases with the increase in altitude.

   Hence, the correct option is (b)

8. Sulphur dioxide present in atmosphere does not contribute to global warming.

   Hence, the correct option is (c)

9. Oxygen is the most abundant element in earth's crust.

   Hence, the correct option is (c)

10. Alloying is the process of mixing a metal with metal or non-metal to form a homogeneous mixture.

    Hence, the correct option is (a)

11. H_2O_2 is used in the laboratory preparation of oxygen.

    Hence, the correct option is (c)

12. Liquid oxygen is used as a supporter of combustion in rockets and space ships.

    Hence, the correct option is (b)

13. Magnesium burns in an atmosphere of CO_2.

    Hence, the correct option is (b)

14. Soda water contains excess of CO_2 in dissolved state.

    Hence, the correct option is (b)

15. Dry ice is used in the refrigeration of sea food.

    Hence, the correct option is (b)

16. Due to increased pressure in the deep sea, more amount of oxygen gets dissolved in water and this excessive intake of oxygen by a person affects and leads to several problems like nausea, dizziness, etc. Hence, a cylinder in which oxygen is diluted with inert gas like He has to be carried.

    Hence, the correct option is (a)

17. Ozone when present in the troposphere is a major pollutant that leads to global warming, while the ozone present in the stratosphere acts as a shield from UV rays reaching the earth's surface.

    Hence, the ozone layer of the stratosphere acts as a shield.

    Hence, the correct option is (b)

18. O_2 is collected by downward displacement of water and CO_2 is collected by upward displacement of air. O_2 is insoluble in water, whereas CO_2 in soluble in water.

    Hence, the correct option is (b)

19. Acid rain, nitrogen fixation and lightening processes are associated with the formation of metal

    Example:

    HNO_3 upon reaction with salts present in the soil gets converted to corresponding metal nitrates. Formation of auroras involves collision of electrons with molecules of N_2 and O_2 and emission of beautiful radiations. It does not result in formation of nitrates.

    Hence, the correct option is (d)

20. Correct sequence of the reactions is:

    (i) exosphere (ii) ionosphere

    (iii) mesophere (iv) stratosphere

    (v) troposphere

    Hence, the correct option is (d)

21. **Correct sequence of the reactions is:**
(i) carbon dioxide (ii) argon
(iii) oxygen (iv) nitrogen
Hence, the correct option is (a)

22. Sodium burns in oxygen with a brilliant golden yellow flame.
Hence, the correct option is (a)

23. $H_2O_2 \rightarrow H_2O + O_2$
(X) (Y)
$NO + O_2 \rightarrow NO_2$
(Y) (Z)
(reddish brown)
O_2 (Y) is neutral towards litmus while NO_2 is acidic, and hence, turns moist litmus from blue to red.
Hence, the correct option is (b)

24. Stratosphere has a temperature range of −60°C to −15°C, troposphere has a temperature range from 17°C to −51°C, mesosphere has a temperature range from −15°C to −120°C and thermosphere has a maximum temperature up to 2000°C.
Hence, the correct option is (a)

25. Since air consists of an active component, i.e., oxygen, it oxidises tungsten filament or any other metal used as a filament. Hence, electric bulbs are filled with an inert gas like argon or chemically inert nitrogen.
Hence, the correct option is (a)

26. (i) Oxygen is prepared by heating of hydrogen peroxide.
(ii) Carbon burns with sparkles and cracking sound to give CO_2.
(iii) Sulphur burns with a brilliant blue flame to give SO_2.
(iv) P_2O_5 appears as dense white fumes when phosphorus is burnt with oxygen.
Hence, the correct option is (a)

27. Holes are created in the ozone layer due to the attack of CFCs which are released from refrigerators and air conditioners.
Hence, the correct option is (b)

28. X is an acidic gas since it changes blue litmus to red. Y is neutral since it does not respond to either red or blue litmus test.
Hence, the correct option is (b)

29. Burning of meteorites takes place in the mesosphere, aeroplanes fly in the stratosphere, reflection of radio waves takes place in the ionosphere. Magnetosphere absorbs ionising radiations and most of the weather phenomena occur in the troposphere.
Hence, the correct option is (b)

30. A → d Tin-coated iron articles are used to preserve edible food materials.
B → c Enamelling is done to washbasins and ovens to prevent rust and provide smooth appearance.
C → b Engine parts are periodically coated with oil grease to have durability.
D → a Iron trunks and sanitary pipes are coated with zinc to prevent corrosion.
Hence, the correct option is (b)

31. Magnesium catches fire when it reacts with oxygen and continues to burn in an atmosphere of N_2.
Hence, the correct option is (b)

32. As we move to higher altitudes, fountain pen ink leaks out because of lower atmospheric pressure. The pressure built up in the ink pen is more when compared to the outside pressure. Hence, it leaks out.
Hence, the correct option is (a)

33. Aluminium, when exposed to the atmosphere, reacts with air, i.e., O_2 and forms Al_2O_3. This layer of Al_2O_3 (alumina) makes aluminium passive.
Hence, the correct option is (c)

34. The usage of refrigerators and air conditioners releases chlorofluoro carbons which don't contribute to SPM.
Hence, the correct option is (d)

35. CO_2 and water vapour are greenhouse gases present in the atmosphere. Their percentage increase in atmosphere increases the temperature of the earth and contributes to global warming. These are the major contributors to global warming.
Hence, the correct option is (d)

36. The increase in the proportion of CO_2 in air leads to global warming.
Hence, the correct option is (b)

37. (i) P_2O_5 on dissolution in water gives phosphoric acid.
(ii) CO_2 is a non-supporter of combustion, but allows burning of active metals.
(iii) Oxygen turns alkaline pyrogallol brown.
(iv) SO_2 when passed through potassium dichromate turns the solution from orange to green.
Hence, the correct option is (b)

38. Many fuel gases contain hydrogen as a major constituent because of its high calorific value.

Hence, the correct option is (b)

39. Sulphur is the non-metal which burns with a blue-coloured flame. SO_2 turns orange-coloured $K_2Cr_2O_7$ green due to the formation of $Cr_2(SO_4)_3$.

Hence, the correct option is (b)

40. When carbon dioxide gas is passed through lime water, it gives a white precipitate due to the formation of calcium carbonate which is insoluble in water.

Hence, the correct option is (c)

41. (i) Carbon monoxide → (D) reduction of O_2 intake

(ii) Increased levels of CH_4, CO_2, O_3 → (E) global warming

(iii) CFC's → (A) ozone depletion

(iv) SO_2, NO_2 → (C) acid rain

(v) SPM → (B) formation of smog

42. A → b Galvanization is the process of coating zinc on iron to prevent rusting.

B → d The process of coating a mixture of silicates on the surface of iron at high temperature is called enamelling.

C → a Bridges are coated with tar or red lead oxide to prevent corrosion.

D → a, e Electric poles are coated with red lead oxide or tar to prevent rusting.

43. A → b H_2O_2 is used as a raw material for the preparation of O_2 in the laboratory.

B → d $CaCO_3$ is used as a raw material for the laboratory preparation of CO_2.

C → c Zinc granules are used for laboratory preparation of hydrogen gas.

D → b Nitre on heating gives oxygen gas.

44. The component of air that is collected by its upward displacement is carbon dioxide.

45. The envelope of gases which surrounds the planet earth is called atmosphere.

46. The two inert gases present in atmosphere are argon and neon.

47. The percentages by volume of inactive and active component of air are 78% and 21%, respectively.

48. The device used to measure the atmospheric pressure is barometer.

49. Collision of high energetic electrons from the sun with the molecules like N_2 and O_2, present in the atmosphere, causes delicate colours of auroras.

50. Ozone absorbs ultraviolet rays.

51. The principal products of combustion of glucose are carbon dioxide and water.

52. Water vapour in the atmosphere helps in the formation of fog, mist, clouds, etc.

53. Greenhouse effect helps to maintain temperature of the earth.

54. The gases that are responsible for acid rain are NO_2, and SO_2.

55. It decomposes to give KNO_2 and oxygen.

$$KNO_3 \rightarrow KNO_2 + O_2 \uparrow$$

56. The substance which alters the rate of reaction but by itself does not take part in the chemical reaction is called a catalyst.

57. $2H_2O_2 \xrightarrow{MnO_2} 2H_2O + O_2$

58. Oxygen is neutral towards litmus.

59. When a paper soaked in acidified potassium dichromate paper is exposed to SO_2 gas, it turns to green due to the formation of chromic sulphate.

60. The factors influencing the rusting are the presence of moisture and oxygen.

61. The process of mixing of a particular metal uniformly with small quantities of different metals in their molten state in order to improve the mechanical properties of the metal is called alloying.

62. Carbon dioxide cannot be prepared by heating sodium carbonate and potassium carbonate.

63. A mixture of 95% oxygen and 5% CO_2 is called carbogen.

Short Answer Type Questions

64. The order of the properties of the components of air, nitrogen, oxygen, helium, carbon dioxide and water vapour, in the order of their percentages by volumes is

(A) Colourless, odourless gas, acidic in nature, and neither combustible nor a supporter of combustion (Carbon dioxide)

(B) Colourless, odourless gas, inert in nature, and di-lutes the activity of active component of air (Nitro-gen)

(C) Colourless, odourless gas, and forms acidic and basic compounds with non-metals and metals, re-spectively (Oxygen)

(D) Colourless gas, inert in nature, present in trace amounts (Helium)

(E) Gaseous form, present in variable amounts, and chemically active along with the active component of air (Water vapour)

Hence, the correct order is BCDAE.

65. Certain gaseous molecules present in the atmosphere absorb infrared rays and reradiate the heat in all direc-tions and thus, the temperature of earth is maintained. This process is called greenhouse effect.

66. Various methods of minimizing air pollution are as follows:

(i) Safe disposal of waste products.

(ii) Equipment like scrubbers and precipitators are to be used in industries to prevent the emission of harmful gases.

(iii) Synthesis of ecofriendly chemicals.

(iv) Arresting deforestation and increasing plantation or greenery.

67. (a) **Respiration**: Oxygen is required for respiration of living beings. In respiration, burning of glucose takes place. Oxygen inhaled during respiration is utilized in oxidizing the glucose to carbon dioxide and water, which is accompanied with evolution of energy.

$$C_6H_{12}O_6 \rightarrow 6CO_2 + 6H_2O + \text{energy}$$

(b) **Cutting and welding**: A mixture of hydrogen and oxygen on burning gives oxyhydrogen flame of 2800°C temperature, whereas a mixture of hydrogen and acetylene produces oxyacetylene flame which has 3300°C temperature. These flames easily melt the metals and hence, used for cutting or welding them.

(c) **Explosion**: A mixture of coal, petroleum jelly and liquid oxygen, called cartridge, is used for blasting rocks.

68. Uses of carbon dioxide

(i) It is used in soft drinks.

(ii) It is used in refrigeration system.

(iii) It is used as a fire extinguisher.

(iv) It is used in the manufacture of different chemicals like H_2SO_4, HNO_3, etc.

69. Different ways of minimizing global warming are as follows:

(i) reduction in the usage of fossil fuels

(ii) controlling deforestation

(iii) restricting the use of CFCs

70. (a) (i) The air present in atmosphere is used for breathing.

(ii) The moisture and dust particles present in air help in the formation of clouds.

(iii) The atmosphere protects us from harmful radiations.

(b) In troposphere, temperature decreases with increase in altitude. But, in stratosphere, temperature increases with increase in altitude. In stratosphere, temperature does not alter much up to a height of about 25 km from the earth's surface Above this, temperature increases with height due to the absorption of highly energetic U.V radiations. Here the temperature rises from −60°C to −15°C. Due to this increase of temperature with height this layer is called inversion layer.

71. Ozone depletion: Ozone present in troposphere contributes to greenhouse effect. Ozone present in stratosphere plays a vital role in protecting the life on earth's surface from harmful UV radiations. Ozone layer acts as a shield as it absorbs harmful UV radia-tions. Pollutants, such as CFCs, upon reaching strato-sphere react with ozone and thus deplete the ozone layer over a period of time. Hence, UV radiations reach tropospheric layer due to the holes created in ozone and affect plant and animal life.

Prevention: Discovery of alternative substance for CFCs used in refrigeration and aerosols.

72. Effects of acid rain are as follows:

(i) The fertility of the soil is lost or reduced.

(ii) Crops are damaged.

(iii) Pollutes water bodies like rivers, seas, etc.

(iv) Corrodes marble statues, monuments or buildings, etc.

73. The constituents of air and their percentages by weight are given below:

nitrogen – 78.084%

oxygen – 20.947%

argon – 0.934%

carbon dioxide – 0.033%

water vapour – 0 to 4%

74. Physical properties of CO_2

(i) It is colourless and odourless gas.

(ii) It is highly soluble in water.

(iii) CO_2 is acidic in nature.

(iv) It is heavier than air.

75. (A) Nascent hydrogen is also called newly born hydrogen. It is denoted by [H]. Nascent hydrogen can reduce compounds that do not readily react with normal hydrogen. Nascent hydrogen is produced in many reactions such as reaction of metals with acids.

(B) Platinum catalytic converter is a device used in motor vehicles (a) that converts toxic gases and pollutants in exhaust gases to less toxic/non-toxic gases by means of oxidation or reduction. It converts carbon monoxide which is released by motor vehicles to carbon dioxide. Compared with carbon dioxide, carbon monoxide is more harmful to human life. (b) It also converts nitrogen oxides of automobile exhausts to nitrogen and oxygen gases. Since nitrogen oxides causes acid rain and also leads to the formation of smog, their conversion into nitrogen and oxygen by platinum catalytic converter reduces the air pollution. Catatylic converter also helps in the conversion of unburnt hydrocarbons into carbon dioxide and water vapour.

76. Catalytic addition of hydrogen to some unsaturated carbon compounds is called hydrogenation. This principle is used in the process of hydrogenation of oils or hardening of oils.

Hydrogenation of oils: Vegetable oils, containing greater percentage of carbon and oxygen but containing less percentage of hydrogen cannot be solidified easily.

Examples: ground nut oil, sunflower oil

Animal oils such as ghee which contain hydrogen in greater percentage get solidified easily under normal conditions. Vegetable oils also get solidified when hydrogen gas is passed through them at high pressure and high temperature in the presence of nickel catalyst.

Examples: palm oil, vanaspathi, soap

77. Important uses of hydrogen are as follows:

(i) In the synthesis of industrial chemicals such as ammonia, HCl, CH_3OH, etc.

(ii) It is used in the manufacture of fuel gases such as water gas, coal gas, semi-water gas, etc.

(iii) It is used for welding of metals.

(iv) It is used as a good reducing agent in the extraction of some metals from their oxides.

78. Nitrogen is required by plants and animals to synthesize proteins. Free nitrogen cannot be assimilated by plants. Hence, the nitrogen present in the atmosphere is converted into nitrogen compounds which can be easily assimilated by plants. The process of conversion of atmospheric nitrogen into nitrates is called nitrogen fixation.

During lightening, N_2 combines with O_2 to form NO which further reacts with O_2 to form NO_2. This gas dissolves in the water droplets of clouds and forms HNO_3. During precipitation, it reaches soil and reacts with metal carbonates to form corresponding nitrates, and these nitrates can be assimilated by plants.

$$N_2 + O_2 \rightarrow 2NO$$

$$2NO + O_2 \rightarrow 2NO_2$$

$$4NO_2 + 2H_2O + O_2 \rightarrow 4HNO_3$$

$$4HNO_3 + MCO_3 \rightarrow M(NO_3)_2 + CO_2 + H_2O$$

Leguminous plants contain symbiotic bacteria in their root nodules which absorb atmospheric nitrogen and convert it into various compounds of nitrogen. These compounds are easily assimilated by plants and also the soil becomes enriched with nitrogen compounds.

79. Water gas is a mixture of equal volumes of carbon monoxide and hydrogen.

Water gas can be prepared by passing steam over red hot coke.

$$C + \underset{\text{steam}}{H_2O} \rightarrow \underset{\text{water gas}}{CO + H_2}$$

80. (i) Reaction with sodium (Na): Sodium reacts with O_2 vigorously at room temperature to form sodium oxide

$$4Na_2 + O_2 \rightarrow 2\,Na_2O$$

(ii) Reaction with magnesium (Mg): Magnesium reacts with oxygen upon slight heating to form magnesium oxide

$$2Mg + O_2 \rightarrow 2MgO$$

(iii) Reaction with sulphur: Sulphur when heated in an atmosphere of oxygen, burns to form sulphur dioxide.

$$S + O_2 \rightarrow SO_2$$

(iv) Reaction with phosphorus: When phosphorus is heated in an atmosphere of oxygen, it burns to produce phosphorus pentoxide.

$$4P + 5O_2 \rightarrow 2P_2O_5$$

81. Methods of prevention of acid rain:

(i) Minimizing the use of fossil fuels. Fossil fuels such as petrol and diesel are replaced by CNG to a great extent in some metropolitan cities.

(ii) Using non-conventional sources of energy.

(iii) Safe disposal of industrial wastes.

82. Human activities responsible for air pollution are the following:

(i) burning of fossil fuels

(ii) deforestation

(iii) emission of polluted gases from vehicles

(iv) agricultural activities which involve usage of fertilizers, pesticides, etc.

(v) lack of civic sense of the people

Essay Answer Type Questions

83. Principle: Hydrogen peroxide in the presence of a catalyst, i.e., manganese dioxide (MnO_2) undergoes decomposition to give water and oxygen at room temperature.

$$2H_2O_2 \xrightarrow{MnO_2} 2H_2O + O_2$$

Experiment: MnO_2 is taken in a clean and dry conical flask. H_2O_2 solution is added dropwise through the thistle funnel which is fitted to a conical flask with the help of a rubber stopper.

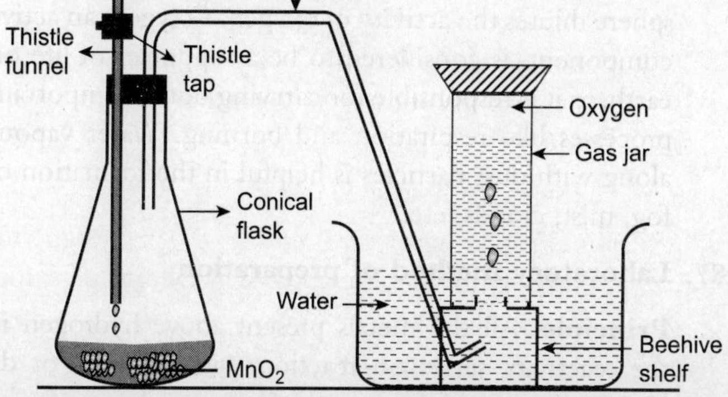

Laboratory preparation of oxygen from H_2O_2

Observation: The oxygen gas evolved, passes through a delivery tube into the beehive shelf placed in a trough of water. The oxygen gas evolves with effervescence in the gas cylinder inverted over the beehive shelf. The gas evolved rekindles a glowing splinter.

Method of collection of oxygen gas: O_2 gas evolved is collected by downward displacement of water.

Precautions:

(a) heating of reaction mixture should be avoided

(b) MnO_2 used should be devoid of impurities

84. General methods of preparation of CO_2

(a) **Combustion**: CO_2 is released into atmosphere when carbon-containing fuels like coal, natural gas, etc., are burnt.

Examples: $C + O_2 \rightarrow CO_2 + \text{heat}$

$CH_4 + 2O_2 \rightarrow CO_2 + 2H_2O + \text{heat}$

(b) **Decomposition of metal carbonates**: Metal carbonates on strong heating decompose to produce CO_2 gas and corresponding metal oxides.

Exceptions: sodium carbonate and potassium carbonate

Examples: $CaCO_3 \xrightarrow{\Delta} CaO + CO_2\uparrow$

$CuCO_3 \xrightarrow{\Delta} CuO + CO_2\uparrow$

$ZnCO_3 \xrightarrow{\Delta} ZnO + CO_2\uparrow$

(c) **Decomposition of metal hydrogen carbonates**: Active metal hydrogen carbonate like sodium hydrogen carbonate, commonly called baking soda, on heating produces CO_2 gas along with the formation of corresponding metal carbonate and water.

$$2NaHCO_3 \rightarrow Na_2CO_3 + H_2 + CO_2$$

Sodium bicarnonate or sodium hydrogen carbonate (sodium carbonate)

(d) **Action of dilute acids on metal carbonates and metal hydrogen carbonates**: Metal carbonates and hydrogen carbonates when treated with dil acids liberate CO_2 gas along with the formation of corresponding salts.

$$Na_2CO_3 + H_2SO_4 \rightarrow Na_2SO_4 + H_2O + CO_2\uparrow$$

$$Ca(HCO_3)_2 + 2HNO_3 \rightarrow Ca(NO_3)_2 + 2H_2O + 2CO_2\uparrow$$

85. **Rusting**: The process of conversion of iron into its hydrated form of oxide in a humid atmosphere is called rusting. The hydrated form of its oxide is called rust.

$$4Fe(s) + 3O_2 \rightarrow 2Fe_2O_3\ (s)$$

$$Fe_2O_3\ (s) + XH_2O\ (l) \rightarrow \underset{\textbf{rust}}{Fe_2O_3.XH_2O\ (s)}$$

(X indicates number of water molecules which is variable)

Iron gets corroded due to the formation of rust. The rust is a brownish, flaky substance which easily crumbles from the surface of metal. Hence, it weakens the iron structures.

Note: Iron does not get rusted in dry atmosphere.

Prevention: Iron is used to make different structures for varied purposes like the manufacture of machinery and tools for industrial purposes, construction of bridges, railway tracks and manufacture of furniture, bodies of cooking stoves, refrigerators, buckets, suitcases and other household goods. To prevent rusting of iron, different methods and processes are employed.

(i) **Coating**: The metal iron is coated with other substances which prevent the exposure of iron to humid air which in turn prevents rusting.

(a) **Coating with red lead oxide or tar**: The bridges, electric poles, etc., are coated with red lead oxide paint or tar which protects iron from rusting.

(b) **Coating with enamel paint**: Doors and windows, bodies of cars, buses and other automobiles, etc., are given a first coat of red lead oxide paint followed by enamelled paint so as to enhance the appearance of the structure.

(c) **By enamelling**: The processes of coating of mixture of silicates on the surface of iron at high temperatures is called **enamelling**. It also gives a good appearance to the articles. Articles like bodies of cooking stoves, refrigerators, plates, wash basins, ovens, etc., are given this type of coating.

(d) **Coating with oil or grease**: The movable machine or engine parts are coated with a layer of oil or grease which not only prevents rusting but also lubricates them. They cannot be coated with other substances because it wears off since these parts keep moving.

(ii) **Galvanization**: Iron sheets are dipped in molten zinc and then passed through heavy rollers. As a result, the iron sheets get coated with zinc metal. This process is called **galvanization** and iron coated with zinc is called galvanized iron.

Examples: Tin roof, buckets, tubs, iron trunks, etc.

(iii) **Tinning**: The process in which a protective layer of tin is given on iron sheets is called **tinning**.

The process is similar to galvanization.

Example: Containers or tins used to preserve edible food materials like oil, meat, vegetables, etc.

(iv) **Electroplating**: The metal iron is coated with another metal by the process called electrolysis. The metals used for coating are either chromium or nickel.

Examples: Bicycle handles, rims, bumpers of car, etc.

(v) **Alloying**: The process of mixing a particular metal uniformly with small quantities of different metals in their molten state in order to improve the mechanical properties of the metal is called alloying. Substances like carbon and chromium are added to iron to form a homogeneous mixture called stainless steel, an alloy by which it is made corrosion resistant.

Percentage composition:

chromium – 12% to 20%

carbon – 0.07% to 0.1%

Examples: surgical instruments, tools, utensils, cutlery, etc.

86. Nitrogen and oxygen which are major components of the atmosphere have very important associations with life. Nitrogen being an inactive component of atmosphere dilutes the activity of oxygen. Oxygen, an active component, is considered to be a supporter of life on earth, as it is responsible for carrying out the important processes like respiration and burning. Water vapour along with dust particles is helpful in the formation of fog, mist, clouds, etc.

87. **Laboratory method of preparation**

Principle: All the metals present above hydrogen in the reactivity series on reaction with dil HCl or dil H_2SO_4 liberate hydrogen gas. Zinc metal is preferred for this reaction.

$$Zn + 2HCl \rightarrow ZnCl_2 + H_2\uparrow$$

$$Zn + H_2SO_4 \rightarrow ZnSO_4 + H_2\uparrow$$

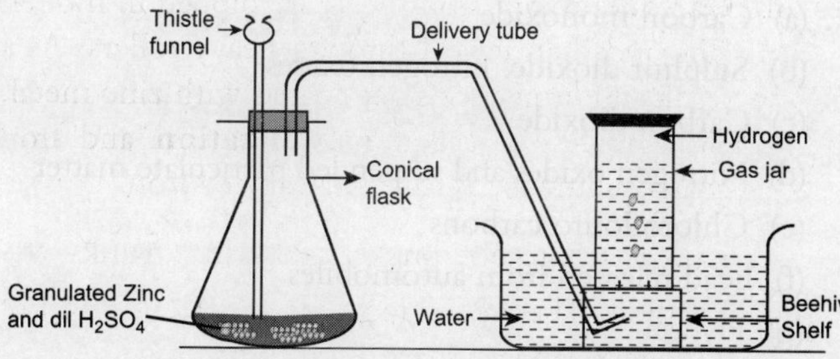

Laboratory preparation of hydrogen

Experiment: Some granulated zinc pieces are taken in a flat-bottom flask fitted with a two-holed air-tight cork. In one hole, a thistle funnel is inserted and in another hole, a long delivery tube is inserted. Dil H_2SO_4 is added to the flask dropwise through the thistle funnel.

Observation: Effervescence is observed in the initial stages of the reaction. Then, a colourless and odourless gas evolves.

Collection of gas: Hydrogen is collected by the downward displacement of water.

88. (a) **Reaction with lime water ($Ca(OH)_2$)**: CO_2 reacts with lime water, i.e., $Ca(OH)_2$ to form a milky white precipitate, i.e., $CaCO_3$.

$$Ca(OH)_2 + CO_2 \rightarrow CaCO_3\downarrow$$

When excess CO_2 is passed through the above solution, the precipitate dissolves due to the formation of $Ca(HCO_3)_2$.

$$CaCO_3 + H_2O + CO_2 \rightarrow Ca(HCO_3)_2$$

(b) **Reaction with metals**: Metals like Na, K and Ca react with CO_2 to form corresponding metal carbonates while Mg and Al give corresponding oxides.

$$4Na + 3CO_2 \rightarrow 2Na_2CO_3 + C$$

$$2Mg + CO_2 \rightarrow 2MgO + C$$

(c) **Reaction with non-metals**: CO_2 when reacts with red hot coke gets reduced to CO, a very poisonous gas.

$$\underset{\text{(coke)}}{C} + CO_2 \xrightarrow{\Delta} 2CO$$

89. (a) **Troposphere**

(i) The layer of atmosphere which begins at the earth's surface and extends up to 20 km height above the surface is called **troposphere**.

(ii) It holds the maximum percentage of the total mass of the atmosphere.

(iii) The density of air and temperature gradually decrease with height. As we move to the upper layers the temperature drops from about 17°C to –51°C. The fall in temperature with increase in height at the rate of 6°C/km is called **lapse rate**.

(iv) Most of the weather phenomena occur in this layer due to rapid variation in temperature.

(v) The height and thickness of this layer vary from the equator to the poles.

(b) **Stratosphere**

(i) The layer of atmosphere above the troposphere which extends up to 50 km above the earth's surface is called **stratosphere**.

(ii) It holds 19% of the atmospheric gases.

(iii) Temperature does not alter much up to a height of about 25 km from the earth's surface. Above this, temperature increases with height due to the absorption of highly energetic UV radiations. Here, the temperature rises from –60°C to –15°C. This increase of temperature with height is called **inversion layer**. The region that extends from 25 km to 40 km above the earth's surface is called **ozonosphere** or **ozone layer**. This layer absorbs harmful UV radiations and thus protects life on the earth.

(iv) Aeroplanes fly in this layer.

90. (a) **Air pollution**: The atmospheric composition of gases change due to the addition of other gases and suspended particles into atmosphere mainly by human-induced activities. This built up of other gases and suspended particulate matter is toxic to organisms living on the earth's surface. The variation in the composition of atmospheric air due to the release of harmful gases is called **air pollution**.

(b) (i) **Ozone depletion**: Ozone present in the troposphere contributes to greenhouse effect. Ozone present in the stratosphere plays a vital role in protecting life on the earth's surface from harmful UV radiations. Ozone layer acts as a shield as it absorbs highly energetic harmful UV radiations.

Pollutants, such as CFCs, upon reaching stratosphere react with ozone and thus, deplete the ozone layer over a period of time. Hence, UV radiations reach the tropospheric layer due to the holes created in ozone and affect both plant and animal life.

Prevention: Discovery of alternative substance for CFCs used in refrigeration.

(ii) **Hazards caused by carbon monoxide**: As the percentage of CO increases in atmosphere, it affects the respiratory system. CO has 200 times more affinity for haemoglobin over oxygen and forms a stable compound called carboxy haemoglobin which causes suffocation and sometimes it is even fatal to human life.

Prevention: Reduction in the burning of fossil fuels, cigarettes, etc.

As the pollutants increase in atmospheric air, they affect both plant and animal life, causes respiratory problems, damage monuments, etc. Particularly, the lead particles from smoke of motor engines cause damage to the nervous system.

91.

Impurities	Substances used for removal
(a) AsH_3, PH_3	Silver nitrate solution
(b) H_2S	Lead nitrate solution
(c) CO_2, SO_2, NO_2	Caustic potash
(d) H_2O (water vapour)	$CaCl_2$ or P_2O_5 (drying agent)

92. (a) Carbon monoxide
(b) Sulphur dioxide, nitrogen oxides
(c) Carbon dioxide
(d) Nitrogen oxides and suspended particulate matter
(e) Chloroflouro carbons
(f) Lead released from automobiles
(g) Fly ash
(h) Sulphur dioxide

93. The required dinegative ion is sulphide ion (S^{2-}), because sulphide ion has 18 electrons; this is equal to the atomic number of argon. One molecule of sulphur reacts with one molecule of oxygen to give one molecule of sulphur dioxide. This sulphur dioxide dissolves in water to give sulphurous acid. SO_2 reacts with oxygen and changes to sulhpur trioxide. This dissolves in water to give sulphuric acid which causes acid rains.

$$S + O_2 \rightarrow SO_2$$

$$SO_2 + H_2O \rightarrow H_2SO_3$$

Competition Wing

Level 1: Apply your Concepts

1. Corrosion of marble statues and monuments is neither directly nor indirectly an effect of global warming.
2. Auroras appear in the layer of the atmosphere which is known as thermosphere.
3. Chlorofluorocarbons deplete the ozone layer.
4. catalyst
   The catalyst alters the rate of a reaction.
5. MnO_2
   In the laboratory preparation of oxygen from hydrogen peroxide, MnO_2 is used as a catalyst.
6. Aeroplanes usually fly in the zone of stratosphere.
7. Meteorites burn up in mesosphere.
8. The percentage of noble gases is 0.94 per cent and that of CO_2 is 0.03 per cent in atmosphere.
9. Oxygen is neutral towards litmus as it is neither acidic nor basic.
10. Gases like nitrogen dioxide, sulphur dioxide in atmosphere cause acid rain.
11. When food grains are kept in the atmosphere of carbon dioxide, it prevents the grain from destruction by insects.
12. CO_2 can be collected by upward displacement of air as CO_2 is denser than air.
13. It provides enough temperature for nitrogen and oxygen to combine to form nitric oxide.
14. Carbogen is a mixture of 95 per cent oxygen and 5 per cent carbon dioxide.
15. Dust particles help in the formation of cloud.
16. The pollutant that is not released into the air because of the combustion of coal is CFCs.
17. Ammonia (NH_3), an important raw material in the manufacture of fertilizers, is manufactured industrially by a process called Haber's process.
18. Water gas, an industrially important fuel, is a mixture of CO and H_2 gases.
19. Liquid hydrogen is used as a rocket fuel.
20. Oxygen is neutral towards litmus.
21. Chemical formula of white lead is $Pb(OH)_2.PbCO_3$.
22. The atmospheric pressure is maximum at sea level and is found to be equal to 760 mm of Hg.
23. In the ionosphere, a layer of atmosphere, TV waves do not get reflected. Hence, artificial satellites are used for transmission of TV waves.
24. Nascent hydrogen is a strong reducing agent.
25. Liquid oxygen is used for burning fuels in rockets and space ships.
26. Thermosphere consists of ions and free elections and the temperature in the thermosphere can reach a maximum of 2000°C because of the absorption of high energy radiations. Both A and R are correct but R is the exact explanation of A.
   Hence, the correct option is (a).
27. O_2, SO_2, and NO_2 are not greenhouse gases. Gases such as CO_2, H_2O, etc., absorb IR radiations and are called greenhouse gases. Thus, A is wrong but R is correct.
   Hence, the correct option is (d).
28. Ozone when present in the troposphere is a major pollutant that leads to global warming, while ozone present in the stratosphere acts as a shield from UV rays reaching the earth's surface.
   Hence, the correct the answer is (b).
29. Burning of meteorites takes place in the mesosphere, aeroplanes fly in the stratosphere, reflection of radio waves takes place in the ionosphere. Magnetosphere absorbs ionising radiations and most of the weather phenomena occur in the troposphere.
   Hence, the correct the answer is (b).
30. The reaction of iron with steam is a reversible reaction.
   Hence, the correct the answer is (c).
31. Neon is used in advertisement glow tubes.
   Hence, the correct the answer is (a).
32. SI unit of atmospheric pressure is Pascal.
   Hence, the correct the answer is (b).
33. Oxygen gas is called acid formerly.
   Hence, the correct the answer is (d).
34. Ozone present in the stratosphere plays a vital role in protecting the life on earth's surface from harmful UV rays.

Hence, the correct the answer is (b).

35. Chromium metal is used in the alloying of iron to prevent corrosion.

Hence, the correct the answer is (d).

36. As we move to higher altitudes, fountain ink pen leaks out because of lower atmospheric pressure. The pressure built up in the ink pen is more when compared to the outside pressure. Hence, it leaks out.

Hence, the correct the answer is (a).

37. Holes are created in the ozone layer due to the attack of CFCs which are released from refrigerators and air conditioners.

Hence, the correct the answer is (b).

38. Due to acid rain, sculptures and monuments get damaged and also water bodies like rivers, oceans get acidified. This acidified water affects the aquatic life which leads to death and decay of aquatic animals.

Hence, the correct the answer is (d).

39. Since sodium, magnesium and potassium are active metals, they catch fire when they react with oxygen and continue to burn in an atmosphere of N_2, while tungsten (W) which burns in presence of oxygen, does not continue to burn in an inert atmosphere of N_2.

Hence, the correct the answer is (d).

40. 'X' is highly soluble in water. Hence, it cannot be collected by water. It is collected by the upward displacement of air as it is heavier than air.

Hence, the correct the answer is (c).

41. (i) Stratosphere (ii) Troposphere
(iii) Ionosphere (iv) Exosphere
(v) Mesosphere

Hence, the correct the answer is (c).

42. (i) Formation of nitric oxide
(ii) Formation of nitrogen dioxide
(iii) Formation of nitric acid
(iv) Formation of metal nitrates

Hence, the correct the answer is (b).

43. Meteorites burn up in the mesosphere due to the presence of relatively thick atmosphere. Meteorites collide with molecules present in this layer, and thus emit, light known as shooting stars. While in the thermosphere, the thin atmosphere is not enough to produce friction for the meteorites to burn.

Hence, the correct the answer is (a).

44. Aeroplanes fly in the stratosphere due to the absence of convection current. This is because the temperature gradually increases with increase in altitude due to the absorption of highly energetic UV radiations. Since there is no turbulence in the atmosphere of the stratosphere, aeroplanes usually fly in the stratosphere.

Hence, the correct the answer is (d).

45. 'A' can be SO_2 or NO_2 because they pollute air and cause acid rain to pollute water. 'B' can be CO_2 since it does not cause acid rain. Its presence in water is essential for aquatic plants. It is considered as an air pollutant as it results in global warming.

Hence, the correct the answer is (c).

46. Tin does not react with the components of food material while Zn reacts and leads to spoilage of food. Hence, tin-coated containers are preferred over zinc-coated ones as tin is less reactive than Zn.

Hence, the correct the answer is (c).

47. Anhydrous calcium chloride is deliquescent in nature which absorbs moisture and forms a solution. Thus, $CaCl_2$ solution formed does not allow the dust particles and other suspended particulate matter to rise.

$$\underset{(X)}{CaCO_3} + HCl \rightarrow \underset{(Y)}{CaCl_2} + CO_2 + H_2O$$

Hence, the correct the answer is (c).

48. Marble is made of $CaCO_3$ which gets dissolved when it reacts with acids like H_2SO_4 or HNO_3 of acid rains. The major pollutants which contribute to acid rain, NO_2 and SO_2 are released into the atmosphere. The NO_2 and SO_2 percentage content in the atmosphere can be decreased by using equipment like scrubbers. In a scrubber, powdered $CaCO_3$ is taken which undergoes decomposition to give CaO. This quick lime combines with SO_2 to form $CaSO_3$ which is removed as slurry.

$$\underset{\text{Base}}{CaO} + \underset{\text{acid}}{SO_2} \rightarrow CaSO_3\downarrow$$

Hence, it is a neutralisation reaction.

Hence, the correct the answer is (a).

49. Since air consists of an active component that is oxygen, it oxidises tungsten filament or any other metal used as a filament. Hence, electric bulbs are filled with inert gas like argon or chemically inert nitrogen.

Hence, the correct the answer is (a).

50. The process of cloud formation takes place throughout the year while the formation of mist takes place only at certain times at particular temperatures.

Hence, the correct the answer is (b).

51. Catalytic convertors consist of ceramic honey comb like structures with platinum catalyst spread out. The increased surface area of the catalyst provides many reactive sites where the less oxidised products like CO and NO are converted to CO_2 and N_2 which are released into the atmosphere.

Hence, the correct the answer is (c).

52. $H_2O_2 \rightarrow H_2O_2 + O_2$
(X)
$NO + O_2 \rightarrow NO_2$
(Y) (Z)
(reddish brown)

O_2 (Y) is neutral towards litmus while NO_2 is acidic, and hence, turns moist blue to red.

Hence, the correct the answer is (b).

53. Due to a very thin atmosphere in the thermosphere, only a few molecules present here absorb high energetic radiations, and hence, the temperature of molecules or ions formed is great but the ambient temperature is very low.

Hence, the correct the answer is (c).

54. Due to the absorption of highly energetic radiations, i.e., UV radiations by the stratosphere, the temperature is high when compared to the troposphere. The high temperature of the stratosphere does not allow the water vapour to reach the stratosphere due to the absence of convection current. Hence, cloud formation does not take place in the stratosphere. Cloud formation requires convection currents and also dust particles for condensation of water droplets.

Hence, the correct the answer is (d).

55. CO_2 and water vapour are greenhouse gases present in the atmosphere. Their percentage increase in the atmosphere increases the temperature of the earth and contributes to global warming. These are the major contributors to global warming.

Hence, the correct the answer is (d).

56. Aluminium, when exposed to the atmosphere, reacts with air, i.e., O_2, and forms Al_2O_3 which is chemically inert. This layer of Al_2O_3 (alumina) makes aluminium passive.

Hence, the correct the answer is (c).

57. The usage of refrigerators and air conditioners releases chlorofluorocarbons which does not contribute to SPM.

Hence, the correct the answer is (d).

58. Incomplete combustion of fuels releases CO, NO, etc., that leads to photochemical smog and acid rain but not global warming.

Hence, the correct the answer is (c).

59. Leguminous plants consist of nodules in their roots with *Rhizobium* bacteria. These bacteria convert atmospheric nitrogen into its corresponding metal nitrates. These nitrates can be readily assimilated by plants. Hence, they do not require additional nitrogenous fertilisers.

Hence, the correct the answer is (d).

60. 'X' is an acidic gas since it changes blue litmus to red. 'Y' is neutral since it does not respond to either red or blue litmus.

Hence, the correct the answer is (b).

61. A → b, c, e Oxides of nitrogen contribute to acid rain, global warming and formation of smog.
B → d, e CFC contributes to the depletion of the ozone layer and global warming
C → a fly ash causes clogging of drainage.
D → c Suspended particulate matter involved in the formation of smog.

62. A → b $SO_2 + H_2O \rightarrow H_2SO_3$
B → g, h $2NO_2 + H_2O \rightarrow HNO_2 + HNO_3$
C → c $P_2O_5 + 3H_2O \rightarrow 2H_3PO_4$
D → e $CO_2 + H_2O \rightarrow H_2CO_3$

63. A → e The major constituent of carbogen is oxygen.
B → d, a Nitrogen dilutes the activity of oxygen. Nitrogen has an inert nature, hence, it is used to preserve food items.
C → f, a CO_2 is used in the making of white lead. CO_2 is also used in the preservation of food stuffs.
D → b, c Nascent hydrogen acts as a good reducing agent. Nascent hydrogen can be replenished by using Kipps apparatus.

Level 2: Review Your Concepts

64. Increased levels of oxygen increase the rate of combustion. Fuel would burn at a faster rate and become dangerous and it will be difficult to extinguish fires. It also would increase the rate of corrosion of metals and increase the rate of respiration which would affect the human system.

65. The order of change of temperature in different layers of the atmosphere according to their heights from above the earth's surface is
   (a) The temperature decreases with an increase in height at a rate of 6°C/km (Troposphere)
   (b) The temperature increases from –60°C to 15°C with an increase in height and is called the inversion layer (Stratosphere).
   (c) The temperature decreases from –15°C to –120°C (Mesosphere)
   (d) The temperature increases with height and can reach to maximum of 2000°c at the top of this layer (Thermosphere)
   (e) High temperature because of absorption of harmful ionising radiations (Exosphere)

   The order is DCBAE.

   Hence, the correct order is DCBAE.

66. When we suck one end of a straw dipped into the coconut water, some air from inside the straw is drawn out. A partial vacuum is created within the straw and as a result coconut water is pushed up by the atmospheric pressure to fill up the vacuum and reaches the persons mouth. Hence, we can drink the coconut water.

67. CNG does not produce any harmful gas, and thus, it reduces the maintenance cost and it is a clean fuel. While petrol and diesel contain N and S which upon combustion produce NO_2 and SO_2, respectively. These lead to acid rain. Hence, CNG can be a substitute for petrol and diesel.

68. In the interior of cities, the density of population is more, as a result a large volume of traffic exists which leads to an increase in the gaseous contents such as CO_2, methane and nitrous oxides which contribute to global warming. Hence, the temperature in the interior of the cities is higher than in the outskirts of the cities.

69. In 100 L of air, volume of nitrogen = 78.10 L

$$\text{Volume of nitrogen in 750 L} = \frac{78.1 \times 750}{100}$$

$$= 585.75 \text{ L}$$

Volume of oxygen in 100 L of air = 21 L

$$\text{Volume of oxygen in 750 L} = \frac{21 \times 750}{100}$$

$$= 157.5 \text{ L}$$

Volume of CO_2 in 100 L of air = 0.03 L

$$\text{Volume of } CO_2 \text{ in 750 L} = \frac{0.03 \times 750}{100}$$

$$= 0.225 \text{ L}$$

$$= 225 \text{ mL}$$

70. The vapour density of oxygen is 16 and that of the air is 14.4. Hence, due to higher vapour density of oxygen its amount in air decrease on higher altitudes such as mountains, i.e., more denser molecules experience more gravitational pull.

71. 14 electrons in the M-shell and 2 electrons in the N-shell correspond to the metal 'Fe.' X is nitrogen which is filled in air tight food packets to prevent oxidation and Y is oxygen which is required for combustion. In presence of oxygen and water vapour (Z) metal iron (M) gets rusted to form a compound, i.e., $Fe_2O_3 . XH_2O$. X = nitrogen Y = oxygen, Z = water vapour and M = Fe.

72. In the process of galvanising, zinc is coated on the iron. Zinc can react with acids present in food material and as a result food items cannot be consumed. However, tin cannot react with acids present in food items. Hence, tinned iron sheets are extensively used for making boxes to store edible substances.

73. It is dangerous to sleep in a closed room with coke burning in improperly designed chulhas because coal undergoes incomplete combustion and produces carbon monoxide which is a harmful gas and leads to respiratory problems.

74. (A) Since X is used in white washing, X is $Ca(OH)_2$, Y is CO_2 and Z is $CaCO_3$ as it is used for construction of monuments.

$$\underset{X}{Ca(OH)_2} + \underset{Y}{CO_2} \rightarrow \underset{Z}{CaCO_3} + H_2O$$

$$CaCO_3 + H_2O + CO_2 \rightarrow Ca(HCO_3)_2.$$

   (B) By passing steam over red-hot coke, water gas is formed. The required mixture 'X' is water gas. Carbon dioxide is a non-supporter of combustion and it turns lime water milky. Catalytic oxidation of water gas gives hydrogen gas and carbon dioxide. So, the required compound 'Y' is carbon dioxide.

(a) X → Carbon (coke); A → carbon monoxide B → Hydrogen C → carbon dioxide D → Carbonic acid.

(b) It is Bosch process for the preparation of hydrogen gases.

(c) Unreacted carbon monoxide is removed by passing the gas through ammonical cuprous chloride solution

(d) $C+H_2O \longrightarrow CO+H_2$

$$CO+H_2+H_2O \xrightarrow[500°C]{Fe_2O_3} CO_2+H_2$$

$$CO_2+H_2O \xrightarrow{\text{High pressure}} H_2CO_3$$

$$CuCl+CO+2H_2O \longrightarrow CuCl.CO.2H_2O$$

75. The presence of water vapour in atmosphere influences the climatic conditions. Water vapour present in the atmosphere gets condensed on dust particles during night time (winter nights) because of low temperature. Depending upon the temperature, the water vapour produces snow, fog, mist, hails and other phenomena. When water vapour condenses on dust particles and remains suspended in atmosphere, it is called fog.

76. Burning of candle produces CO_2 and water. When the cylinder containing CO_2 is inverted into water, CO_2 dissolves in water and as a result the water level slightly rises in the glass jar. Thus, it indicates that CO_2 is soluble in water.

77. During acid rain, the nitric acid formed as a result of lightning process in very dilute form is washed down to earth and reacts with metal carbonates to form nitrates. $CaCO_3 + 2HNO_3 \rightarrow Ca(NO_3)_2 + CO_2 + H_2O$. Nitrates so formed act as excellent nutrients for the growth of plants.

Level 3: Assess Your Concepts

78. A = ionosphere or thermosphere, B = troposphere,

C = mesosphere, D = stratosphere. Increasing order of five layers as per altitude from the surface of earth are: B < D < C < A.

79. The element X is sulphur which burns in oxygen to produce compound Y which (SO_2) turns acidified potassium dichromate paper to green. When moist blue litmus paper is introduced to SO_2, it turns red due to formation of compound Z which is H_2SO_3.

$$S + O_2 \rightarrow SO_2;\ SO_2 + H_2O \rightarrow H_2SO_3$$

$$SO_2 + K_2Cr_2O_7\ H_2SO_4 \rightarrow K_2SO_4 + \underset{\text{green}}{Cr_2(SO_4)} + H_2O$$

80. (A) Aqua purifiers consist of energy source which radiates UV rays. Oxygen is converted to ozone in presence of ultraviolet rays. The ozone decomposes into oxygen and nascent oxygen in presence of UV rays. The nascent oxygen has ability to kill the harmful microorganisms present in water, and hence, water gets purified.

$$3O_2 \rightarrow 2O_3$$

$$O_3 \rightarrow O_2 + [O]$$

(B) The electronic configuration of the metal could be 2,8,8,2 and the metal could be calcium. Oxyacid of carbon (Z = 6) is carbonic acid. The normal salt is calcium carbonate. Marble contains $CaCO_3$ as the major component. Binary acid of chlorine is HCl.

(a) The gas evolved is carbon dioxide

$$CaCO_3 + 2HCl \rightarrow CaCl_2 + H_2O + CO_2\uparrow$$

(b) The non-metal with 6 electrons in valence M shell could be sulphur (2, 8, 6). Higher oxyacid of sulphur is sulphuric acid. If H_2SO_4 is used in place HCl, insoluble calcium sulphate is formed which forms a layer over marble chips and the further reaction is hindered.

$$CaCO_3 + H_2SO_4 \rightarrow CaSO_4\downarrow + CO_2 + H_2O$$

(c) CO_2 is collected by upward displacement of air as it heavier than air.

81. Active metals like Na and Mg react with carbon dioxide and form corresponding oxide and carbon monoxide in trace amounts which is a harmful gas and also a supporter of combustion. Hence, fires caused by metals like Na and Mg cannot be extinguished by CO_2.

82. Electric precipitator removes the suspended particulate matter which are charged particles coming from thermal power plants, cement plants, steel plants so that smoke and ash entering the atmosphere is minimised. Catalytic converter contains catalysts such as platinum on ceramic comb which convert harmful gases to less harmful gases, such as CO to CO_2 and oxides of nitrogen to nitrogen.

CHAPTER

5

Water

Remember

Before beginning this chapter, you should be able to:

- have knowledge of layers of the earth.
- have basic concept of hydrosphere.

Key Ideas

After completing this chapter, you should be able to:

- know about the different sources, forms of water and importance of water.
- explain the physical properties and uses of water, and depletion of water table.
- learn the different types of water (hard and soft), causes of hardness and methods of removal of different kinds of hardness.
- understand causes of water pollution and the process of purification of water.
- study about the volumetric composition of water by means of electrolysis.

Scientific Crypt

A Tribute to Michael Faraday (1791 – 1867)

Michael Faraday was an English chemist and physicist who gained worldwide reputation for his commendable contributions to the fields of eletromagnetism and electrochemistry. It is largely due to his efforts that electricity became viable for use in day to day life and technology.

Faraday received only basic school education and at the tender age of 14, he became apprenticed to a local bookbinder and bookseller. During his apprenticeship, he read many books and developed a passion and interest in science particularly electricity. At the end of his apprenticeship, he attended lectures of eminent English chemists like Humphry Davy. This gave a breakthrough for Faraday's career as he was later appointed as secretary and then became chemical assistant to Humphry Davy. Faraday's early chemical work was carried out under Humphry Davy, which resulted in Faraday's mentor relationship with Davy.

Michael Faraday's major and the most significant contribution to Chemistry was study of electrolysis and his laws of electrolysis. His other contributions to Chemistry include discovery of benzene, system of oxidation numbers, liquefaction of gases, alloys of steel, various kinds of optical glass etc. Invention of early form of Bunsen burner which is universally used in science laboratories is another feather in his cap.

He became the source of inspiration for the later scientists which is evident from the fact that the eminent Nobel laureate, Albert Einstein kept Faraday's photograph on his study wall alongside pictures of Issac Newton and Clerk Maxwell.

FUN TIME

CROSSWORD

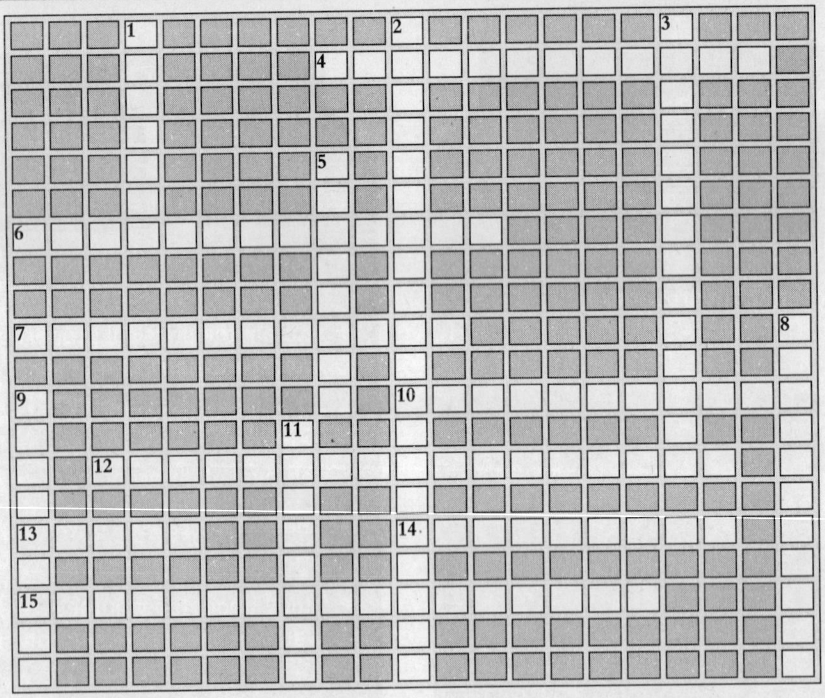

Across

4. The amount of heat required to raise the temperature of unit mass of a substance by 1°C
6. Scanty rainfall and drought conditions lead to ______
7. The process of removal of the salinity of sea water
10. The compound added for the removal of permanent hardness
12. The type of hardness caused by the presence of chloride salts
13. The liquid with the highest specific heat capacity
14. The purest form of natural water
15. The hardness caused by the presence of bicarbonate salts

Down

1. The electrode at which hydrogen is liberated during electrolysis of water
2. The decrease in the level of water table
3. The principle involved in desalination process
5. The common name of hydrated sodium aluminium silicate
8. The common name of compound added in Clark's method for removal of hardness
9. Water which can form lather with soap
11. Water which forms precipitate with soap

INTRODUCTION

Our planet Earth is unique and different than other planets in many ways out of which the most prominent reason is the habitation of a wide variety of flora and fauna and water is responsible for sustaining that on our planet. Water is the most abundant resource on Earth.

The Wonder Liquid - Water

The significance of water in the sustenance of the biosphere dates back to the evolution of aquatic life in oceans millions of years ago. It is believed that complex chemical reactions between the minerals in sea water took place in the presence of sunlight which resulted in the origin of unicellular organisms such as bacteria and fungi. The role of water is not confined to the evolution of life alone. Water is the essential constituent required for photosynthesis which is the only process that supports life. Being the major component in all living cells, water plays the most crucial role in all biological processes.

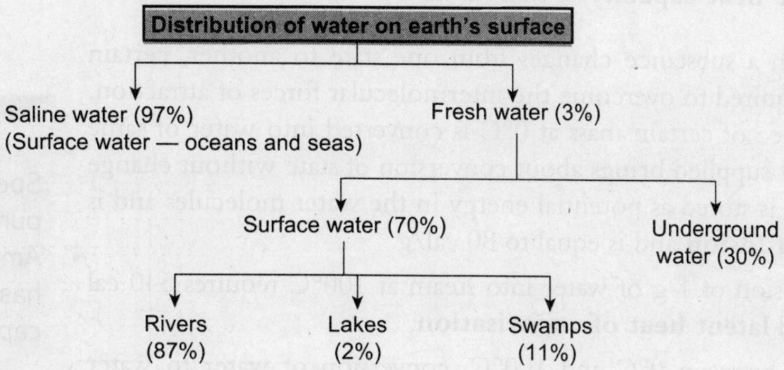

Distribution of Water on the Earth

The distribution of water over the earth depends on the following factors:

- Climate
- Temperature
- Rainfall

Since these factors are variable in different geographical regions, the distribution of rainfall is not uniform on the earth. Some places receive high rainfall throughout the most part of the year and hence have abundant water resources. Some places experience scanty rainfall and hence face acute water shortage leading to drought conditions.

In India, the contrasting nature of distribution of water is much more conspicuous due to the vast area of the country and wide range of terrain such as mountains, plateaus and plains.

In India, the coastal areas usually get affected by floods frequently because of excessive rainfall. In some landlocked regions such as Thar desert, the absence of rains results in frequent droughts.

Physical Properties of Water

Water possesses certain significant physical properties which are responsible for making it a vital liquid. Some of the important properties are listed below.

1. **Nature:** It is a colourless, odourless and tasteless liquid.

2. **Freezing Point:** Water freezes to ice at 0°C under normal atmospheric pressure, i.e., 760 mm of Hg.
3. **Boiling Point:** Water gets converted into steam at 100°C under normal atmospheric pressure, i.e., 760 mm of Hg. The boiling point of water is proportional to external pressure.
4. **Density:** In general, solids possess greater densities than liquids. Therefore, for such liquids, the density decreases with an increase in temperature as the liquids expand on heating. However, in the case of water, it is different. Ice has lower density than water at the same temperatrure. As ice gets converted into water at 0°C, its density increases and this trend continues till the temperature rises to 4°C. Beyond 4°C, water shows normal trend of decrease in density with increase in temperature. Therefore, density of water is maximum at 4°C (1 g/cc). From 4°C to 0°C, water undergoes expansion while all other liquids undergo contraction. Since this trend is opposite to the normal trend, this is called **anomalous expansion of water**.

Table 5.1 Density of water at different temperatures

Temperature	Density
0°C	0.91 g/cc (ice)
0°C	0.97 g/cc (water)
4°C	1 g/cc
>4°C	<1 g/cc

5. **Specific Heat:** The amount of heat energy required to raise the temperature of unit mass of a substance through 1°C is called **specific heat capacity** of that substance.
6. **Latent Heat:** When a substance changes from one state to another, certain amount of heat is required to overcome the intermolecular forces of attraction. For instance, when ice of certain mass at 0°C is converted into water of same mass at 0°C, the heat supplied brings about conversion of state without change in temperature. This is stored as potential energy in the water molecules and is called **latent heat of fusion** and is equal to 80 cal/g.

   Similarly, the conversion of 1 g of water into steam at 100°C requires 540 cal heat and this is called **latent heat of vaporisation**.

   At any temperature between 0°C and 100°C, conversion of water to water vapour takes place rather slowly. This process is called **evaporation**. The rate of evaporation increases with increase in temperature.

Konnect

Specific heat capacity of pure water is 1 calorie/g/°C. Among all substances, water has the highest specific heat capacity.

7. **Conductivity:** Pure water is a poor conductor of electricity. However, the presence of dissolved salts renders normal water a good conductor.
8. **Solvent Property:** Water can dissolve most of the substances in it. Hence, it is known as **universal solvent**.

Forms of Water

Water is the most abundant component on the earth's surface. In fact from 70 to 75% of the earth's surface is occupied by water. Although the term 'water' is mostly relevant for liquid state, the occurrence of this substance in other states in nature is also considerable.

In very cold regions of world such as the Arctic circle and the Antarctica, water occurs in the form of snow or ice. High mountains also contain water in the form of ice due to very low temperatures prevailing there. Water exists as water vapour in the atmospheric air. Water vapour is present in a condensed form in clouds, fog, mist, etc. Liquid state is the most common state of water. Basically, water is available in two forms namely surface water and underground water.

Water is also present in combined form along with the molecules of some salts.

This water is called **water of crystallization** and those substances are known as **hydrated salts.** For example, $CuSO_4.5H_2O$

The substsances which do not possess this water of crystallisation are said to be **anhydrous salts.** Ex: Anhydrous copper sulphate is devoid of water of crystallisation.

Sources of Water

1. **Surface Water:** It is the water present on the surface of the earth. The water present in oceans, seas, rivers, springs, etc., comes under surface water.
   - **Oceans and Seas:** These are the largest sources of water. Almost 97% of water available on the earth is present in oceans and seas. This water contains huge amount of dissolved salts in addition to other impurities. Due to the presence of high proportion of dissolved salts (especially 2.5% common salt) which makes the water salty and renders the water unfit for usage and consumption, this called **saline water**.
   - **Desalination:** The process of removal of dissolved salts from the sea water is known as **desalination**. Desalination is carried out by reverse osmosis technique. In this method, sea water which contains dissolved salts is taken in the inner vessel and pure water is taken in the outer vessel. These two vessels are separated by a semi-permeable membrane. Pressure greater than osmotic pressure is applied on the sea water with the help of a piston, as a result of which pure water from the inner vessel passes into the outer vessel, leaving behind the dissolved salts. Hence, desalination of sea water takes place.
   - **Rivers and Lakes:** Rainwater from higher altitudes flows down the hills and forms rivers. Apart from this rainwater, water formed by melting of ice and snow flows into the rivers. Since water takes a long course and flows over land surface from higher altitudes, it contains various impurities and soluble salts. As the proportion of dissolved salts is less as compared to saline water, it is considered as fresh water and is available for consumption for various activities.
   - **Rainwater:** It is the main source of natural water. Since it directly comes from the atmosphere, it is the purest form of water. The initial showers of rainwater contain dust particles and other microorganisms. The later part of rainwater is devoid of any impurities. Therefore, it is considered as the purest form of natural water.
2. **Underground Water:** A part of the rainwater reaches the water bodies such as rivers and lakes. A part of the rainwater seeps into the soil and reaches the bottom layers. The rainwater as well as some water from river water seeps through the soil and fills the empty spaces and cracks in the deep layers of the earth. This phenomenon is called **infiltration** and the water is called **underground water**. As water infiltrates through the open spaces in the soil, it first passes through the zone of aeration where the soil is unsaturated. At greater depths, known as **recharge area**, water fills in more spaces until the zone of saturation is reached. At this level, the groundwater pressure is equal to the atmospheric pressure and this is known as **water table**. Below the water table, there is an underground layer of water bearing permeable rock or unconsolidated materials from which groundwater can be usefully extracted using a water well. This zone is called **aquifer**.

> **Info Bytes!**
>
> The underground water during seepage gets filtered through various layers of soil, and hence, it does not contain suspended impurities.

Water in the water tube or aquifer can be drawn out by using hand pumps or tube wells. This water is called **well water** and it contains soluble impurities. The depth of well varies from place to place.

Groundwater while travelling through a network of cracks and fissures emerges from below the surface of the earth. At this point, the aquifer surface meets the ground surface and water flows onto the surface of the earth with high pressure. This spring water is devoid of suspended impurities but contains dissolved salts and minerals. Due to the presence of rare minerals, it is used for medicinal purposes.

Uses of Water

Some of the main uses of water are listed below.

1. Essential constituent for the reaction of photosynthesis which is the process providing support for life as well as making food for plants and animals.
2. Medium for all biochemical processes taking place in plants and animals.
3. Medium for transport of nutrients and minerals to the living cells in living beings.
4. Exchange of gases through blood by the process of respiration.

5. Germination of seeds.
6. Growth of plants.
7. Regulation of body temperature.

Water Cycle

Water which is so essential in so many ways derives its major source from rains. Water is added to the atmosphere in the form of water vapour by various processes. The water vapour so added to the atmosphere, being lighter than air, reaches the upper atmosphere. There, due to lower temperature, it gets condensed to form tiny water droplets which remain suspended in air. These small water droplets associated with the dust particles form larger aggregates called **micelles**. They appear as clouds and when the quantity of water in the clouds increases, it causes rain. This rainwater can form various types of water bodies in the form of surface water and can help recharge Groundwater level. This natural process of adding water to atmospheric air and its subsequent condensation to rainwater is called **water cycle**. Thus, water cycle builds a natural balance in the ecosystem.

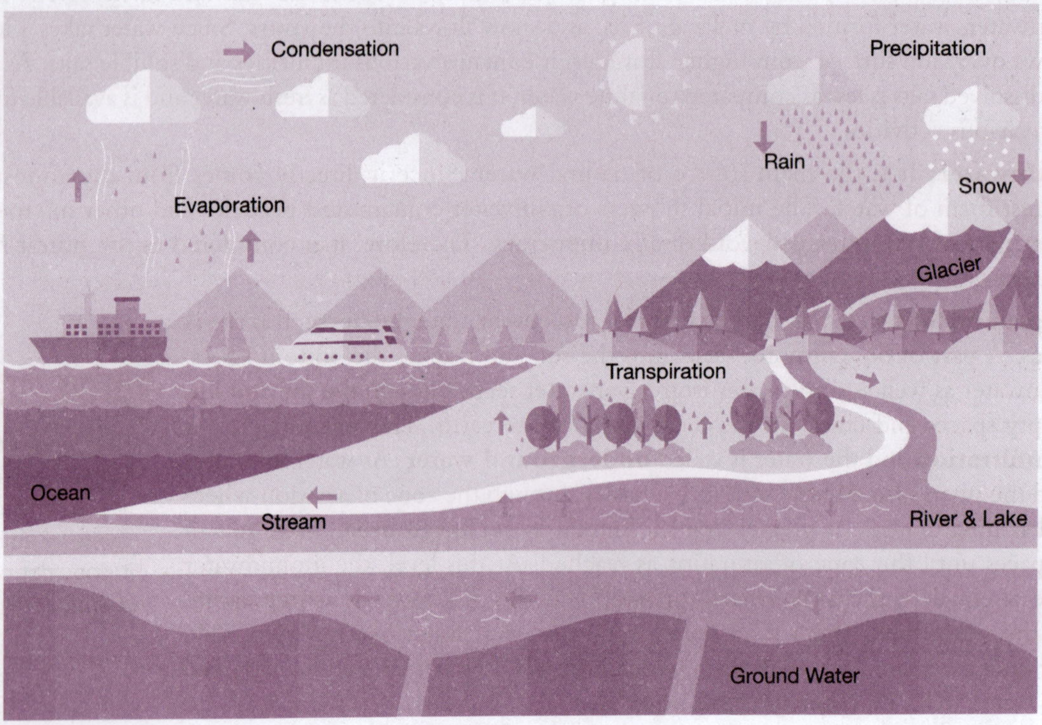

Figure 5.1 Water cycle

Water Scarcity

Scanty rainfall and drought conditions may lead to water scarcity. This in addition to reducing availability of water for human consumption, affects vegetation very badly. Water shortage results in wilting and drying up of plants and finally in the death of the vegetation. As rivers dry up in summer season, water is stored by constructing dams. This water is used for agricultural activities and also for the generation of hydel power.

Konnect

Jaisalmer, a city in the heart of India's Thar Desert, boasts of a lake called Gadsisar Lake. Constructed in the 14th century, it served as a vital reservoir in this arid region.

Depletion of Water Table

Sea water, which is the major proportion of water on the earth's surface, is saline and not suitable for consumption. Only river water and underground water making up to 0.01% are the sources of water. River water being limited and rivers drying up during the summer season, the dependence on underground water is inevitable.

The underground water is drawn out by using various devices such as hand pumps and tube wells. This water is again replenished by means of seepage of water into the ground during rainy season. When there is an imbalance between underground water and its replenishment, the level of water table may go down. This is called **depletion of water table**. This is more common in times of scanty rainfall.

Causes of Depletion

1. **Scanty Rainfall or Draught Conditions:** As long as there is a balance between the usage of underground water and its replenishment by rainfall, there is no question of depletion. But during long periods of scanty rainfall or in the absence of rainfall, this balance is disturbed. Usage of underground water continues more or less at the same level while its replenishment becomes very less or almost nil. This results in the depletion of water table.
2. **Deforestation:** Big trees in dense forests bind the soil particles through the roots. As a result, they help in reducing the water flow and help in the seepage of rainwater through the soil. Deforestation results in reduction of forest area which allows the rainwater flow rapidly into large water bodies. Seepage becomes less thereby leading to imbalance in the replenishment of underground water. Moreover, trees are one of the sources of water vapour which condenses to form clouds and results in rain.
3. **Increasing Population:** Increasing population forces increased demand for construction. This leads to depletion of water table by decreasing the area of seepage and increasing the demand for water.
4. **Increasing Industrialisation:** Every industry requires water for usage in various ways. Increase in number of industries leads to tremendous increase in usage of water which does not match the rate of replenishment. Thus, it also eventually leads to the depletion of water table.
5. **Increased Agricultural Activities:** Due to erratic rainfall, the canal irrigation becomes rather impractical in certain areas. As a result, agriculture mostly depends on groundwater for irrigation. The increased demand for agriculture results in the depletion of water table.

The above activities in the long run lead to tremendous depletion of groundwater level and eventually to acute shortage of water.

Water being the most precious and essential natural resource, and the percentage of available water being less, it should be used judiciously. Several steps should be taken in day-to-day life both by the citizens as well as authorities for preventing depletion of water table.

Water Management

In view of the lesser abundance of available fresh water and the various natural factors affecting water cycle, water is considered as an invaluable natural resource. Therefore, water management is an important area to be dealt with.

Water management as such involves two major aspects. One is prevention of wastage of water by providing water supply through pipes without leakage. At the individual level, minimising the wastage in daily activities is an important step. Another aspect is utilising the rainwater to recharge the groundwater. This is called **water harvesting** or **rainwater harvesting**. This can be done by installing water harvesting systems in the households.

Adoption of drip irrigation system in agriculture can also effectively help to minimise the usage of water in agricultural practices. In drip irrigation, water is supplied to the plants using narrow tubings which deliver water directly at the base of the plant. Irrigation by closed pipes instead of open canals can be of help in this direction since it reduces the loss of water by evaporation.

In regions with scanty rainfall, a substance called **cetyl alcohol** is sprayed on the water in reservoirs meant for storage of large quantities of water. This reduces rate of evaporation of water.

Growing some plants under plastic covers also minimises water loss as the water vapour condenses on the inner surface of plastic cover and is given back to soil.

Methods of Water Conservation

- Rainwater harvesting
- Recycling of wastewater
- Use of modern and efficient irrigation methods such as drip irrigation
- Creation of awareness in public for judicious use of water in daily life activities

Hard and Soft Water

Underground water is the main source of water used for various purposes. Since this water remains in the bottom layers of earth's crust for a long time, it contains many dissolved salts. Depending on the type of dissolved salts, water can be classified into two types:

1. **Soft Water:** Water which can freely form lather with soap is called **soft water**.
2. **Hard Water:** Water which does not form lather with soap and forms a precipitate or scum is called **hard water**.

Info Bytes!

Ever noticed scaling on your heaters or kettles? That's caused by hard water. The famed Indian River, the Ganges, particularly in its upper reaches, is known to be a naturally soft water source.

Causes of Hardness

If the sample of water contains calcium and magnesium bicarbonates, chlorides and sulphates, they do not allow the formation of much lather. Therefore, these salts cause hardness of water.

Disadvantages of Hardness

Due to the presence of various dissolved salts in water, hard water is not suitable for use for various purposes, some of which are listed below.

1. Not suitable for drinking.
2. Due to very poor lather formation, it is not effective for washing, cleaning and bathing purposes.
3. Scale formation in boilers results in loss of heat and wastage of fuels in industries.
4. Not effective for dyeing of fabrics due to improper fixing of dye to the fabric.

Types of Hardness

Among the various salts, presence of bicarbonates in water results due to the dissolution of CO_2 gas in rainwater. This water flows across a wide area with different types of rocks. Calcium carbonate and magnesium carbonate present in the rocks react with the water containing CO_2 thereby forming the corresponding bicarbonates. Bicarbonates being highly soluble in water impart hardness to water.

The hardness caused by these bicarbonate salts is called **temporary hardness**.

$$CaCO_3 + H_2O + CO_2 \rightarrow Ca(HCO_3)_2$$

$$MgCO_3 + H_2O + CO_2 \rightarrow Mg(HCO_3)_2$$

If water dissolves other minerals in it, such as chlorides and sulphates; they also cause hardness of water. However, these salts cannot be removed by boiling. Hence, the hardness imparted by these salts is called **permanent hardness**.

Removal of Temporary Hardness

1. **Boiling:** However, when water is subjected to boiling, these bicarbonates get converted into insoluble carbonates and can be removed by filtration. Since the hardness is removed by simple boiling, it is called temporary hardness and the water is called **temporary hard water**.

$$Ca(HCO_3)_2 \xrightarrow{\Delta} CaCO_3 + H_2O + CO_2$$

$$Mg(HCO_3)_2 \xrightarrow{\Delta} MgCO_3 + H_2O + CO_2$$

2. **Clark's Method:** This method involves the addition of slaked lime to water either in solid or liquid form. This also results in conversion of soluble bicarbonates into insoluble carbonates. On filtration, soft water is obtained.

$$Ca(HCO_3)_2 + Ca(OH)_2 \longrightarrow 2CaCO_3 \downarrow + 2H_2O$$

$$Mg(HCO_3)_2 + Ca(OH)_2 \longrightarrow CaCO_3 \downarrow MgCO_3 \downarrow + 2H_2O$$

Removal of Permanent Hardness

There are various methods adopted to remove permanent hardness.

1. **Addition of Washing Soda (Sodium Carbonate):** This method can remove both temporary as well as permanent hardness from water.

   Bicarbonate salts as well as sulphate and chloride salts undergo double decomposition reaction with sodium carbonate. In these reactions, the insoluble carbonates formed get precipitated and are removed by filtration.

$$Ca(HCO_3)_2 + Na_2CO_3 \rightarrow CaCO_3\downarrow + 2NaHCO_3$$

$$MgSO_4 + Na_2CO_3 \rightarrow MgCO_3\downarrow + Na_2SO_4$$

$$CaCl_2 + Na_2CO_3 \rightarrow CaCO_3\downarrow + 2NaCl$$

2. **Permutit Process:** Hydrated sodium aluminium silicate ($Na_2Al_2Si_2O_8.xH_2O$) is called **permutit**. The sample of hard water is allowed to pass through a cylindrical tube filled with permutit. As the water passes through permutit, the calcium and magnesium ions of hard water are replaced by sodium ions. Sodium ions do not cause any precipitation with soap and do not hinder the formation of lather. Thus, the water is said to be softened.

   After some time, the entire permutit contains Ca^{2+} and Mg^{2+} in place of Na^+ ions. This is called **exhausted permutit**. This can be regenerated by sending sodium chloride solution through exhausted permutit.

3. **Ion Exchange Method:** As the name indicates, this method involves exchange of hardness-causing ions by other ions. In this method, the apparatus consists of two cylindrical tubes A and B known as cation exchanger and anion exchanger, respectively.

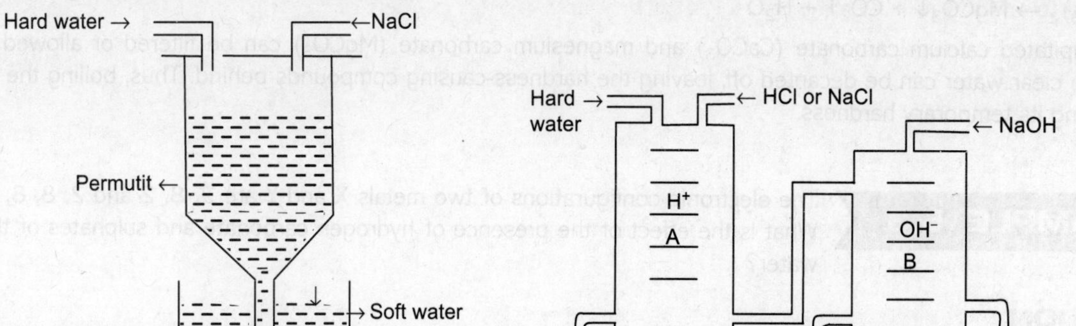

Figure 5.2 Permutit process (above) and Ion exchange process (below)

These ion exchangers contain porous solids which do not dissolve in water but swell in water. These solids are called **ion exchange resins**. They contain mobile groups or ions which can be exchanged with other ions. The resin-containing groups or ions capable of exchanging cations are called **cation exchange resins** and the resin-containing groups or ions capable of exchanging anions are called **anion exchange resins**. H-cation exchanger results in exchange of Ca^{2+} or Mg^{2+} ions by H^+ ions. **Na-cation exchanger** results in exchange of Ca^{2+} or Mg^{2+} ions by Na^+ ions. Hard water is first passed through tube A where all the positive ions are displaced by H^+ or Na^+

ions depending on the type of resin used. The water is then passed through tube B where all the negative ions are displaced by OH^- ions present in anion exchange resin. Thus, the water coming out of ion exchange apparatus now contains only pure water. This is also called **demineralised water.** When the cation exchanger and anion exchanger get depleted of H^+ and OH^- ions, the ion exchange resins are regenerated by passing HCl solution or NaCl solution as the case may be and NaOH solution through the tubes A and B, respectively.

$$MgCl_2 + 2H^+ - Resin \rightarrow Mg - Resin + 2HCl$$

$$RNH_3OH + Cl^- \rightarrow RNH_3Cl + OH^-$$

$$H^+ + OH^- \rightarrow H_2O$$

Once hardness is removed, the water can be used for various day-to-day activities, industries, etc. In addition to these naturally added components, i.e., dissolved salts, many other components are added to the water by human activities. These components are called **pollutants.**

EXAMPLE 5.1 Why does ice float on the water despite being solid?

SOLUTION

Most solids are denser than their liquid form, causing them to sink in their respective liquids. However, water behaves differently. When water freezes to form ice, its molecules arrange themselves in a hexagonal pattern that occupies more space and thus reduces its density. As a result, ice has a lower density than liquid water. This peculiar behaviour of water, where its solid form (ice) is less dense than its liquid form, causes ice to float on water. This unique property has important ecological implications, especially for aquatic life during cold conditions, as it ensures that water bodies don't freeze solid from the bottom up.

EXAMPLE 5.2 Boiling is an effective method to remove the temporary hardness of water. Explain.

SOLUTION

The temporary hardness of water is primarily caused by the presence of dissolved calcium and magnesium bicarbonates. When water is boiled, these bicarbonates decompose to produce insoluble carbonates, which precipitate out of the water.

The chemical reactions involved are:

$Ca(HCO_3)_2 \rightarrow CaCO_3\downarrow + CO_2\uparrow + H_2O$

$Mg(HCO_3)_2 \rightarrow MgCO_3\downarrow + CO_2\uparrow + H_2O$

The precipitated calcium carbonate ($CaCO_3$) and magnesium carbonate ($MgCO_3$) can be filtered or allowed to settle, after which the clear water can be decanted off, leaving the hardness-causing compounds behind. Thus, boiling the water can help in removing its temporary hardness.

EXAMPLE 5.3 The electronic configurations of two metals X and Y are 2, 8, 2 and 2, 8, 8, 2, respectively. What is the effect of the presence of hydrogen carbonate and sulphates of these metals on water?

SOLUTION

Elements X and Y are Mg and Ca, respectively. Hydrogen carbonates or bicarbonates of Ca and Mg impart temporary hardness while sulphates of Ca and Mg impart permanent hardness to water.

EXAMPLE 5.4 In permutit process, what is the role of the addition of the concentrated solution of the solid compound obtained due to the reaction between NaOH with HCl? Explain.

SOLUTION

In permutit process, sodium permutit that is $Na_2Al_2Si_2O_8.xH_2O$ is used. When hard water is treated with sodium permutit, Ca^{+2} and Mg^{+2} ions are exchanged with the Na^+ ions present in the permutit. After long use, most of the sodium ions present in permutit are replaced with calcium and magnesium ions, and hence, it becomes ineffective. Sodium hydroxide reacts with HCl to form NaCl. Concentrated NaCl solution is added to regenerate the permutit.

EXAMPLE 5.5 Jini took a container completely filled with water with some ice cubes floating on it. He observed the container, expecting that water to overflow after the ice melted. Can you predict what he would finally see?

SOLUTION

The water would not overflow after the melting of the ice cubes because the volume of water obtained from the ice cubes is equal to the volume of water displaced by the ice cubes. The container would be filled up to the brim.

EXAMPLE 5.6 Why is water called universal solvent?

SOLUTION

Water can dissolve most of the substances in it, and hence, it is known as universal solvent.

Water Pollution

Water of rivers and lakes are contaminated with unwanted and harmful substances. Polluted water changes the physical, chemical and biological characteristics which in turn affect the biosphere

Causes of and various methods to control water pollution are summarized in Table 5.2.

Table 5.2 Cause and control of water pollution

Causes of water pollution	Types of pollutants	Effects on environment	Measurement to control water pollution
Defecation by living beings (excreta of animals and humans)	Microorganisms (tapeworm, round worm, hookworm, Amoeba, etc.)	Water-borne diseases at times lead to epidemics	• Usage of pit latrines • Conversion of cow dung into biogas and the left over slurry can be used as manure
Industrial operation	Poisonous metallic salts (mercury, cadmium, chromium and arsenic)	Affects aquatic organisms	• Removal of metallic salts by chemical treatment of water before discharging it
Agricultural activities	Residual amount of artificial fertilisers, pesticides, insecticides and fungicides	Pollutes underground water	• Usage of natural manure in place of artificial fertilisers • Usage of natural pesticides • Avoiding spraying of chemicals in rainy season • Usage of drip irrigation
Thermal pollution (steel and thermal power plants) and **Atomic reactors**	Hot water	Favourable for growth of algae leading to decrease in dissolved O_2 which affects aquatic life	• Cooling and recycling of water in the industry • Cooling by cooling towers before discharging it into water bodies

Purification of Water

Many steps are taken by authorities to control water pollution. One such important programme is 'Ganga Action Plan.' This plan envisages the enforcement of laws to force the industries to set up water treatment plants. In spite of taking all the control measures, water from natural sources still contains some suspended impurities and microorganisms. Although it can be used safely for other activities, it cannot be used for the purpose of drinking or human consumption. Therefore, it is necessary to subject this water to purification.

The purification of water basically involves two steps:

1. Removal of suspended impurities
2. Removal of microorganisms

Removal of Suspended Impurities

(a) **Sedimentation:** River water is pumped into settling tanks and allowed to settle without any disturbance. The suspended impurities being larger particles settle down on standing.

(b) **Addition of Chemicals:** The above process makes water only semi-clear. This is passed into a mixing chamber where alum and lime are added to the water and it is agitated with huge mechanical blades. Later on, this water is pumped into a sedimentation tank. Alum hastens the process of precipitation of suspended impurities. During the precipitation process, some bacteria also get trapped and removed.

(c) **Filtration through Sand and Gravel:** The clear water obtained is pumped into a sand and gravel filter. This removes all remaining traces of suspended impurities.

Removal of Microorganisms

Addition of bleaching powder releases chlorine which helps in killing the harmful bacteria and the pure water obtained is stored in storage tanks.

The water so obtained at the end of the above purification process is devoid of suspended impurities and harmful bacteria. This water is fit for drinking and is called **potable water**. Potable water contains dissolved gases, such as O_2 and CO_2, and also some dissolved salts especially common salt. These salts play an important role in the metabolic activities. They also provide taste to water. Therefore, this water is very much suitable for human consumption.

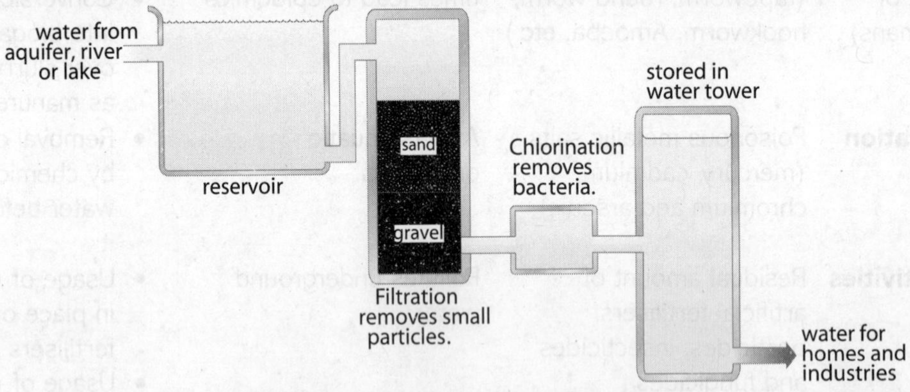

Figure 5.3 Purification of water process

Distilled Water

Since most of the chemical reactions take place in water, laboratory work requires pure water for carrying out various tests and reactions. For this purpose, the dissolved salts should be removed from water to get pure water. This is done by subjecting water for purification by the process of distillation.

Info Bytes!

Distilled water can taste 'flat' as it lacks the minerals and impurities that give regular water its taste.

Distillation Using Liebig Condenser

The water to be purified is taken in a distillation flask and subjected to boiling. The steam formed as a result of boiling when passed through Liebig condenser condenses due to cooling and gets collected in the receiver flask. The dissolved salts are left behind in the distillation flask.

Distillation Using Continuous Water-Still

The sample of water is warmed by condensing steam prior to subjecting the water for boiling in the still. The advantage of the process is that it requires usage of lesser amount of fuel for boiling the water in the still as it had already been heated by condensing steam.

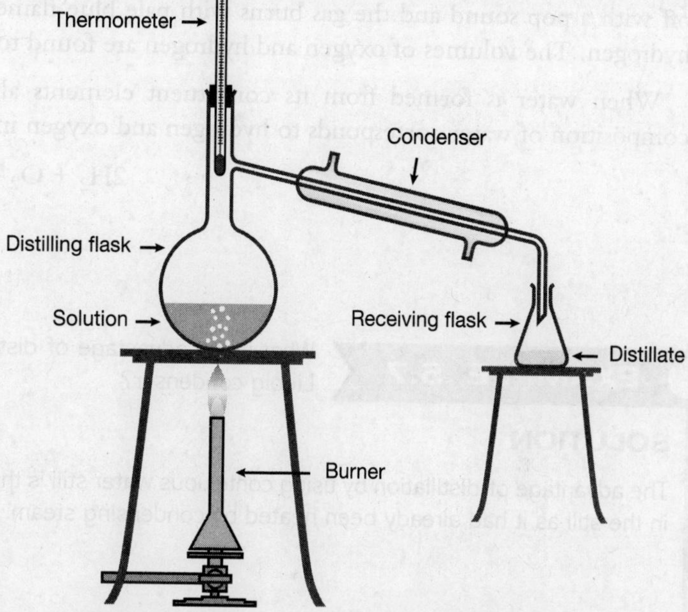

Figure 5.4 Distillation using Liebig Condenser

Uses of Distilled Water

1. It is used exclusively for chemical work in laboratories.
2. It has a bland and insipid taste and in fact considered as tasteless since the mineral salts and dissolved gases only impart taste and freshness to water.
3. It is not a substitute for potable water. Although it is a pure form of water, it does not contain the required mineral salts and dissolved gases. The nutrients from body fluids get dissolved in this water and are sent out, thus, leading to deficiency of vital nutrients.
4. The saline water from seas can be subjected to distillation and to the water so obtained, little amount of common salt is added for making it suitable for use as potable water.

Determination of Volumetric Composition of Water by the Process of Electrolysis

Decomposition is a chemical change and can be brought about by using various forms of energy like light, electricity, etc. The decomposition of a substance by passing electricity is called **electrolysis**.

Principle: Since pure water is a poor conductor of electricity, little amount of sulphuric acid is added to water. This acidulated water on passage of electricity decomposes to give hydrogen and oxygen in 2 : 1 volume ratio.

$$2H_2O \rightarrow 2H_2 + O_2$$

Process: The acidulated water is filled in two test tubes without any air bubbles. The two test tubes are inverted over two iron nails connected to positive and negative terminals of a battery. These iron nails act as electrodes. The iron nail connected to positive terminal of the battery is called **anode** and the one connected to negative terminal is called **cathode**.

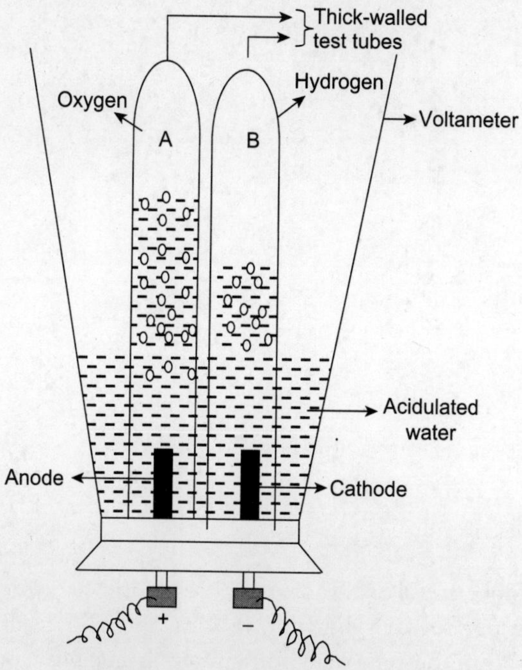

Figure 5.5 Electrolysis of water

On passing electricity for some time, two gases are collected in the two test tubes. Corresponding decrease in the volumes of solution in the test tubes indicates the volumes of gases formed. The gases in the respective test tubes can be identified by introducing a burning splinter. In test tube A the splinter burns brilliantly. In test tube B, the splinter is put off with a pop sound and the gas burns with pale blue flame. The former is identified as oxygen, whereas the latter as hydrogen. The volumes of oxygen and hydrogen are found to be in 1 : 2 ratio.

When water is formed from its constituent elements also, the combination reaction reveals that the volumetric composition of water corresponds to hydrogen and oxygen in 2 : 1 ratio.

$$2H_2 + O_2 \rightarrow 2H_2O$$

EXAMPLE 5.7

What is the advantage of distillation by using continuous water still over distillation by using Liebig condenser?

SOLUTION

The advantage of distillation by using continuous water still is that it requires usage of lesser amount of fuel for boiling the water in the still as it had already been heated by condensing steam.

EXAMPLE 5.8

Explain the continuous water-still method of distillation in brief.

SOLUTION

In a continuous water still, water is constantly fed into a boiling chamber and heated. As it boils, steam rises and moves to a condenser where it cools and returns to a liquid state, producing distilled water. The remaining impurities are left in the boiling chamber. This method allows for the continuous production of distilled water, making it efficient for large-scale needs.

POINTS TO REMEMBER

- ✔ Among the different sources of water, rain water is considered to be the purest.
- ✔ Although distilled water is a pure form of water, we use potable water for drinking.
- ✔ Specific heat of water, which is 1 cal g^{-1} $°C^{-1}$ is the highest for any known substance. The latent heat of fusion is 80 cal/g/°C and latent heat of vaporisation is 540 cal/g/°C.
- ✔ Water shows anomalous expansion. Density of water is maximum at 4°C which is equal to 1 g/cc.
- ✔ The boiling point is directly proportional to external pressure.
- ✔ Due to the presence of calcium and magnesium salts, water does not form lather and such water is called hard water.
- ✔ Hardness in water may be classified into temporary hardness and permanent hardness. Temporary hardness can be removed by boiling or Clark's method and permanent hardness is removed by permutit process or ion exchange method.
- ✔ Pollution of water is caused by defecation by living beings, industries, agricultural operations, thermal power plants, etc.
- ✔ Water pollution can be controlled by converting human excreta, cow dung, etc., into biogas, use of natural fertilisers, pesticides and by adopting drip irrigation technique.
- ✔ The volumetric composition of water is hydrogen and oxygen in the ratio of 2 : 1.

DW

PRACTICE QUESTIONS CLASSROOM WING

Very Short Answer Type Questions

Directions for questions from 1 to 5:
Fill in the blanks.

1. In the ion exchange process, the cation exchanger results in the exchange of ______ and ______ ions.

2. The activity that does not lead to an acute shortage of water in the long run is ______.

3. ______ hardness is removed by Clark's method.

4. ______ is added to prevent the evaporation of water.

5. Watering plants by using narrow tubes is called ______.

Directions for questions from 6 to 41:
For each of the questions, four choices have been provided. Select the correct alternative.

6. Which of the following chemicals lead to water pollution?
   (a) Fertilisers (b) Insecticides
   (c) Pesticides (d) All the above

7. Freezing point of water is 0°C at ______.
   (a) 76 cm of Hg
   (b) 760 cm of Hg
   (c) 76 mm of Hg
   (d) 7.6 mm of Hg

8. The salts of which among the pairs of metals cause greater water pollution?
   (a) Calcium, aluminium
   (b) Mercury, cadmium
   (c) Calcium, cadmium
   (d) Calcium, mercury

9. Identify the set of pure and impure water among the following.
   (a) rainwater and sea water
   (b) rainwater and distilled water
   (c) sea water and river water
   (d) river water and groundwater

10. Chemical treatment of surface water can be carried out by the addition of:
    (a) bleaching power (b) alum
    (c) oxygen (d) carbon dioxide

11. Density of water is less than 1g/c.c ______.
    (a) at 4°C (b) above 4°C
    (c) below 4°C (d) both (b) and (c)

12. Latent heat of vaporisation of water is ______.
    (a) 270 cal/g (b) 540 cal/g
    (c) 80 cal/g (d) 180 cal/g

13. Which of the following processes can be used to remove both temporary and permanent hardness?
    (a) Clark's method
    (b) Addition of washing soda
    (c) Boiling
    (d) All the above

14. Which of the following terms is not related to underground water?
    (a) Infiltration (b) Aquifer
    (c) Water table (d) Potable water

15. Which of the following types of water is suitable for drinking?
    (a) Soft water
    (b) Demineralised water
    (c) Potable water
    (d) Distilled water

16. When the water gets converted into ice, its volume:
    (a) decreases
    (b) increases
    (c) remains the same
    (d) initially decreases and then increases

17. Which of the following dissolved gases are present in drinking water?
    (a) Oxygen and nitric oxide
    (b) Oxygen and carbon monoxide
    (c) Oxygen and carbon dioxide
    (d) Oxygen and nitrogen

18. Which of the following salts is responsible for temporary and permanent hardness of water, respectively?
    (a) $Mg(HCO_3)_2$ and Na_2SO_4
    (b) $Ca(HCO_3)_2$ and $MgCl_2$
    (c) $MgSO_4$ and $Mg(HCO_3)_2$
    (d) $CaCl_2$ and $CaSO_4$

19. Arrange the following terms in sequence from source to supply.
(1) Chlorination (2) Sedimentation
(3) Filtration (4) Storage water tank
(5) Lakes
(a) 53142 (b) 13425
(c) 52314 (d) 23145

20. Arrange the terms in sequence of water cycle starting from water bodies.
(1) Precipitation (2) Condensation
(3) Water vapour (4) Infiltration
(5) Groundwater table
(a) 54231 (b) 32145
(c) 35412 (d) 52314

21. Which of the following chemical substances can be used for removing permanent hardness of water by precipitation reaction?
(a) Baking soda (b) Washing soda
(c) Alum (d) Quick lime

22. Wealthy but not healthy agriculture can be achieved by:
(a) introducing biogas plants
(b) using natural pesticides
(c) using drip irrigation
(d) using artificial fertilisers

23. Match the following:

Column A		Column B	
A.	Rainwater	(a)	Free of suspended impurities
B.	Rivers and lakes	(b)	Purest form of natural water
C.	Underground water	(c)	Water obtained after reverse osmosis
D.	Demineralised water	(d)	Water coming out of an ion exchange apparatus
		(e)	Fresh water for consumption for various activities

(a) A → e; B → b; C → a; D → d, e
(b) A → b; B → e; C → a; D → d
(c) A → b; B → a; C → d; D → e
(d) A → b; B → a, e; C → b; D → d

24. Arrange the steps in a sequence for the formation of rainfall.
(1) Formation of micelles
(2) Condensation
(3) Evaporation
(4) Formation of clouds
(5) Precipitation
(a) 3 5 4 2 1 (b) 3 2 4 1 5
(c) 3 2 1 4 5 (d) 1 2 3 5 4

25. A divalent metal salt X, which contributes to hardness of water, combines with washing soda and forms an insoluble salt Y and common salt. Salt Y is also used for the laboratory preparation of CO_2. Identify X and Y, respectively.
(a) $CaSO_4$, $CaCO_3$
(b) $MgSO_4$, $MgCO_3$
(c) $CaCl_2$, $CaCO_3$
(d) $MgCl_2$, $MgCO_3$

26. Which of the following processes is not involved in the purification of drinking water?
(a) Sedimentation (b) Filtration
(c) Chlorination (d) Distillation

27. Which of the following is a biodegradable substance?
(a) Detergent
(b) Pesticide
(c) Polythene
(d) Waste obtained from a biogas plant

28. Match the following:

Column A		Column B	
A.	Distilled water	(a)	Drinking purpose
B.	Potable water	(b)	Laboratory work
C.	Spring water	(c)	Dissolved salts and rare minerals
D.	Acidulated water	(d)	Medicinal purposes
		(e)	Electrolysis

(a) A → b; B → a; C → d, c; D → e
(b) A → c; B → b; C → c, e; D → d
(c) A → b; B → c; C → d; D → e
(d) A → a; B → c; C → d, e; D → b

29. The amount of heat energy required to increase the temperature of X g of water by 10°C is found to be 15 cal. Calculate X.
(a) 0.5 g (b) 15 g
(c) 1.5 g (d) 7.5

30. Arrange the steps in a sequence for the conversion of atmospheric water vapour into underground water.
(1) Infiltration in recharge area
(2) Water table
(3) Infiltration in zone of aeration

(4) Precipitation
(5) Aquifer
(a) 4 1 3 2 5 (b) 4 3 1 2 5
(c) 4 3 1 5 2 (d) 4 1 3 5 2

31. Arrange the steps in a sequence for the removal of microorganisms during the purification of drinking water.
(1) Lime feeder
(2) Mechanical mixing
(3) Alum feeder
(4) Sedimentation tank
(5) Passing through gravel and sand
(6) chlorine feeder
(a) 3 1 2 4 5 6 (b) 3 2 1 4 5 6
(c) 5 1 2 3 6 4 (d) 1 2 4 3 5 6

32. What is the latent heat of fusion and latent heat of vaporisation of 10 g of ice and water, respectively?
(a) 800 cal, 800 cal
(b) 540 cal, 540 cal
(c) 800 cal, 5400 cal
(d) 540 cal, 800 cal

33. Which of the following types of water does not contain dissolved gases such as oxygen and carbon dioxide?
(a) potable water (b) distilled water
(c) saline water (d) soft water

34. The volumetric composition of water is:
(a) 1 : 2 ratio of hydrogen and oxygen, respectively
(b) 1 : 8 ratio of hydrogen and oxygen, respectively
(c) 1 : 1 ratio of hydrogen and oxygen, respectively
(d) 2 : 1 ratio of hydrogen and oxygen, respectively

35. The solvent water is used in car radiators. Which of the following properties of water is exploited?
(a) High solubility
(b) Poor conductivity
(c) Maximum density
(d) High specific heat

36. **Assertion (A)**: The Clark's method involves removal of permanent hardness.
Reason (R): The Clark's method involves the addition of slaked lime which results in the removal of bicarbonates as insoluble carbonates.
(a) Both (A) and (R) are true and (R) is the correct reason for (A).
(b) Both (A) and (R) are true but (R) is not the correct reason for (A).
(c) (A) is true but (R) is false.
(d) (A) is false but (R) is true.

37. Which among the following is based on the principle that boiling point decreases with decrease in atmospheric pressure?
(a) Cooking food at sea level takes longer period of time.
(b) Cooking food at higher altitudes takes longer period of time.
(c) Working principle of air coolers.
(d) Working principle of a pressure cooker.

38. When the temperature of water rises from 0°C to 10°C, the density of water:
(a) decreases gradually
(b) decreases up to 4°C and then increases
(c) increases up to 4°C and then decreases
(d) increases gradually

39. Water-containing salt X, of a divalent metal, when treated with a compound Y gives much lather with soap. Further, an insoluble compound $MgCO_3$ and salt of a monovalent metal sulphate are formed. Identify X and Y, respectively.
(a) $CaCl_2$, Na_2CO_3
(b) $MgSO_4$, Na_2CO_3
(c) $MgCl_2$, $NaHCO_3$
(d) $CaSO_4$, $Mg(HCO_3)_2$

40. The volumetric composition of water is:
(a) 1 : 2 ratio of hydrogen and oxygen, respectively
(b) 1 : 8 ratio of hydrogen and oxygen, respectively
(c) 1 : 1 ratio of hydrogen and oxygen, respectively
(d) 2 : 1 ratio of hydrogen and oxygen, respectively

41. **Assertion (A)**: The products of electrolysis of water are hydrogen and oxygen.
Reason (R): In electrolysis process of water, hydrogen ions are attracted to anode and hydroxyl ions are attracted to cathode.
(a) Both (A) and (R) are true and (R) is the correct reason of (A).
(b) Both (A) and (R) are true but (R) is not the correct reason of (A).
(c) (A) is true but (R) is false.
(d) (A) is false but (R) is true.

Directions for questions from 42 to 44:
Match the entries given in Column A with the appropriate ones in Column B. More than one suitable content of Column B can also be considered correct for an entry in Column A and some content given in Column B may not be the appropriate one for any entry in Column A.

42. Match the statements of Column A with those of Column B.

Column A (Causes of Water Pollution)		Column B (Effect on Environment)
A. Atomic reactors	(a)	Water-borne diseases
B. Industrial processes	(b)	Underground water pollution
C. Thermal power plants	(c)	Destruction of aquatic organisms
D. Human and animal excretes	(d)	Decrease in content of dissolved O_2 in water
Agricultural activities	(e)	Affecting marine life

43.

Column A		Column B
A. Potable water	(a)	Electrolysis
B. Distilled water	(b)	Irrigation
C. Acidulated water	(c)	Pure water
D. River water	(d)	Laboratory purpose
	(e)	Human consumption

44.

Column A		Column B
A. Sedimentation	(a)	Baking powder
B. Filtration	(b)	Antacid
C. Chlorination	(c)	Soft drinks
D. Permutit	(d)	Purification of drinking water

Directions for questions from 45 to 64:
Answer the following questions.

45. Identify the form of water that is the least suitable for drinking purposes.

46. Which chemical, when added to water, removes both types of hardness?

47. Which practices in agriculture help or minimize the usage of water?

48. Name the most vital process where water takes part in the reaction in which one of the products is a supporter of life.

49. What is an aquifer?

50. Underground water does not contain suspended impurities. Why?

51. What is meant by rainwater harvesting?

52. Distinguish between hard water and soft water.

53. Compare the density of water at 4°C with that below and above 4°C.

54. What are the values of latent heat of fusion of ice and latent heat of vaporisation for water?

55. Why is spring water used for medicinal purpose?

56. Name the substance added to water stored in reservoirs in regions with scanty rainfall. Give reason.

57. What is permutit? Give its formula?

58. Why is ordinary water a good conductor of electricity?

59. How are springs formed?

60. What is desalination?

61. Define electrolysis.

62. What is depletion of water table?

63. Distinguish between temporary hardness and permanent hardness.

64. Why is rainwater considered the purest form of natural water?

Short Answer Type Questions

65. A base consisting of a divalent metal cation and monovalent anion, formed by the dissolution of the oxide of a divalent metal in water, is used in the removal of temporary hardness of water. Identify the base.

66. The different forms of water are given here. Arrange them in the order of their characteristics given below.

Demineralized water, rainwater, potable water, saline water and aquifer.

(A) Water fit for drinking purposes.

(B) Underground water that can be made accessible using a well.

(C) Water containing dissolved salts unfit for usage.

(D) Water devoid of all types of mineral ions.

(E) Purest form of natural water coming directly from the atmosphere.

67. The different steps involved in the process of purification of water are as follows. Arrange them in the regular order of the process of purification.

(A) Filtration through sand and gravel.

(B) Sedimentation for removing suspended impurities.

(C) Addition of alum and lime.

(D) Addition of bleaching power which releases chlorine that helps in killing bacteria.

(E) Mechanical mixing.

68. How are bicarbonates added to water? How can they be removed by boiling? Give equations.

69. Explain the removal of temporary hardness of water by Clark's method. Give equations.

70. (A) Give the characteristics of potable water.

(B) What produces more severe burns, boiling water or steam? Why?

71. Explain the role of alum in the purification of water.

72. Describe the various stages of purification of drinking water

73. Draw a neat labelled diagram for the electrolysis of water.

74. Explain the process by which both removal of temporary hardness and permanent hardness is possible.

75. Write a short note on water management.

76. Draw a neat line sketch of water cycle.

77. What is meant by depletion of water table? Explain in detail.

78. How can you harvest water in household?

79. Draw a line sketch of distribution of water on earth's surface.

80. List important uses of water.

81. Discuss five important physical properties of water.

82. Describe various sources of water.

83. (A) Is hard water preferred for washing clothes? Justify.

(B) Between Zeolite and ion exchange methods, which water softening method gives demineralized water? Why?

Essay Answer Type Questions

84. Explain the electrolysis of water to determine the volumetric composition of water with a diagram.

85. Give reasons for the following:

(a) Sea water is unfit for usage and consumption.

(b) River water is considered as fresh water.

(c) Underground water does not contain suspended impurities.

(d) Distilled water is used for laboratory processes.

86. Explain water cycle and its role in raising the groundwater table.

87. What are the disadvantages of hard water? Explain the various methods of removal of permanent hardness of water with diagrams.

88. Discuss the various steps involved in making potable water.

89. (A) Mention the causes for water pollution.

(B) Mention different types of pollutants.

(C) Mention the control measures for water pollution.

90. (A) Explain the different causes of depletion of water table.

(B) What steps should be taken in day-to-day life to prevent depletion of water table?

91. Mention suitable terms for the following statements:

(a) Decrease in density of water on decreasing temperature from 4°C to 0°C which is opposite to the normal trend.

(b) The underground layer of water bearing permeable rock present below the water table

(c) The natural process of adding water to atmospheric air and its subsequent condensation to rainwater.

(d) Type of chemical reaction carried out when electricity is passed through water.

PRACTICE QUESTIONS COMPETITION WING

Level 1: Apply your Concepts

Directions for questions from 1 to 15:
State whether the following statements are true or false.

1. Respiration does not involve the use of water as an important medium.
2. Drinking water mainly contains small amounts of salts of sodium, magnesium and calcium metals.
3. Carbon dioxide on dissolution in water forms carbon monoxide.
4. 1 g of water at 100°C on heating forms 1g of steam at the same temperature by absorbing 640 cal of energy.
5. 1g of pure water at 4°C occupies a volume of 1 cm^3
6. Underground water is free from suspended impurities.
7. Saline water contains large amounts of dissolved salts.
8. 1 g of pure water at 4°C occupies a volume of 0.97 cc.
9. Water containing calcium bicarbonate produces scum with soap.
10. Hard water is fit for dyeing clothes.
11. Cation exchange resin is regenerated by passing HCl solution.
12. Salt is added to pure water to increase its electrical conductivity.
13. Two volumes of hydrogen and one volume of oxygen compose one volume of water.
14. Permanent hardness is removed by Clark's method.
15. Specific heat of water is 1 cal/g/°C.

Directions for questions from 16 to 25:
Fill in the blanks.

16. _________ is sprayed in water reservoirs to reduce the rate of evapo-ration of water in regions of scanty rainfall.
17. Hydrated sodium aluminium silicate is called ______.
18. The exhausted permutit contains _______ and ______ ions in place of Na^+ ions.
19. In sedimentation process, alum ______ the process of precipitation of suspended impurities.
20. Addition of ______ releases ______ which helps in killing the harmful bacteria present in water.
21. Addition of acid to water, ______ the conductivity.
22. In electrolysis of water ______ gas is liberated at cathode.
23. The change of water into water vapour at 30°C at slow rate is called ______.
24. Small water droplets associated with dust particles to form larger aggregates called ______
25. Percentage of water in animals varies from ______ to ______.

Directions for questions from 26 to 60:
For each of the questions, four choices have been provided. Select the correct alternative.

26. **Assertion (A)**: Water is called a universal solvent.

    Reason (R): Pure water is a good conductor of electricity

    (a) Both (A) and (R) are true and (R) is the correct explanation of (A).
    (b) Both (A) and (R) are true, but (R) is not the correct explanation of (A).
    (c) (A) is true and (R) is false.
    (d) (A) is false and (R) is true.

27. **Assertion (A)**: Water has a high specific heat capacity.

    Reason (R): The density of water increases with an increase in temperature up to 4°C.

    (a) Both (A) and (R) are true and (R) is the correct explanation of (A).
    (b) Both (A) and (R) are true, But (R) is not the correct explanation of (A).
    (c) (A) is true and (R) is false.
    (d) (A) is false and (R) is true.

28. Density of water is maximum:

    (a) at 0°C (b) at 4°C
    (c) above 4°C (d) below 4°C

29. Which of the following substances used in agriculture does not cause water pollution to a large extent?
(a) Manures (b) Pesticides
(c) Fertilisers (d) Insecticides

30. Metals present in permutit are:
(a) Na and K (b) Na and Al
(c) Al and K (d) K and Al

31. Which among the following liquids has the highest specific heat?
(a) Petrol (b) Mercury
(c) Oil (d) Water

32. Which among the following types of water is a poor conductor of electricity?
(a) Saline water (b) Tap water
(c) River water (d) Distilled water

33. Which of the following is not the control measure of water pollution?
(a) Usage of natural manure
(b) Usage of drip irrigation
(c) Usage of fertilisers
(d) Usage of natural pesticides

34. The pair of ions which does not cause hardness of water is:
(a) sulphate, chloride
(b) bicarbonate, chloride
(c) bicarbonate, sulphate
(d) nitrate, phosphate

35. Regeneration of anion exchange resin is carried out by passing:
(a) sodium hydroxide solution
(b) sodium chloride solution
(c) sodium bicarbonate solution
(d) All the above

36. Spring water usually contains:
(a) Dissolved salts
(b) Minerals
(c) Suspended impurities
(d) Both (a) and (b)

37. Which of the following forms of water does not contain dissolved gases such as oxygen and carbon dioxide?
(a) Potable water (b) Distilled water
(c) Saline water (d) Soft water

38. Which of the following chemical substances can be used for removing permanent hardness of water by precipitation reaction?
(a) Baking soda (b) Washing soda
(c) Alum (d) Quick lime

39. When the temperature of water rises from 0°C to 10°C, the density of water:
(a) decreases gradually
(b) decreases up to 4°C and then increases
(c) increases up to 4°C and then decreases
(d) increases gradually

40. **Assertion (A)**: The removal of permanent hardness of water can be done by Clark's method.

Reason (R): In the Clark's method, slaked lime is added which results in the removal of bicarbonates as insoluble carbonates.

(a) Both (A) and (R) are true and (R) is the correct reason for (A).
(b) Both (A) and (R) are true but (R) is not the correct reason for (A).
(c) (A) is true but (R) is false.
(d) (A) is false but (R) is true.

41. Arrange the process in sequence for the purification of drinking water.
(1) Lime feeder, alum feeder
(2) Filtration
(3) Mechanical mixing
(4) Chlorination
(a) 1324 (b) 1243
(c) 2345 (d) 2341

42. Arrange statements in sequence of increasing order of heat content.
(1) Ice of 10 g mass at 10°C
(2) Water of 10 g mass at 10°C
(3) Ice of 10 g mass at 40°C
(4) Water of 10 g mass at 40°C
(5) Steam of 10 g mass at 10°C
(a) 13245 (b) 54312
(c) 12534 (d) 12543

43. What is the latent heat of fusion and latent heat of vaporisation of 10 g of ice and water, respectively?
(a) 800 cal and 800 cal
(b) 540 cal and 540 cal
(c) 800 cal and 5400 cal
(d) 540 cal and 800 cal

44. Which of the following properties of iceberg led to the sinking of the Titanic ship?
(a) Heavy water currents
(b) Relatively higher density of ice

(c) 9/10 of iceberg submerged below sea water and 1/10 above the sea water

(d) None of the above

45. Which of the following processes is not involved in making surface water potable?

(a) Sedimentation (b) Chlorination
(c) Filtration (d) Distillation

46. The solvent water is used in car radiators. Which of the following properties of water is exploited?

(a) High solubility
(b) Poor conductivity
(c) Maximum density
(d) High specific heat

47. A divalent metal salt X, which contributes to hardness of water, combines with washing soda and forms an insoluble salt Y and common salt. Salt Y is also used for the laboratory preparation of CO_2. Identify X and Y, respectively.

(a) $CaSO_4$, $CaCO_3$
(b) $MgSO_4$, $MgCO_3$
(c) $CaCl_2$, $CaCO_3$
(d) $MgCl_2$, $MgCO_3$

48. The amount of heat energy required to increase the temperature of 20 g of water by 1°C is ______.

(a) 10 cal (b) 20 cal
(c) 15 cal (d) 2 cal

49. On passing electricity through acidulated water, the gaseous products obtained are collected in two separate test tubes A and B. The volume of the gas collected in test tube A is double the volume of gas collected in test tube B. Identify the two gases in test tubes A and B.

(a) Hydrogen and oxygen
(b) Oxygen and hydrogen
(c) Hydrogen peroxide and oxygen
(d) Oxygen and water vapour

50. Which of the following types of water is a bad conductor of electricity?

(a) Distilled water
(b) Water obtained in ion-exchange process
(c) Mineral water
(d) Both (a) and (b)

51. The pressure cooker reduces the cooking time because of:

(a) increase in the boiling point of water
(b) high specific heat of water
(c) decrease in the boiling point of water
(d) high latent heat of vaporisation

52. Wealthy but not healthy agriculture can be achieved by:

(a) introducing biogas plants
(b) using natural pesticides
(c) using drip irrigation
(d) introducing artificial fertilisers

53. Two persons A and B got burns, one with boiling water at 100°C and other due to steam at 100°C, respectively. Which person is affected more?

(a) A
(b) B
(c) Both A and B to the same extent
(d) none of the above

54. Aquatic animals are able to survive in water bodies like rivers and oceans during winter when the atmospheric temperature is –10°C. This is because:

(a) density of ice is less than water
(b) density of water is minimum at 4°C
(c) ice is a poor conductor of heat
(d) both (a) and (c)

55. Which of the following elements is used for the purification of surface water to make it free from germs so that it can be used for drinking purpose?

(a) Oxygen
(b) Fluorine
(c) Chlorine
(d) Carbon

56. Which of the following is the application of the highest specific heat capacity of water?

(a) Cooling of soft drink bottles in ice
(b) Cooling of earth's atmosphere after a hail storm
(c) Cool breeze from air coolers
(d) Bursting of water pipes during winter in cold countries

57. Water-containing salt X of a divalent metal, when treated with a compound Y gives much lather with soap. Insoluble compound $MgCO_3$ and salt of a monovalent metal sulphate are formed. Identify X and Y, respectively.

(a) $CaCl_2$, Na_2CO_3
(b) $MgSO_4$, Na_2CO_3
(c) MgCl $NaHCO_3$
(d) $CaSO_4$, $Mg(HCO_3)_2$

58. The amount of heat energy required to increase the temperature of X g of water by 10°C is found to be 15 cal. Calculate X.
(a) 0.5 g (b) 15 g
(c) 1.5 g (d) 7.5 g

59. The water obtained in ion-exchange process is:
(a) devoid of dissolved salts and minerals
(b) devoid of only minerals
(c) potable
(d) called mineral water

60. Which among the following is based on the principle that boiling point decreases with decrease in atmosphere pressure?
(a) Cooking food at sea level takes longer period of time.
(b) Cooking food at higher altitudes takes longer period of time.
(c) Working principle of air coolers.
(d) Working principle of pressure cooker.

Directions for questions from 61 to 63:
Match the entries given in Column A with the appropriate ones in Column B. More than one suitable content of Column B can also be considered correct for an entry in Column A and some content given in Column B may not be the appropriate one for any entry in Column A.

61.

	Column A		Column B
A.	Defecation by living beings	(a)	Arsenic, mercury, etc.
B.	Industrial operation	(b)	Insecticides, fungicides, etc.
C.	Thermal pollution	(c)	*Amoeba*, fungicides, etc.
D.	Agricultural activities	(d)	Favourable for growth of algae

62.

	Column A		Column B
A.	Removal of hardness by boiling	(a)	Resins
B.	Clark's method	(b)	Can remove temporary and permanent hardness
C.	Addition of washing soda	(c)	Decomposition reaction
D.	Ion exchange method	(d)	Addition of slaked lime

63.

	Column A		Column B
A.	Specific heat of water	(a)	250 cal/g°C
B.	Latent heat of fusion of ice	(b)	0°C
C.	Latent heat of vaporisation of water	(c)	100°C
D.	Temperature at which melting of ice starts under normal atmospheric pressure	(d)	1 cal/g°C
E.	Temperature at which boiling of water starts under normal atmospheric pressure	(e)	80 cal/g°C
		(f)	540 cal/g°C

Level 2: Review Your Concepts

64. A small amount of sulphuric acid is added in the process of electrolytic decomposition of water. Two gases, the one liberated at the negative electrode put off the burning splinter and burns with blue flame and another gas at the positive electrode, glows the burning splinter and is a non-combustible gas. Write the gases liberated at negative and positive electrode.

65. Passing the hard water sample through a chemical exchange the ions with the ion of the same charge. Identify the chemical, the ion that re-places and the type of hardness being removed.

66. Why is sea water not suitable for drinking? How is it made potable?

67. Hot water bags are generally used for reducing body pain. Can they also be used to keep us warm in winter? Explain.

68. Usually, solid objects are denser than liquids but, ice floats on water. Why?

69. Calculate the amount of heat energy required to increase the temperature of 10 g of water through 12°C.

70. During summer vacations, Aryan went for a trip to Tirupathi in an old car along with his family. During the journey, the driver stopped the car beside a hotel and brought a can full of water and poured it into the radiator of the car. Aryan's son, Mouryan wanted to know the reason for pouring water into the radiator and asked his father who is a mechanical engineer by profession the reason. Aryan explained the role of water in the radiator of the car engine. Can you predict the explanation given by Aryan?

71. Calculate the ratio of the amount of heat energy lost during the conversion of 20 g of water at 0°C to ice at 0°C to heat energy gained during the conversion of same amount of water at 100°C to steam at 100°C.

72. (A) Two open containers A and B are filled with water and in container A, cetyl alcohol is added. Both the containers are placed at 40°C. Predict the level of water in the two containers after some time and give reasons.

(B) A liquid has a specific heat of 0.9 J/g/°C. 100g of this liquid is subjected to heating at 40°C. By supplying 4200 J of heat, to what temperature can the liquid be heated?

73. The electronic configurations of two metals X and Y are 2, 8, 2 and 2, 8, 8, 2, respectively. What is the effect of the presence of hydrogen carbonate and sulphates of these metals in water?

74. A group of students went for an excursion to Shimla in the month of November. A science teacher also accompanied them. There the temperature fell to −10°C. They took some ice cubes and subjected them to heating while keeping a thermometer in the container. The students monitored the readings of thermometer till the entire ice melted into water. All of them went to their science teacher and showed him their observations. He asked them to discuss among themselves and give a proper justification for the observations on the readings at various stages.

75. An element with electronic configuration 2, 8, 1 forms a compound with carbonate. How does this compound remove both temporary and permanent hardness of water?

76. In permutit process, what is the role of the addition of the concentrated solution of the solid compound obtained due to the reaction between NaOH with HCl? Explain.

77. Master Vishnu and his sister Jishnu went to their uncle's village to spend their summer vacation. One day, Jishnu was pestering her uncle for a soft drink. Vishnu's uncle took both of them to a shop where soft drink bottles were kept in an insulated box containing ice. Vishnu's uncle who is a physical science teacher, with an intention of testing Vishnu, posed a question to him regarding the concept involved in cooling of soft drinks by keeping them in ice. Vishnu who is a student of TIME, IITF impressed his uncle by explaining the above phenomenon with respect to the concept of latent heat of fusion of ice. Can you also explain the concept like Vishnu?

Level 3: Assess Your Concepts

78. Why is ion exchange process preferred over permutit process for the purification of water?

79. In cold countries, water pipes burst in winter. Explain.

80. Generally when a person jumps into water in any water body, he is expected to sink. But he tends to float in the Dead Sea. How do you account for this?

81. During the conversion of surface water to potable water, chlorination is an important step. Give reasons.

82. Thermal pollution of water leads to the death of biotic life. Explain.

83. (A) Is pure water fit for dinking? Justify

(B) Mention any three purposes for which it is suitable?

AT

ANSWER KEYS

Crossword

Across

4. Specific heat
6. Water scarcity
7. Desalination
10. Washing soda
12. Permanent hardness
13. Water
14. Rain water
15. Temporary hardness

Down

1. Cathode
2. Depletion of water table
3. Reverse Osmosis
5. Permutit
8. Slaked lime
9. Soft water
11. Hard water

Classroom Wing

Very Short Answer Type Questions

1. Ca^{+2} and Mg^{+2}
2. large human consumption
3. Temporary
4. Cetyl alcohol
5. drip irrigation
6. (d)
7. (a)
8. (b)
9. (a)
10. (a)
11. (d)
12. (b)
13. (b)
14. (d)
15. (c)
16. (b)
17. (c)
18. (b)
19. (c)
20. (b)
21. (b)
22. (d)
23. (b)
24. (c)
25. (c)
26. (d)
27. (d)
28. (a)
29. (c)
30. (b)
31. (a)
32. (c)
33. (b)
34. (d)
35. (d)
36. (d)
37. (b)
38. (c)
39. (b)
40. (d)
41. (c)
42. (i)-(E), (ii)-(C), (iii)-(D), (iv)-(B), (v)-(A)
43. A → e, B → d, c, C → a, D → b
44. A → b, B → c, C → d, D → a

Competition Wing

Level 1: Apply your Concepts

1. True
2. True
3. False
4. False
5. True
6. True
7. True
8. False
9. True
10. False
11. True
12. True
13. False
14. False
15. True
16. Acetyl alcohol
17. permutit
18. Ca^{+2}, Mg^{+2}
19. hastens
20. bleaching powder, chlorine
21. increases
22. hydrogen
23. evaporation
24. micelles
25. 70 per cent, 90 per cent
26. (c)
27. (b)
28. (b)
29. (a)
30. (b)
31. (d)
32. (d)
33. (c)
34. (d)
35. (a)
36. (d)
37. (b)
38. (b)
39. (c)
40. (d)
41. (a)
42. (a)
43. (c)
44. (c)
45. (d)
46. (d)
47. (c)
48. (b)
49. (a)
50. (d)
51. (a)
52. (d)
53. (b)
54. (d)
55. (c)
56. (c)
57. (b)
58. (c)
59. (a)
60. (b)
61. A → c, B → a, C → d, D → b
62. A → c, B → d, C → b, D → a
63. A → d, B → e, C → f, D → b, E → c

Hints and Explanations

CLASSROOM WING

Very Short Answer Type Questions

1. In the ion exchange process, the cation exchanger results in the ex-change of Ca^{+2} and Mg^{+2} ions.
2. The activity that does not lead to an acute shortage of water in the long run is large human consumption.
3. Temporary

   Temporary hardness is removed by Clark's method.
4. Cetyl alcohol

   Cetyl alcohol is added to prevent the evaporation of water.
5. drip irrigation

   Watering plants by using narrow tubes is called drip irrigation.
6. Fertilizers, insecticides and pesticides consist of chemicals added during agricultural activities. When these are let into water bodies, they harm the aquatic life and if this water is used for drinking purpose it affects human system.

   Hence, the correct option is (d)
7. Freezing point of water is 0°C at 76 cm of Hg

   Hence, the correct option is (a)
8. Salts of mercury and cadmium cause greater water pollution.

   Hence, the correct option is (b)
9. Rain water and sea water are pure and impure water, respectively.

   Hence, the correct option is (a)
10. Chemical treatment of surface water can be carried out by the addition of bleaching powder.

    Hence, the correct option is (a)
11. Density of water is less than 1 g/cc above and below 4°C.

    Hence, the correct option is (d)
12. Latent heat of vaporization of water is 540 cal/g.

    Hence, the correct option is (b)
13. Addition of washing soda can remove both temporary as well as permanent hardness of water.

    Hence, the correct option is (b)
14. The term potable water is not related to underground water.

    Hence, the correct option is (d)
15. Potable water is suitable for drinking purpose.

    Hence, the correct option is (c)
16. When the water gets converted to ice, its volume increases as mass of substance remains same. As a result, density of ice is less than that of water.

    Hence, the correct option is (b)
17. Oxygen and carbon dioxide are the two dissolved gases present in drinking water as they impart freshness to water.

    Hence, the correct option is (c)
18. Bicarbonates of calcium and magnesium; chlorides and sulphates of calcium and magnesium are responsible for temporary and permanent hardness, respectively.

    Hence, the correct option is (b)
19. (i) Lakes

    (ii) sedimentation

    (iii) filtration

    (iv) chlorination

    (v) storage water tank

    Hence, the correct option is (c)
20. (i) water vapour

    (ii) condensation

    (iii) precipitation

    (iv) infiltration

    (v) Ground water table

    Hence, the correct option is (b)
21. Washing soda can be used for removing permanent hardness by precipitation reaction.

    Hence, the correct option is (b)
22. By introducing artificial fertilisers, crop yield is improved but at the same time it contributes to water pollution.

    Hence, the correct option is (d)
23. A $\rightarrow$ b Rainwater is the purest form of natural water.

B → e River and lake water are considered as fresh water, and hence, available for consumption for various activities.

C → a Underground water during seepage gets filtered through various layers of soil, and hence, it does not contain suspended impurities.

D → d The water coming out of an ion-exchange apparatus contains only pure water and is called dematerialised water.

Hence, the correct option is (b)

24. (i) Evaporation

(ii) Condensation

(iii) Formation of micelles

(iv) Formation of clouds

(v) Precipitation

Hence, the correct option is (c)

25. Divalent metal salt X which contributes to hardness of water is $CaCl_2$ which combines with Na_2CO_3. It gives salt Y, calcium carbonate and sodium chloride.

$CaCl_2 + Na_2CO_3 — CaCO_3 + 2NaCl$

Hence, the correct option is (c)

26. Distillation process is not involved in the purification of drinking water.

Hence, the correct option is (d)

27. The waste obtained from biogas plant can be used as manure as it is an organic matter.

Hence, the correct option is (d)

28. A → b Distilled water is used in a laboratory for chemical reactions taking place in water.

B → a Potable water is used for drinking purpose.

C → d, c Spring water is devoid of suspended impurities but contains dissolved salts and minerals.

Due to the presence of rare minerals, it is used for medicinal purposes.

D → e Pure water is a bad conductor of electricity, little amount of sulphuric acid is added to make acidulated water.

Hence, the correct option is (a)

29. The specific heat of water is 1 cal/g/°C.

∴ Heat required for increasing 10°C temperature of X g water is 10 X cal.

∴ 10X = 15

∴ X = 1.5 g

Hence, the correct option is (c)

30. (i) Precipitation

(ii) infiltration in zone of aeration

(iii) infiltration in recharge area

(iv) water table

(v) aquifer

Hence, the correct option is (b)

31. (i) alum feeder

(ii) lime feeder

(iii) mechanical mixing

(iv) sedimentation tank

(v) passing through gravel and sand

(vi) chlorine feeder

Hence, the correct option is (a)

32. Latent heat of fusion of 10 g of ice is 10 × 80 = 800 cal

Latent heat of vaporisation of 10 g of water is 10 × 540 = 5400 cal.

Hence, the correct option is (c)

33. Potable water, soft or sea water contain dissolved gases such as oxygen and carbon dioxide but distilled water does not contain O_2 and CO_2 because during distillation these dissolved gases are distilled off.

Hence, the correct option is (b)

34. The volumetric composition of water is 2 : 1 of hydrogen and oxygen.

Hence, the correct option is (d)

35. Water has high specific heat, which means that water needs a large amount of heat to become hot.

Hence, the correct option is (d)

36. Clark's method is used to remove temporary hardness. In this process slaked lime is added, which results in conversion of soluble bicarbonates into insoluble carbonates. On filtration, soft water is obtained.

Hence, the correct option is (d)

37. As we move to higher altitudes, pressure decreases, and hence, boiling point decreases. Water boils at low temperatures on the hills, and thus, the cooking of food takes longer time.

Hence, the correct option is (b)

38. Density of water is maximum at 4°C due to anomalous expansion of water. Hence, when the temperature of water is raised from 0°C to 10°C, the density increases up to 4°C, then decreases gradually.

Hence, the correct option is (c)

39. Divalent metal salt X, i.e., $MgSO_4$ is treated with compound Y, i.e., Na_2CO_3 to form $MgCO_3$ and Na_2SO_4.

$MgSO_4 + Na_2CO_3 \rightarrow MgCO_3 + Na_2SO_4$

Hence, the correct option is (b)

40. The volumetric composition of water is 2 : 1 of hydrogen and oxygen.

Hence, the correct option is (d)

41. During the electrolysis of water the electrolytes in water dissociates as H^+ and OH^- ions which move to cathode and anode, respectively. Oxygen and hydrogen are produced.

Hence, the correct option is (c)

42. (i) Atomic reactors → (E) Effect on marine life

(ii) Industrial processes → (C) Destruction of aquatic organism

(iii) Thermal power plants → (D) Decrease in content of dissolved O2 in water

(iv) Human and animal excretes → (B) Underground water pollution

(v) Agricultural activities → (A) Water-borne diseases

∴ (i) → (E); (ii) → (C); (iii) → (D); (iv) → (A); (v) → (B)

43. A – e Potable water is fit for human consumption.

B – d, c Distilled water is pure water which is used for laboratory purpose.

C – a Acidulated water is used as an electrolyte in electrolysis process.

D – b River water is used for irrigation purposes.

44. A – b Addition of alum hastens the rate of sedimentation.

B – c Filtration is the process by which suspended impurities can be removed.

C – d Chlorination is the process used for disinfecting drinking water.

D – a Permutit process is used to soften the hard water.

45. Demineralized (distilled) water is not fit for drinking purposes whereas the other forms are suitable.

46. Addition of washing soda helps to remove both types of hardness whereas other chemicals help to remove only one type of hardness.

47. Drip irrigation is an agricultural practice that helps minimise the usage of water.

48. Photosynthesis is the most vital process in which water takes part in the reaction.

49. Below the water table, there is an underground layer of water bearing permeable rock or unconsolidated materials from which ground water can be usefully extracted using a water well. This is called aquifer.

50. The underground water, during seepage gets filtered through the layers of soil and hence, does not contain suspended impurities.

51. Utilizing the rain water to recharge the ground water is called water harvesting or rain water harvesting.

52. Water which can freely form lather with soap is called soft water and water which does not form lather with soap and forms precipitate is called hard water.

53.

Temperature	Density
0°C (below 4°C)	< 1g/cc
4°C	1 g/cc
>4°C	<1 g/cc

54. The value of latent heat of fusion of ice and latent heat of vaporization of water are 80 cal/g and 540 cal/g, respectively.

55. Spring water is devoid of suspended impurities but contains dissolved salts and minerals. Due to the presence of rare minerals, it is used for medicinal purpose.

56. In regions with scanty rainfall, a substance called cetyl alcohol is sprayed on the water in reservoirs meant for storage of large quantities of water. This reduces the rate of evaporation of water.

57. Hydrated sodium aluminium silicate is called permutit. Formula of permutit is $Na_2\ Al_2Si_2O_8\ x\ H_2O$.

58. Ordinary water contains some dissolved salts which enables it to conduct electricity.

59. Ground water while travelling through a network of cracks and fissures emerges from below the surface of the earth. At this point, the aquifer surface meets the ground surface and water flows on to the surface of the earth with high pressure. This is called spring water.

60. The process of removal of dissolved salts from sea water is known as desalination.

61. The decomposition of a substance by passing electricity is called electrolysis.

62. When there is an imbalance between underground water and its replenishment, the level of water table may go down. This is called depletion of water table.

63.

Temporary hardness	Permanent hardness
It is caused by bicarbonates of calcium and magnesium.	It is caused by chlorides and sulphates of calcium and magnesium.
It can be removed by boiling by the addition of washing soda and Clark's method.	It can be removed by the addition of washing soda, permutit process and ion exchange method.

64. Rain water is the main source of natural water since it directly comes from the atmosphere, and it is the purest form of water. The initial showers of rain water contain dust particles and other micro-organisms. The later part of the rain water is devoid of any impurities. Therefore, it is considered as the purest form of natural water.

Short Answer Type Questions

65. The base is Cal$(OH)_2$. It consists of a divalent metal cation Ca^{+2} and a monovalent anion OH^-. It is formed by the dissolution of oxide of the metal cation, i.e., CaO, in water and is used in the removal of temporary hardness of water.

66. The different forms of water, arranged in the order of their charac-teristics are as follows:

(D) Demineralised water – water devoid of all types of mineral ions.

(E) River water – the purest form of natural water coming directly from the atmosphere.

(A) Potable water – water fit for consumption purposes.

(C) Aquifer – an underground form of water that can be extracted using a well.

(B) Saline water – water containing dissolved salts unfit for usage.

Thus, the order is DEACB.

67. The different steps involved in the process of purification of water in order are

(C) Addition of alum and lime

(E) Mechanical mixing

(B) Sedimentation for removing suspended impurities

(A) Filtration through sand and gravel

(D) Addition of bleaching powder releases chlorine which helps kill bacteria.

Hence, the correct order is CEBAD.

68. The presence of bicarbonates in water results due to the dissolution of CO_2 gas in rain water. This water flows across a wide area with different types of rocks. Calcium carbonate and magnesium carbonate present in the rocks react with the water containing CO_2 thereby, forming the corresponding bicarbonates. Bicarbonates being highly soluble in water impart hardness to water. The hardness caused by these bicarbonate salts is called temporary hardness.

When the water containing temporary hardness is subjected to boiling, these bicarbonates get converted to insoluble carbonates and can be removed by filtration.

$$Ca(HCO_3)_2 \rightarrow CaCO_3 + H_2O + CO_2$$

$$Mg(HCO_3)_2 \rightarrow MgCO_3 + H_2O + CO_2$$

69. **Clark's method:** This method involves the addition of slaked lime to water either in solid or in liquid form. This results in conversion of soluble bicarbonates to insoluble carbonates. On filtration, soft water is obtained.

$$Ca(HCO_3)_2 + Ca(OH)_2 \rightarrow 2CaCO_3 \downarrow + 2H_2O$$

$$Mg(HCO_3)_2 + Ca(OH)_2 \rightarrow CaCO_3 \downarrow + MgCO_3 \downarrow + 2H_2O$$

70. (A) Characteristics of potable water are given below:

(i) It should be free from suspended impurities and microorganisms.

(ii) It should contain dissolved gases such as O_2 and CO_2.

(iii) It should also contain some dissolved salts especially common salt.

(B) Though both water and steam are at the same temperature 100°C, steam has more energy than boiling water. It possesses the additional latent heat of vaporization (540 cals/g).

When steam touches our skin and condenses to produce water, it gives out 540cal/g more heat than boiling water at the same temperature.

Therefore, burns produced by steam are more severe than those produced by boiling water.

71. Alum is added during sedimentation process to hasten the process of precipitation of suspended impurities. During the precipitation process, some bacteria also get trapped and are removed.

72. (i) Removal of suspended impurities

(a) **Sedimentation**: River water is pumped into settling tanks and allowed to settle without any disturbance. The suspended impurities being larger particles settle down on standing.

(b) **Addition of chemicals**: The above process makes water only semi-clear. This is passed into mixing chamber where alum and lime are added to water and it is agitated with huge mechanical blades. Later on, this water is pumped into sedimentation tank. Alum hastens the process of precipitation of suspended impurities. During the precipitation process, some bacteria also get trapped and removed.

(c) **Filtration through sand and gravel**: The clear water obtained is pumped into sand and gravel filter. This removes all remaining traces of suspended impurities.

(ii) Removal of microorganisms

Addition of bleaching powder releases chlorine which helps in killing the harmful bacteria and the pure water obtained is stored in storage tanks.

73.

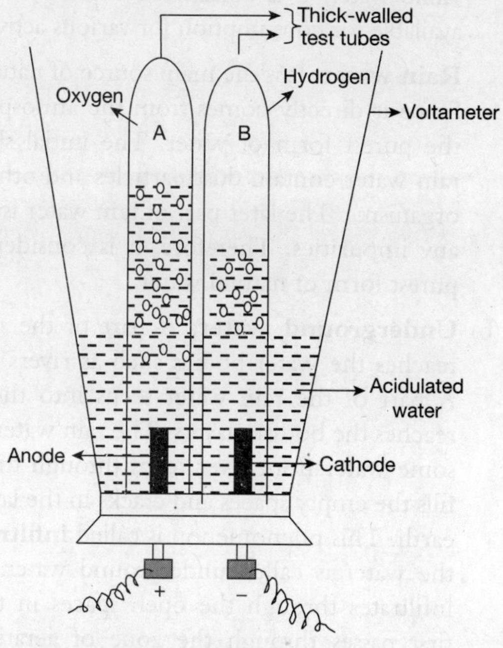

Electrolysis of water

74. By the addition of washing soda, we can remove both temporary as well as permanent hardness from water. Bicarbonate salts as well as sulphate and chloride salts undergo double decomposition reaction with sodium carbonate. In these reactions, the insoluble carbonates formed get precipitated and are removed by filtration.

$$Ca(HCO_3)_2 + NaCO_3 \rightarrow CaCO_3 \downarrow + 2NaHCO_3$$

$$MgSO_4 + Na_2CO_3 \rightarrow CaCO_3 \downarrow + 2NaCl$$

$$CaCl_2 + Na_2CO_3 \rightarrow CaCO_3 \downarrow + 2NaCl$$

75. Water management as such involves two major aspects. One is prevention of wastage of water by providing water supply through pipes without leakage. At the individual level, minimizing the wastage in daily activities is an important step. Another aspect is utilizing the rain water to recharge the ground water. This is called **water harvesting** or **rain water harvesting**. This can be done by installing water harvesting systems in the households.

76.

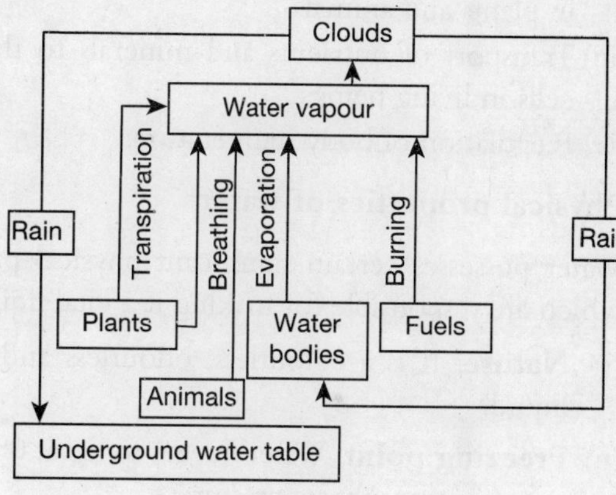

Water cycle

77. Sea water is the only proportion of water on the earth's surface which is saline and is not suitable for consumption. Only river water and underground water, constituting 0.01%, are sources of water. River water being limited and rivers drying up during the summer season, the dependence on underground water is inevitable. The underground water is drawn out by using various devices such as hand pumps and tube wells. This water is again replenished by means of seepage of water into the ground during rainy season. When there is an imbalance between underground water and its replenishment, the level of water table may go down. This is called depletion of the water table.

78. (1) At the individual level, minimizing the wastage in daily activities.

(2) Utilizing the rain water to recharge the ground water which is called rain water harvesting.

79.

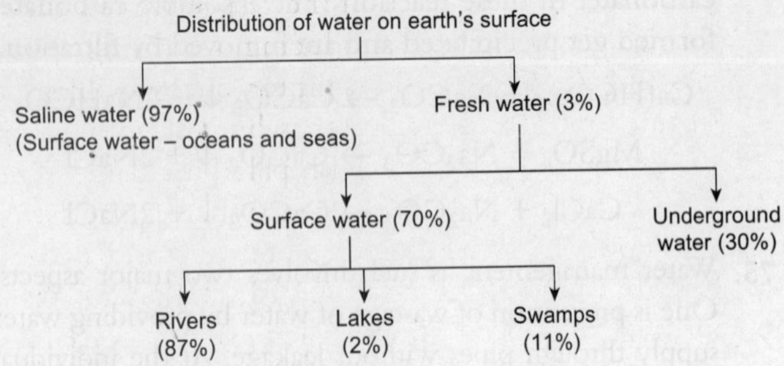

80. Important uses of water:

(i) Essential constituent for the reaction of photosynthesis which is the process providing support for life as well as making food for plants and animals.

(ii) Medium for all biochemical processes taking place in plants and animals.

(iii) Transport of nutrients and minerals to the living cells in living beings.

(iv) Regulation of body temperature.

81. Physical properties of water

Water possesses certain significant physical properties which are responsible for making it a vital liquid.

(i) **Nature**: It is a colourless, odourless and tasteless liquid.

(ii) **Freezing point**: Water freezes to ice at 0°C under normal atmospheric pressure.

(iii) **Boiling point**: Water gets converted to steam at 100°C under normal atmospheric pressure.

(iv) **Specific heat**: The amount of heat energy required to raise the temperature of unit mass of a substance through 1°C is called the specific heat capacity of that substance. Specific heat capacity of pure water is 1 calorie/g°C. Among all substances, water has the highest specific heat capacity.

(v) **Latent heat**: When a substance changes from one state to the other, certain amount of heat is required to break the intermolecular forces of attraction. For instance, when ice of certain mass at 0°C is converted to water of same mass at 0°C, the heat supplied brings about conversion of state without change in temperature. This is stored as potential energy in the water molecules and is called latent heat of fusion and is equal to 80 cal/g.

Similarly, the same conversion of 1 g of water at 100° C to water vapour requires 540 cal heat and this is called **latent heat of vaporization.**

At any temperature between 0°C and 100°C, conversion of water to water vapour takes place rather slowly. This process is called evaporation. The rate of evaporation increases with increase in temperature.

82. Sources of Water

(a) **Surface water**: It is the water present on the surface of the earth. The water present in oceans, seas, rivers, springs, etc., comes under surface water.

Oceans and Seas: These are the largest sources of water. Almost 97% of water available on earth is present in oceans and seas. This water contains huge amount of dissolved salts in addition to other impurities. Due to the presence of high proportion of dissolved salts (especially 2.5% common salt) the water gets salty and is rendered unfit for usage and consumption, and this water is called **saline water.**

Rivers and lakes: Rain water from higher altitudes flows down the hills and forms rivers. Apart from this rain water, water formed by melting of ice and snow flows into the rivers. Since water takes a long course and flows over land surface from higher altitudes, it contains various impurities and soluble salts. As the proportion of dissolved salts is less than in saline water, it is considered as fresh water and is available for consumption for various activities.

Rain water: It is the main source of natural water. Since it directly comes from the atmosphere, it is the purest form of water. The initial showers of rain water contain dust particles and other microorganisms. The later part of rain water is devoid of any impurities. Therefore, it is considered as the purest form of natural water.

(b) **Underground water**: A part of the rain water reaches the water bodies such as rivers and lakes. A part of the rain water seeps into the soil and reaches the bottom layers. The rain water as well as some water from river seeps through the soil and fills the empty spaces and cracks in the layers of the earth. This phenomenon is called **infiltration** and the water is called underground water. As water infiltrates through the open spaces in the soil, it first passes through the zone of aeration where the soil is unsaturated. At greater depths, known as recharge area, water fills in more spaces until the zone of saturation is reached. At this level, the ground water pressure is equal to the atmospheric pressure and this is known as water table. Below the water table, there is an underground layer of water bearing permeable rock or unconsolidated materials from which ground water can be usefully extracted using a water well. This is called **aquifer.**

83. (A) No. Hard water is not preferred for washing clothes as it forms poor lather with the soap. Lather formation by soap is very essential as it traps dirt from the clothes and prevent it from getting deposited back on the cloth by making it remained suspended in water. So, dirt can easily get removed off from clothes along with water. When hard water is used with soap, the calcium and Magnesium ions present in hard water combines with the soap molecules and forms a white curdy precipitate known as scum. Hence, much of the soap get wasted and clothes doesn't get cleaned due to the lack of required lather formation. So, soft water is preferred instead of hard water for washing clothes.

(B) Water obtained by Ion exchange method is demineralized water. In zeolite method, only the cations, i.e., calcium and magnesium ions are exchanged with the hydrogen ions of zeolite mineral but not the anions. In ion exchange process which uses cation and anion exchangers, both the cations and anions present in hard water are exchanged with H^+ and OH^- ions. These H^+ and OH^- ions from cation and anion exchangers later combine to form pure water.

Essay Answer Type Questions

84. Volumetric composition of water: Decomposition is a chemical change and it can be brought about by using various forms of energy like light, electricity, etc. The decomposition of a substance by passing electricity is called **electrolysis**.

Principle: Since water is a poor conductor of electricity, a little amount of sulphuric acid is added to water. This acidulated water, on passage of electricity, decomposes to give hydrogen and oxygen in 2 : 1 volume ratio.

$$2H_2O \rightarrow 2H_2 + O_2$$

Process: The acidulated water is filled in two test tubes without any air bubbles. The two test tubes are inverted over two iron nails connected to positive and negative terminals of a battery. These iron nails act as electrodes. The iron nail connected to the positive terminal of battery is called anode and the one connected to the negative terminal is called cathode. On passing electricity for some time, two gases are collected in the two test tubes. Corresponding decrease in the volumes of solution in the test tubes indicates the volumes of gases formed. The gases in the respective test tubes can be identified by introducing a burning splinter. In test tube 'A' the splinter burns brilliantly. In test tube 'B', the splinter is put off with a pop sound and the gas burns with pale blue flame. The former is identified as oxygen, whereas the latter as hydrogen. The volumes of oxygen and hydrogen are found to be in 1 : 2 ratio. When water is formed from its constituent elements the combination reaction reveals that the volumetric composition of water corresponds to hydrogen and oxygen in 2 : 1 ratio.

$$2H_2 + O_2 \rightarrow 2H_2O$$

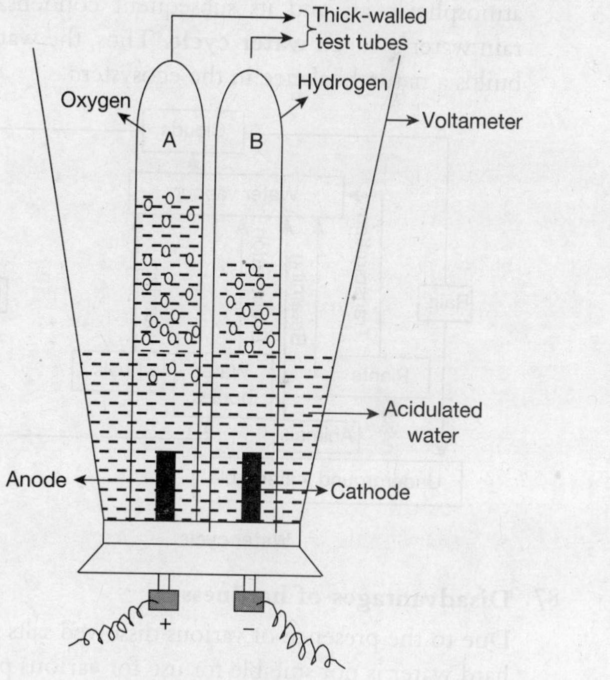

Electrolysis of water

85. (a) The presence of high proportion of dissolved salts makes sea water unfit for usage and consumption.

(b) River water takes a long course and flows over land from higher altitudes. As the proportion of dissolved salts is less than that in saline water, it is considered as fresh water.

(c) The underground water during seepage gets filtered through various layers of soil and hence, does not contain suspended impurities.

(d) Since most of the chemical reactions take place in water, laboratory work requires pure water for carrying out various tests and reactions. Hence, distilled water is used for laboratory processes.

86. Water which is so essential in so many ways derives its major source from rains. Water is added to the atmosphere in the form of water vapour by various processes. The water vapour so added to the atmosphere, being lighter than air, reaches the upper atmosphere. There, due to lower temperature, it gets condensed to form tiny water droplets which remain suspended in air. These small water droplets associated with the dust particles form larger aggregates called **micelles**. They appear as clouds and when the quantity of water in the clouds increases, it causes rain. This rain water can form various types of water bodies in the form of surface water and can help recharge the ground water level. This natural process of adding water to atmospheric air and its subsequent condensation to rain water is called **water cycle**. Thus, the water cycle builds a natural balance in the ecosystem.

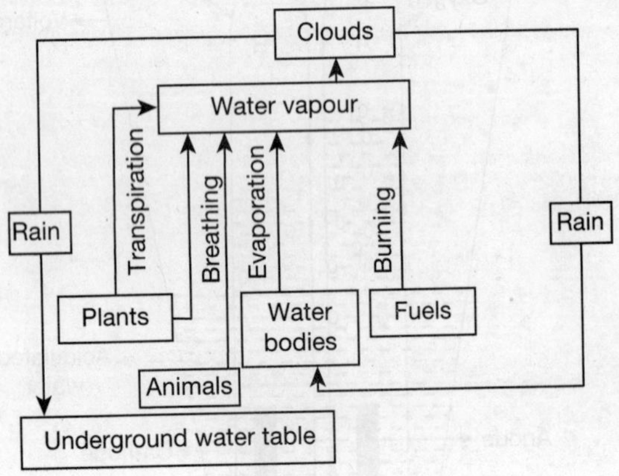

Water cycle

87. Disadvantages of hardness

Due to the presence of various dissolved salts in water, hard water is not suitable for use for various purposes.

(i) Not suitable for drinking.
(ii) Due to very poor lather formation, it is not effective for washing, cleaning and bathing purposes.
(iii) Scale formation in boilers results in loss of heat and wastage of fuels in industries.
(iv) Not effective for dyeing the fabrics due to improper fixing of dye to the fabric.

Removal of temporary hardness

(a) **Boiling**: However, when the water is subjected to boiling, these bicarbonates get converted to insoluble carbonates and can be removed by filtration. Since the hardness is removed by simple boiling, it is called temporary hardness and the water is called **temporary hard water**.

$$Ca(HCO_3)_2 \xrightarrow{\Delta} CaCO_3 + H_2O + CO_2$$

$$Mg(HCO_3)_2 \xrightarrow{\Delta} MgCO_3 + H_2O + CO_2$$

(b) **Clark's method**: This method involves the addition of slaked lime to water either in solid or in liquid form. This also results in conversion of soluble bicarbonates to insoluble carbonates. On filtration, soft water is obtained.

$$Ca(HCO_3)_2 + Ca(OH)_2 \rightarrow 2CaCO_3 \downarrow + 2H_2O$$

$$Mg(HCO_3)_2 + Ca(OH)_2 \rightarrow CaCO_3 \downarrow + MgCO_3 \downarrow + 2H_2O$$

If water dissolves other minerals in it, such as chlorides and sulphates, they also cause hardness of water. However, these salts cannot be removed by boiling. Hence, the hardness imparted by these salts is called **permanent hardness.**

Removal of permanent hardness

There are various methods adopted to remove permanent hardness.

(a) **Addition of washing soda (sodium carbonate)**: This method can remove both temporary as well as permanent hardness from water. Bicarbonate salts as well as sulphate and chloride salts undergo double decomposition reaction with sodium carbonate. In these reactions, the insoluble carbonates formed get precipitated and are removed by filtration.

$$Ca(HCO_3)_2 + Na_2CO_3 \rightarrow CaCO_3 \downarrow + 2NaHCO_3$$

$$MgSO_4 + Na_2CO_3 \rightarrow MgCO_3 \downarrow + Na_2SO_4$$

$$CaCl_2 + Na_2CO_3 \rightarrow CaCO_3 \downarrow + 2NaCl$$

(b) **Permutit process**: Hydrated sodium aluminium silicate is called **permutit**. ($Na_2Al_2Si_2O_8.xH_2O$). The sample of hard water is allowed to pass through a cylindrical tube filled with permutit. As the water passes through permutit, the calcium and magnesium ions of hard water are replaced by sodium ions. Sodium ions do not cause any precipitation with soap and do not hinder the formation of lather. Thus, the water is said to be softened. After some time, the entire permutit contains Ca^{+2} and Mg^{+2} in place of Na^+ ions. This is called exhausted permutit. This can be regenerated by sending sodium chloride solution through exhausted permutit.

(c) **Ion exchange method**: As the name indicates, this method involves exchange of hardness-causing ions by other ions. In this method, the apparatus consists of two cylindrical tubes A and B known as cation exchanger and anion exchanger, respectively.

These ion exchangers contain porous solids which do not dissolve in water but swell in water. These solids are called **ion exchange resins**. They contain mobile groups or ions which can be exchanged with other ions. The resin-containing groups or ions capable of exchanging cations are called cation exchange resins and the resin-containing groups or ions capable of exchanging anions are called **anion exchange resins**. H-cation exchanger results in exchange of Ca^{+2} or Mg^{+2} ions by H^+ ions. **Na-cation exchanger** results in exchange of Ca^{+2} or Mg^{+2} ions by Na^+ ions. Hard water is first passed through tube 'A' where all the positive ions are displaced by H^+ or Na^+ ions depending on the type of resin used. The water is then passed through tube 'B' where all the negative ions are displaced by OH ions present in the anion exchange resin. Thus, the water coming out of ion exchange apparatus now contains only pure water. This is also called **demineralized water**. When the cation exchanger and anion exchanger get depleted of H^+ and OH^- ions, the ion exchange resins are regenerated by passing HCl solution and sodium carbonate solution through the tubes A and B, respectively.

$MgCl_2 + 2H\text{+ Resin} \rightarrow \text{Mg – Resin} + 2HCl$

$RNH_3OH + Cl^- \rightarrow RNH_3Cl + OH^-$

$H^+ + OH^- \rightarrow H_2O$

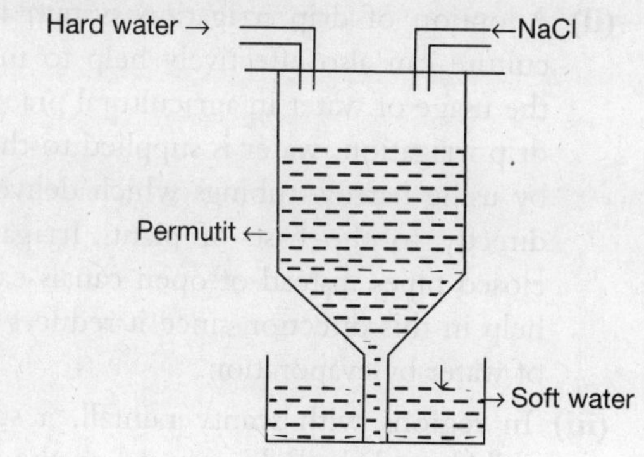

Permutit process

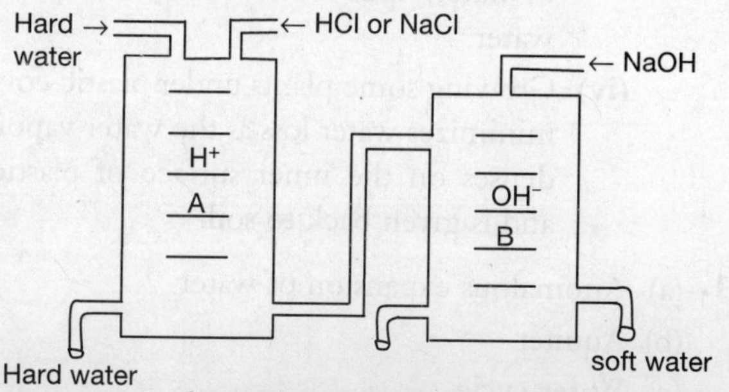

Ion exchange process

88. The purification of water basically involves two steps:

(i) Removal of suspended impurities and

(ii) removal of microorganisms.

(i) **Removal of suspended impurities**

(a) **Sedimentation**: River water is pumped into settling tanks and allowed to settle without any disturbance. The suspended impurities being larger particles settle down on standing.

(b) **Addition of chemicals**: The above process makes water only semi-clear. This is passed into mixing chamber where alum and lime are added to water and it is agitated with huge mechanical blades. Later on, this water is pumped into sedimentation tank. Alum hastens the process of precipitation of suspended impurities. During the precipitation process, some bacteria also get trapped and removed.

(c) **Filtration through sand and gravel**: The clear water obtained is pumped into sand and gravel filter. This removes all remaining traces of suspended impurities.

(ii) **Removal of microorganisms**

Addition of bleaching powder releases chlorine which helps in killing the harmful bacteria and the pure water obtained is stored in storage tanks.

The water so obtained at the end of the above purification process is devoid of suspended impurities and harmful bacteria. This water is fit for drinking and is called potable water. Potable water contains dissolved gases such as O_2 and CO_2 and also some dissolved salts especially common salt. These salts play an important role in the metabolic activities. They also provide taste to water. Therefore, this water is very much suitable for human consumption.

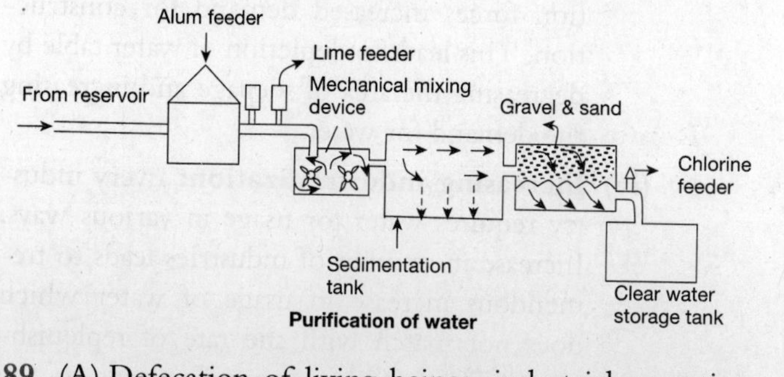

Purification of water

89. (A) Defecation of living beings, industrial operation, agricultural activities, thermal pollution and atomic reactors are the different causes of water pollution.

(B) Microorganisms, poisonous metallic salts, residual amount of artificial fertilizers, pesticides, insecticides and hot water are different types of pollutant.

(C) Usage of pit latrines, conversion of cow dung into biogas and the left over slurry can be used as manure. Removal of metallic salts by chemical treatment of water before discharging it, usage of natural manure in place of artificial fertilizers, usage of natural pesticides, avoiding spraying of chemicals in rainy season, usage of drip irrigation, cooling and recycling of water in the industry, and cooling by cooling towers before discharging it into water bodies are some of the control measures of water pollution.

90. (A) Causes of depletion

(i) Scanty rainfall or draught conditions: As long as there is balance between the usage of underground water and its replenishment by rainfall, there is no question of depletion. But, during long periods of scanty rainfall or in the absence of rainfall, this balance is disturbed. Usage of underground water continues more or less at the same level while its replenishment becomes very less or almost nil. This results in the depletion of water table.

(ii) Deforestation: Big trees in dense forests bind the soil particles through the roots. As a result they help in reducing the water flow and help in the seepage of rain water through the soil. Deforestation results in reduction in forest area which allows the rain water flow rapidly into large water bodies. Seepage becomes less thereby, leading to imbalance in the replenishment of underground water. Moreover, trees are one of the sources of water vapour which condenses to form clouds and results in rain.

(iii) Increasing population: Increasing population forces increased demand for construction. This leads to depletion of water table by decreasing the area of seepage and increasing the demand for water.

(iv) Increasing industrialization: Every industry requires water for usage in various ways. Increase in number of industries leads to tremendous increase in usage of water which does not match with the rate of replenishment. Thus, it also eventually leads to the depletion of water table.

(v) Increased agricultural activities: Due to erratic rainfall, the canal irrigation becomes rather impractical in certain areas. As a result, agriculture mostly depends on ground water for irrigation. The increased demand for agriculture results in the depletion of water table.

The above activities in the long run lead to tremendous depletion of ground water level and eventually to acute shortage of water.

(B) Water, being the most precious and essential natural resource and the percentage of available water being less, should be used judiciously. Several steps should be taken in day-to-day life both by the citizens as well as authorities for preventing depletion of water table.

(i) Water management as such involves two major aspects. One is prevention of wastage of water by providing water supply through pipes without leakage. At the individual level, minimizing the wastage in daily activities is an important step. Another aspect is utilizing the rain water to recharge the ground water. This is called **water harvesting** or **rain water harvesting**. This can be done by installing water harvesting systems in the households.

(ii) Adoption of drip irrigation system in agriculture can also effectively help to minimize the usage of water in agricultural practices. In drip irrigation, water is supplied to the plants by using narrow tubings which deliver water directly to the base of plant. Irrigation by closed pipes instead of open canals can be of help in this direction since it reduces the loss of water by evaporation.

(iii) In regions with scanty rainfall, a substance called cetyl alcohol is sprayed on the water in reservoirs meant for storage of large quantities of water. This reduces rate of evaporation of water.

(iv) Growing some plants under plastic covers also minimizes water loss as the water vapour condenses on the inner surface of plastic cover and is given back to soil.

91. (a) Anomalous expansion of water

(b) Aquifer

(c) Water cycle

(d) Decomposition reaction

Competition Wing

Level 1: Apply Your Concepts

1. **True.** The process of respiration, and all the remaining processes involve water as an important medium.

2. Drinking water mainly contains small amounts of salts of sodium, magnesium and calcium metals.

3. Carbon dioxide on dissolution in water forms carbonic acid.

4. 1 g of water at 100°C on heating forms 1 g of steam at the same temperature by absorbing 540 cal of energy.

5. 1 g of pure water at 4°C occupies a volume of 1 cm^3.

6. Under groundwater is passed through several layers of soil, and hence, it is free from suspended impurities.

7. The water which contains large amounts of dissolved salt is called saline water.

8. 1 g of pure water at 4°C occupies a volume of 1 cc.

9. Soft water produces lather with soap, whereas hard water produces scum with soap.

10. Hard water is unfit for dyeing clothes as it makes colour to fade.

11. Cation exchanger is regenerated by passing HCl solution.

12. Pure water is a bad conductor of electricity. Salt or alkali is added to water to increase its conductivity.

13. $2H_2 \quad + \quad O_2 \quad \rightarrow \quad 2H_2O$

Two volumes   one volume   two volumes

14. Clark's method is used for the removal of temporary hardness.

15. Specific heat capacity of water is 1 cal/g/°C.

16. The chemical that is sprayed in water reservoirs to reduce the rate of evaporation of water, in regions of scanty rainfall, is acetyl alcohol.

17. Hydrated sodium aluminium silicate is called permutit.

18. The exhausted permutit contains Ca^{+2} and Mg^{+2} in place of Na^+ ions.

19. In sedimentation process, alum hastens the process of precipitation of suspended impurities.

20. Addition of bleaching powder releases chlorine which helps in killing the harmful bacteria present in water.

21. Addition of acid to water increases the conductivity.

22. In electrolysis of water, hydrogen gas is liberated at cathode.

23. The change of water into water vapour below 100°C at slow rate is called evaporation.

24. Small water droplets associated with the dust particles form larger aggregates called micelles.

25. Percentage of water in animals varies from 70 to 90 %.

26. As water dissolves most of the substances in it, it is called a universal solvent. (A) is correct. Water containing dissolved ions only conducts electricity. Pure water which is devoid of all kinds of ions is a bad non-conductor of electricity. Thus, (R) is wrong.

    Hence, the correct option is (c).

27. Water has high specific heat. (A) is correct. The density of water in-creases with an increase in temperature from 0°C to 4°C and then decreases. (R) is also correct but (R) is not the correct explanation of (A).

    Hence, the correct option is (b).

28. Density of water is maximum at 4°C.

29. Adding of manure to soil causes less pollution because it is an organic matter and can be decomposed by microorganisms.

30. Metals present in permutit are Na and Al.

31. Water has the highest specific heat among all the substances.

32. Distilled water is a poor conductor of electricity as it is the purest form of water.

33. Usage of fertilisers is not the control measure for water pollution.

34. Nitrate and phosphate ions do not cause hardness of water.

35. Anion exchange resin can be regenerated by passing sodium hydroxide solution because it can replenishes OH^- ions.

36. Spring water is used for medicinal purposes because it contains dissolved salts, and minerals but not suspended impurities.

37. Potable water, soft water and sea water contain dissolved gases such as oxygen and carbon dioxide but distilled water does not contain O_2 and CO_2 because during distillation these dissolved gases are distilled off.

38. Washing soda is used to remove permanent hardness by precipitation reaction.

39. Density of water is maximum at 4°C due to anomalous expansion of water. Hence, when the temperature of water is raised from 0°C to 10°C, the density increases up to 4°C, then decreases gradually.

40. Clark's method is used to remove temporary hardness. In this process slaked lime is added, which results in conversion of soluble bicarbonates into insoluble carbonates. On filtration, soft water is obtained.

41. (i) lime feeder, alum feeder

(ii) mechanical mixing

(iii) filtration

(iv) chlorination

42. (i) ice of 10 g mass at 10°C

(ii) ice of 10 g mass at 40°C

(iii) water of 10 g mass at 10°C

(iv) water of 10 g mass at 40°C

(v) steam of 10 g mass at 10°C

43. Latent heat of fusion of 10 g of water is $10 \times 80 = 800$ cal

Latent heat of vaporisation of 10 g of steam is $10 \times 540 = 5400$ cal

44. Icebergs weigh millions of tons but float on the surface of sea water because the density of ice is less than that of the sea water. Usually 9/10 of icebergs will be below the surface of water and 1/10 above the sea water as a result we cannot estimate the size below water, and hence, when ship hits this heavier ice berg the ship sinks.

45. Distillation process is not involved in making surface water potable.

46. Water has high specific heat, which means that water needs a large amount of heat to become hot.

47. Divalent metal salt X which contributes to hardness of water is $CaCl_2$ which combines with Na_2CO_3 gives insoluble salt Y, i.e., calcium carbonate and sodium chloride.

$$CaCl_2 + Na_2CO_3 \rightarrow CaCO_3 \downarrow + 2NaCl$$

48. Specific heat of water is 1 cal/g/°C.

That means 1 g of water requires 1 cal energy to increase the temperature by 7°C.

2 g of water requires? = $20 \times 1 = 20$ cal

49. On passing electricity through acidulated water it decomposes to hydrogen and oxygen. Volume of hydrogen evolved in test tube A is double the volume of oxygen collected in test tube B.

50. Demineralised water is obtained through ion-exchange process. Distilled and demineralised water doesn't contain any impurities. Hence, they do not conduct electricity. Mineral water is a good conductor of electricity.

51. Cooking in a pressure cooker takes less time because in pressure cooker as pressure increases boiling point increases and food is cooked softer in less time.

52. By introducing artificial fertilisers, crop yield is improved but at the same time it contributes to water pollution.

53. B will get severe burns as latent heat of vaporisation of 540 cal/g is stored within the molecules of steam.

54. Aquatic organisms are able to survive in lakes during winter even though there is ice at the surface because the density of ice is less than that of water; ice is a poor conductor of heat.

55. Chlorine is involved in making surface water potable by the process called chlorination.

56. In air coolers, warm air is sucked by an exhaust fan. The warm air passes through khus-khus mats through which water is dripping. The water absorbs the heat from the air and cools the air.

57. Divalent metal salt X, i.e., $MgSO_4$ is treated with compound Y, i.e., Na_2CO_3 to form $MgCO_3$ and Na_2SO_4.

$$MgSO_4 + Na_2CO_3 \rightarrow MgCO_3 + Na_2SO_4$$

58. The specific heat of water is 1 cal/g/°C. Therefore, the amount of heat required is 1.5 cal for 15 for 10°C raise in temperature.

59. In the ion-exchange method, pure water called demineralised water is obtained which is not potable because it does not contain any minerals and dissolved salts.

60. As we move to higher altitudes, pressure decreases, and hence, boiling point decreases. Water boils at low temperatures on the hills, and thus, the food is cooked for longer hours.

61. A → c Defecation by living beings produces pollutants such as amoeba, fungicides, etc.

B → a Industrial operation produces pollutants such as mercury, arsenic, etc.

C → d Water released from thermal power plants is favourable for growth of algae.

D → b Agricultural activities produce pollutants such as insecticides, fungicides, etc.

62. A → c By the process of boiling we can remove temporary hardness in which bicarbonates present in water decompose to carbonates which are precipitated.

B → d Clark's method involves the addition of slaked lime to water either in solid or liquid form to remove temporary hardness.

C → b Addition of washing soda helps in removing both temporary and permanent hardness.

D → a Ion exchange method consists of solids called ion exchange resins.

63. A → d The value of specific heat of water is 1 cal/g/°C.

B → e The latent heat of fusion of ice is 80 cal/g/°C.

C → f The latent heat of vaporisation of water is 540 cal/g/°C.

D → b Ice melts at 0°C.

E → c Water boils at 100°C.

Level 2: Review Your Concepts

64. The gas that is liberated at the negative electrode and puts off the burning splinter and burns with a blue flame is hydrogen and the gas that is liberated at the positive electrode and glows the burning splinter brightly and is non-combustible is oxygen.

65. Passing the hard water sample through a chemical called permutit exchanges the ions in the hard water with ions of some charge. The Ca^{+2} and Mg^{+2} ions in the hard water are replaced by Na^{+} ions of permutit, which removes the permanent hardness of water.

66. Sea water contains more amount of dissolved salts, and hence, it is unsuitable for drinking. Sea water is made potable through reverse osmosis process.

67. The specific heat capacity of water is very high. Hence, it can lose lot of heat without much decrease in its temperature. The heat lost by water can increase the temperature of the other substances which is in contact with it. Therefore, hot water bags can used to keep out body warm in winter.

68. Though ice is a solid, it has large amount of space between its molecules. These spaces are larger as compared to spaces in water molecules. Thus, the volume of ice is greater than water. Hence, the density of ice is less than of water. A substance with low density than water can float on it.

69. Specific heat capacity of water is 1 cal/g/°C.

1 cal heat is required to increase the temperature of 1 g of water by 1°C.

To increase the temperature of 10 g water by 12°C, 120 calories of heat is required.

70. Specific heat capacity of water is very high. Hence, water can take way lot of heat from the hot engine without significant increase in its temperature.

71. Latent heat of fusion or freezing is 80 cal/g, i.e., 1 g of ice requires 80 cal.

20 g ice requires = 20 + 80 = 1600 cal

Latent heat of vaporisation of water is 540 kg cal/g, i.e., 1 g water requires 540 cal.

20 g water requires = 20 × 540 = 10,800 cal

Ratio = 1600 : 10800 = 1 : 6.75

72. (A) Addition of cetyl alcohol reduces the rate of evaporation of water. Hence, level of water in container A is comparatively higher than the level of water in container B.

(B) Specific heat of liquid = 0.9 J/g

Mass of liquid = 100g

Amount of heat supplied (g) = 4200 J

Difference in temperature $(\Delta t) = \frac{q}{ms}$

$= \frac{4200}{100 \times 0.9} = 46.67°C$

Initial temperature = 40°C

Temperature to which the liquid is heated

= 46.67 + 40 = <u>86.67°C</u>

73. Elements X and Y are Mg and Ca, respectively. Hydrogen carbonates or bicarbonates of Ca and Mg impart temporary hardness while sulphates of Ca and Mg impart permanent hardness to water.

74. The heat energy supplied is completely utilised to convert ice into liquid water. As a result, thermometer does not register any rise in temperature till all the ice cubes melts.

75. Element with electronic configuration 2, 8, 1 is Na and its carbonate is sodium carbonate which is called washing soda. It is used for the removal of both temporary and permanent hardness of water.

$Ca(HCO_3)_2 + Na_2CO_3 \rightarrow CaCO_3 \downarrow + 2NaHCO_3$

$CaSO_4 + Na_2CO_3 \rightarrow CaCO_3 \downarrow + Na_2SO_4$

$CaCO_3$ is insoluble, and hence, it settles down.

In this way washing soda can be used to remove both temporary and permanent hardness of water.

76. In permutit process, we use sodium permutit, i.e., $Na_2Al_2Si_2O_8.xH_2O$. When hard water is treated with sodium premutit, Ca and Mg ions are exchanged with the Na ions present in the permutit. After long use, most of the sodium ions present in permutit are replaced with calcium and magnesium ions, and hence, it becomes ineffective. Sodium hydroxide reacts with HCl to from sodium chloride Concentrated sodium chloride solution is added to regenerate the permutit.

77. The amount of heat energy required to convert 1 g of ice to 1 g of water at 0°C is called latent heat of fusion. Latent heat of fusion of ice is 80 cal/g, i.e., every 1 g of ice requires 80 calories of heat in order to melt. This energy is taken away from the soft drinks, and hence, these drinks are cooled when they are placed in ice.

Level 3: Assess Your Concepts

78. In permutit process, cations which impart hardness to water are removed. In the ion-exchange process both cations and anions are removed in the respective ion exchanger. Hence, water obtained from the ion exchanger is almost free from ions which can be used in the laboratory to carry out experiments.

79. In cold countries, the temperature is below 0°C. The water present in the pipes expands during freezing. As a result, ice exerts huge pressure on the pipes and they burst.

80. Dead sea consists of large quantity of dissolved salts to the extent of saturation. Density of human body is less than the water present in dead sea. Therefore, human body floats.

81. During chlorination, chlorine is added to water, which produces nascent oxygen. This nascent oxygen kills all harmful germs and bacteria present in water.

82. Thermal pollution of water is due to heavy industries such as steel, thermal power plants. These sources discharge large amounts of hot water into the rivers, which helps in the rapid growth of algae. This alga depletes dissolved oxygen in water. This in turn leads to the death of biotic life.

83. (A) Pure water which is free from all cations and anions other than H^+ and OH^- ions is called distilled water. Potable water should contain some ions which are require for the human body. As distilled water does not contain any ions, it cannot provide the minerals required for human body. Moreover, the minerals which are present in the body fluids get dissolved in the water and are excreted. Due to this reason, distilled water cannot be a substitute for potable water though it is the purest form of water.

(B) Distilled water is used for the purpose of preparation of medicines and laboratory reagents as the ions present in normal water interfere with the usual chemical processes supposed to take place in the system.

CHAPTER
6

Chemistry in Daily Life

Remember

Before beginning this chapter, you should be able to:

- Explain basic concepts of matter and its classification.
- Describe physical and chemical properties of certain substances.

Key Ideas

After completing this chapter, you should be able to:

- Explain the properties of metals and non-metals, and their applications in various fields.
- Identify some common alloys, their special properties and uses.
- Describe the preparation, properties of different compounds, like, plaster of Paris, cement, glass, fertilisers, soaps and detergents that find wide applications in our daily life.
- List different types of polymers and plastics.

Scientific Crypt

A Tribute to Joseph Aspdin (1778 – 1855)

Joseph Aspdin (or Aspdin) was the eldest of the six children of Thomas Aspdin, a bricklayer who was living in Hunslet district of Leeds in Yorkshire, England. Aspdin was a British cement manufacturer, who obtained patent for Portland cement. He was baptised on Christmas day in 1788. After getting married to Mary fotherby on 21st May 1811, Aspdin entered his fathers trade. By 1817, he started his own business in central Leeds. During the next few years of his setup of business, he experimented with cement manufacture and he was granted the British patent BP 5022, entitled "An improvement in the mode of producing an artificial stone", in which he coined the term 'Portland cement' by analogy with the portland stone, an oolitic lime stone that is quarried on the channel coast of England, on the Isle of Portland in Dorset. In 1825, in partnership with neighbour in Leeds, William Beverley, Aspdin setup a production plant of Portland cement. In the same year, he obtained a second patent for a method of making lime. In 1841, Aspdin along with his eldest son James barred his youngest son William from the business and took control over the plant. Later, around the time of his departure, William was thought to have developed modifications leading to modern Portland cement. Joseph retired in 1844, transferring his sphere of business to James. Joseph passed away on March 20, 1855, at his home in Wakefield.

FUN TIME

CROSSWORD

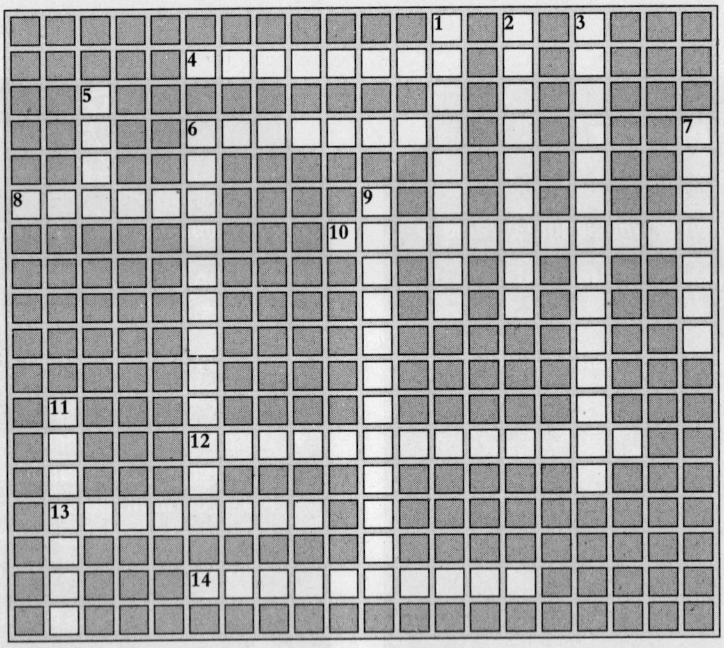

Across

4. The main constituent of pencil lead
6. Non-metal used in the sterilization of drinking water.
8. Calcium sulphate dihydrate is the chemical name of
10. Hydrated copper sulphate is the chemical name of
12. Type of plastic to which polyethylene belongs
13. Mixture of cement, gravel and sand in the ratio of 1 : 2 : 3 by weight.
14. Glass used in soap industry

Down

1. Sodium salt of alkyl hydrogen sulphate.
2. The main constituent of duralumin
3. Calcium sulphate hemihydrate is the chemical name of ______.
5. Sodium salt of fatty acid.
6. Mixture of cement and sand in the ratio of 1 : 4 by weight.
7. Calcined lime is the common name of _______
9. The technique used for manufacture of laboratory glassware from molten glass.
11. Thermometric liquid used in clinical thermometer.

INTRODUCTION

The branch of science that deals with the composition, physical and chemical behaviour of different substances around us is called **Chemistry**. It also deals with the application of these substances in various fields to make our lifestyle easy and comfortable. Along with this, many chemicals are synthesized in the laboratory and in the industry to satisfy different requirements. Moreover, improvisation of the properties of the substances available in nature by altering their composition also comes under the purview of chemistry. Hence, the study of chemistry is indispensable.

Metals, Non-metals and their Uses

Metals find extensive applications because of their specific properties like-lustre, tensile strength, conductivity, malleability, ductility, etc.

The wide range of materials used in our day-to-day life are constituted of basic components called elements. The elements are broadly categorized into metals and non-metals on the basis of their characteristic properties. The various metals and non-metals find applications in various fields either in elemental form or in the form of their compounds. Therefore, before going into the study of chemistry involved in the materials used in our daily life, it is very much appropriate to throw light on the comparative study of properties of metals and non-metals and also the uses of various metals and non-metals along with the properties exploited for the respective uses.

Table 6.1 Comparative study of physical properties of metals and non-metals

Property	Metals	Non-metals
State	Solids at room temperature **Exceptions:** Mercury and gallium are liquids.	Mostly gases. **Exceptions:** Some of the solid non-metals are carbon, sulphur, phosphorus, iodine whereas bromine is a liquid non-metal.
Melting point and boiling point	Very high melting point and boiling point **Exceptions:** Sodium, potassium, mercury have low melting points and boiling points. Gallium has low-melting point but high-boiling point.	Low melting points and boiling points **Exceptions:** Carbon, silicon and boron have high melting points and boiling points.
Hardness	Generally hard **Exceptions:** Sodium and potassium are soft.	Solid non-metals are brittle. **Exception:** Diamond is the hardest naturally occurring substance.
Density	Possess high density **Exceptions:** Lithium, sodium, and potassium have density lower than water (1 gm/cm^3).	Possess low density **Exception:** Diamond
Conductivity	Good conductors of heat and electricity **Exceptions:** Bismuth and tungsten are poor conductors of electricity.	Bad conductors of heat and electricity **Exception:** Graphite and gas carbon are good conductors of electricity.

(Continued)

Table 6.1 Continued

Property	Metals	Non-metals
Lustre	Have lustre	Have no lustre **Exceptions:** Iodine and graphite
Tensile strength (Maximum force which the substance can withstand without breaking)	High tensile strength **Exception:** Zinc has very less tensile strength.	Low tensile strength **Exception:** Carbon fibre, a recently developed allotrope of carbon
Malleability (Ability to be made into thin sheets) and **ductility** (Ability to draw into be thin wires)	Generally malleable and ductile **Exception:** Zinc is not malleable and ductile.	Non-malleable and nonductile **Exception:** Carbon fibres are highly ductile.
Sonorousness	Sonorous	Non-sonorous
Occurrence	Found in combined state **Exception:** Only noble metals are found in free state.	Found in free state as well as in the combined state

Table 6.2 Comparative study of chemical properties of metals and non-metals

Property	Metals	Non-metals
Number of electrons in the valence shell	Have 1 to 3 electrons in their valence shells	Have 4 to 7 electrons in their valence shells **Exceptions:** Hydrogen has one electron in its valence shell because the first shell is its valence shell.
Formation of ions	Lose electrons from their valence shells to form stable cations.	Accept electrons to from stable anions.
Formation of oxides	Metals on heating in air or oxygen react to form their respective oxides. The oxides are either basic or amphoteric in nature. **Example:** Sodium oxide is basic and aluminium oxide is amphoteric. **Exceptions:** Metals like gold and platinum do not form oxides.	Non-metals on heating in air or oxygen form their respective oxides. But the oxides are either acidic or neutral in nature. **Example:** Carbon dioxide and sulphur dioxide are acidic whereas water and carbon monoxide are neutral.
Reaction with acid and water	Metals, which are more reactive than hydrogen, replace hydrogen from the acid as well as from water. **Example:** Sodium reacts with air and water and the reaction is highly exothermic.	Generally, non-metals do not react with water. **Example:** Phosphorus does not react with water.

Table 6.3 Properties and applications of different metals

Name of the metals	Properties	Applications
Gold 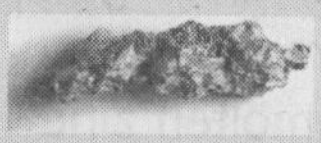	It possesses a yellow lustre, is malleable, ductile and highly resistant to chemicals. It is relatively a soft metal.	• It is used for making jewellery, coins, etc. • Used in dentistry for filling cavities, satellites and ayurvedic medicines.
Silver 	• It possesses a white lustre, is malleable, ductile and is one of the best conductors of heat and electricity. • Compounds of silver, like, silver chloride, silver iodide, etc., are sensitive to light and undergo photolytic decomposition.	• It is used for making coins and ornaments, table cutlery, high-quality glass mirror, silver threads in clothing and electric water purifiers. • It is used in electric circuits for highly expensive electric appliances. • It finds application in ayurvedic medicine and filling cavities in teeth. • Compounds of silver, such as, silver chloride and silver iodide are used in photographic film and photogrey lenses. Silver nitrite or silver iodide is used in cloud seeding for artificial rain.
Copper 	It possesses a reddish brown lustre, is malleable, ductile and is the second best conductor of heat and electricity.	• It is used for the manufacture of electric transmission cables, utensils, statues, etc. • It is used for making printed circuits used in electronic devices. • It is also used for making coins and alloys like, brass, bronze, bell metal, etc.
Iron 	It possesses a grey lustre and is fairly malleable and ductile.	• It is extensively used in the form of an alloy in the construction of ships, buildings, automobiles, railway bridges, railway lines, electric transmission towers, television towers, microwave towers and in a variety of machineries. • It finds wide applications in household articles.
Tin 	It possesses a silvery white lustre, is malleable and less ductile. It has a comparatively low melting point with respect to other metals.	• It is used for coating food cans and cooking vessels which are made of copper and iron. • The process of coating tin over any article is called **tinning**. • It is used in the manufacture of alloys like brass and bronze and fusible alloys which are used in the manufacture of fuse wires.
Lead 	It possesses a silvery grey lustre, is less corrosive, and hence, more durable. It has a comparatively lower melting point and its density is very high.	• It is used for making lead storage batteries used in automobiles. • It is used for covering tin roofs in cold countries, for the manufacture of sanitary pipes and making the tip of bullets. • It is used for making fusible alloy constituted of lead and tin in 1 : 1 ratio by mass.

(Continued)

Table 6.3 Continued

Name of the metals	Properties	Applications
Zinc 	• It possesses a white lustre with a light blue tinge. • Characteristic properties of metals namely, malleability and ductility are not clearly demonstrated in zinc.	• It is used in the process of galvanizing iron sheets. In the galvanisation process, the hot iron sheets are dipped in molten zinc and then passed through hot and heavy rollers. On cooling, a coating of zinc metal is formed over the iron sheets.The coating of zinc protects iron from rusting, and hence, is used for the manufacture of iron roofing, iron tanks, rainwater drain pipes, etc. • It is used as electrode in dry cells. • It is used for making alloys, such as, brass and bronze.
Aluminium 	• It possesses a silvery white lustre, is highly malleable and ductile, is a very good conductor of electricity, is very light in weight and corrosion resistant. • It is the most abundant metal in the earth's crust. • It is relatively a soft metal when compared to other metals.	• It is used for the manufacture of high-voltage electric transmission wire. • It is used for making foils for packing food materials, medicines, etc. • It is used for making alloys, such as, duralumin, magnalium, etc., which are very light in weight and impact resistant. Hence, these alloys are used for the manufacture of aircraft frames and components of automobiles. • These alloys also find application in the manufacture of utensils, household fixtures, etc.
Magnesium 	It possesses a silvery white lustre, burns with a white dazzling flame and its reaction with oxygen is highly exothermic.	• It is used in fire works. • It is used as fuse wires in thermite welding. • It is used in the manufacture of alloys, like, magnalium.
Mercury 	• It is a silvery white metal which is a liquid at normal temperature. Its melting point is –39°C and boiling point is 357°C, it is a very good conductor of electricity and heat. • It can dissolve almost all the metals in itself. The solution of a metal in mercury is called **amalgam**.	• It is used as a thermometric liquid in the laboratory as well as a clinical thermometer. • The gold amalgam and silver amalgam are used in dentistry for filling teeth cavities.

Table 6.4 Properties and applications of different non-metals

Names of the non-metals	Properties	Applications
Chlorine	• It is a greenish yellow, pungent-smelling and poisonous gas. • It is fairly soluble in water and about 2.5-times heavier than water. • It shows bleaching (decolourizing) and sterilizing action.	• It is used for bleaching cotton and jute fabrics. • It is used for the sterilization of drinking water. • It is also used in the manufacture of bleaching powder, hydrochloric acid, insecticides and pesticides, such as, DDT (dichloro diphenyl trichloroethane) and BHC (benzene hexachloride).
Iodine	• It is a bluish grey crystalline solid with lustre. • It is insoluble in water, but soluble in alcohol, carbon tetrachloride and potassium iodide solution.	• Compounds of iodine, such as, sodium iodide or potassium iodide are mixed with common salt to prevent the deficiency of iodine in our diet. • The common salt containing the above compounds of iodine is called **iodized salt**. People suffer from diseases, like, goitre and mental retardation because of the deficiency of iodine in their body. • Other compounds of iodine, like, silver iodide are used for making photographic films as well as for cloud seeding • Tincture of iodine (iodine in mixture of potassium iodide solution and alcohol) is used as a germicide for dressing of wounds. • Iodoform, another compound of iodine, is used in medicines.
Graphite	• It is a crystalline form of carbon. It possesses a dark grey lustre. • It is a good conductor of electricity and bad conductor of heat. • It is highly heat resistant as well as chemical resistant. • It is soft, and hence, can leave an impression on the paper.	• Pencil leads are manufactured by mixing graphite with clay. The hardness of the pencil depends on the amount of clay present in it. The more the amount of clay, the harder is the pencil. • Graphite mixed with fine clay is moulded and sintered into crucibles of desired size and shape. These crucibles are used to melt small quantities of metals. • It is also used as an excellent lubricant in those parts of the machineries where high heat is generated. In the above case, the use of ordinary lubricating oils is restricted as they get charred at high temperatures. • Graphite is used in electrolytic cells as electrodes. • Graphite is used in nuclear reactors as a moderator to slow down the speed of neutrons produced due to the splitting of the atoms of uranium or thorium.

Noble Gases and Their Uses

Noble gases find various applications due to their inert (non-reactive) nature. There are six noble gases which are helium, neon, argon, krypton, xenon and radon. Helium, being the second lightest element and inert in nature, is extensively used for filling weather-observation balloons. Neon is used in advertising sign-boards, whereas argon is used in filli ng up the electric bulbs to improve their efficiency by preventing oxidation of tungsten filament. Krypton and xenon are also used in electric bulbs to slow down the sublimation of hot tungsten filament. Radon, being a radioactive gas is used in cancer treatment.

Some Common Alloys and their Uses

In order to improvise the properties of a metal according to the end use, fused or molten metal is uniformly mixed with other metal(s) and sometimes a non-metal in small quantity. The mixture is then cooled to obtain a solid, called an **alloy**. Every alloy possesses some special properties because of its specific composition. In general, alloying improves the mechanical strength, makes the metal corrosion resistant, and hence, increases the durability.

Table 6.5 Important alloys and their uses

Names of the alloys	Major components	Composition (other components)	Special properties	Applications
Stainless steel	Iron (83%)	Carbon (1%) Chromium (15%) Nickel (1%)	It does not rust and is resistant to mild acids or alkalies.	In utensils, cutlery, surgical instruments and ornamental articles.
Duralumin	Aluminium (95%)	Copper (4%) Manganese (0.5%) Magnesium (0.5%)	It is very light in weight but hard and possesses high tensile strength.	It is used for making frames of aircraft, automobiles and speedboats.
Brass	Copper (60–80%)	Zinc (40–20%)	It possesses a yellow lustre, is harder and stronger than copper but more malleable and ductile than copper.	It is used for making electric switches of various kinds, taps, statues, household utensils and shells of ammunition rounds.
Bronze	Copper (80%)	Zinc (10%), Tin (10%)	It is resistant to corrosion and takes high polish.	It is used for making statues, coins and household utensils.
Alloyed gold	Gold	Silver or copper in small quantities	It possesses a lower melting point and is harder and more impact resistant than pure gold.	It is extensively used in making jewellery and coins.

EXAMPLE 6.1 What are noble gases? Mention their uses.

SOLUTION

Noble gases are those which are inert. There are six noble gases which are helium, neon, argon, krypon, xenon and radon.

Element	Uses
Helium	Filling weather observation balloons
Neon	Advertising sign boards
Argon, krypton and xenon	Filling up electric bulbs
Radon	Cancer treatment

EXAMPLE 6.2 Mention some common alloys and their composition.

SOLUTION

- Brass: Copper (Cu) and Zinc (Zn)
- Bronze: Copper (Cu) and Tin (Sn), though other elements can be added for specialized types of bronze.
- Stainless Steel: Iron (Fe), Carbon (C), and Chromium (Cr). It can also contain Nickel (Ni) and other elements.
- Amalgam: Mercury (Hg) combined with other metals like Silver (Ag), Tin (Sn), and Copper (Cu).

EXAMPLE 6.3

(a) What is the composition of pencil lead?
(b) How is hardness of pencil related to the composition of pencil lead?
(c) How are crucibles made with the help of graphite?
(d) Why is graphite a more preferred lubricant to the ordinary lubricating oils?
(e) What is the role of graphite in nuclear reactor?

SOLUTION

(a) Pencil leads are manufactured by mixing graphite with clay.
(b) The more the amount of clay, the harder is the pencil.
(c) Graphite mixed with fine clay is moulded and sintered into crucibles of desired size and shape.
(d) Graphite is highly resistant to heat, and therefore, used as lubricant in those parts of machinery where high heat is generated due to friction. In the above case, ordinary lubricating oils get charred at high temperatures.
(e) Graphite is used in nuclear reactors as a moderator to slow down the speed of neutrons produced due to splitting of the atoms of uranium or thorium.

EXAMPLE 6.4

An element X is non-malleable and non-ductile. X is extensively used to protect another element Y from corrosion. Identify X and Y, and name the process that is mentioned above. Also compare the reactivity of X and Y.

SOLUTION

Element X is zinc which is non-malleable and non-ductile. Y is iron. The process of protecting iron by coating with zinc is called galvanisation. The element X(Zn) is more reactive than Y (Fe).

EXAMPLE 6.5

Explain the principle involved in the usage of chlorine in sterilisation of drinking water.

SOLUTION

Chlorine is highly soluble in water. On dissolution of chlorine in water, hypochlorous acid is formed which dissociates to give nascent oxygen. Nascent oxygen kills germs and bacteria. Hence, chlorine is used in sterilisation of drinking water.

Some Useful Compounds

In compounds, the constituent elements do not retain their properties and a new set of properties are exhibited by the compounds. Many compounds find applications in various fields. We now discuss some of these compounds.

Sodium Chloride (NaCl)

The major source of sodium chloride is sea water. The salt obtained due to the evaporation of sea water is called **crude salt**, because of the presence of sand and clay particles. Crude salt is dissolved in water, and thus, the soluble component, i.e., sodium chloride is extracted and then recrystallised. **Recrystallisation** is a process to separate a solid solute from the liquid solvent by cooling the hot saturated solution.

A small quantity of sodium iodide or potassium iodide is mixed with sodium chloride and the mixture is called **common salt**, which is inevitable in our daily meal. Other than this, it is used as a preservative for the storage of fish and meat. It is also used as a raw material for the manufacture of other useful compounds, like, baking soda, washing soda, hydrochloric acid, caustic soda and elements like chlorine.

Hydrochloric Acid (HCl)

Hydrochloric acid is prepared industrially by heating common salt and concentrated sulphuric acid. It can also be obtained by passing hydrogen chloride gas through water. It is used in the preparation of silver chloride which finds application in photographic printing paper. It is an important laboratory reagent. Industrially, it is used to clean the surface of metals. In households, hydrochloric acid is used as a bathroom-cleaning agent.

Blue Vitriol ($CuSO_4$)

Blue vitriol is hydrated copper sulphate prepared by dissolving cupric sulphide or cupric oxide or cupric carbonate in dil sulphuric acid. It finds application as an insecticide. Solution of copper sulphate is sprayed over citrus trees and grape vines to kill the insects.

> **Konnect**
>
> Blue Vitriol, also known as Copper Sulphate, was used in ancient India as an emetic – a substance used to induce vomiting.

Marble or Limestone ($CaCO_3$)

Limestone is a metamorphic rock formed from the sea shells. Chemically, limestone is calcium carbonate. Limestone is used as one of the raw materials for the manufacture of cement and glass. Lime (calcium oxide) which is a component of mortar, is manufactured from limestone. Mortar is used in the construction of buildings. Lime is also used for white washing. Marble is extensively used as flooring, statues and monuments.

Zincite or Zinc Oxide (ZnO)

Naturally occurring zinc carbonate is heated strongly to obtain zinc oxide. It is used as a raw material for the extraction of zinc and in the manufacture of paints.

Gypsum ($CaSO_4.2H_2O$) and Plaster of Paris ($CaSO_4.\frac{1}{2}H_2O$)

Gypsum is a naturally occurring mineral. Its chemical composition is calcium sulphate dihydrate ($CaSO_4.2H_2O$). It is used to reduce the acidity of the soil. When gypsum is heated over a long period of time, it partially loses its water of crystallisation and plaster of Paris ($CaSO_4.\frac{1}{2}H_2O$) is obtained.

Plaster of Paris can be moulded into different shapes when it is kneaded with the right proportion of water. The moulded object sets into a hard mass when it is dried. Hence, it is applied on the body parts to set fractured bones properly. It is also used for casting statues, toys and decorative materials. Modern black board chalks and ceiling panels are also made from plaster of Paris.

Compounds of Silicon

Sand or **silicon dioxide** is a naturally occurring mineral. Sand in purified form is used as the raw material for the manufacture of glass and cement.

Sodium silicate is the compound of silicon which is soluble in water and is used in the preservation of eggs. **Silicone** is a polymer manufactured in the industry from silicon. Silicone is highly heat resistant, non-sticky in nature and water repellant as well as a bad conductor of electricity. Hence, it is used in the manufacture of non-stick pans, waterproof clothes, wax polishes, electrical insulators, etc.

Ferrosilicon is an alloy of iron and silicon and is a very hard steel. **Silicon carbide**, a compound of silicon, is the hardest compound and used in all kinds of grinding wheels.

Fertilizers and Their Uses

Fertilisers are compounds or mixtures of compounds which are added to the soil in order to provide the essential nutrients to the plants.

Fertilisers can be categorised into two types depending on the source from which they are obtained.

1. Natural fertiliser
2. Artificial fertiliser

Types of Fertilizers

Natural fertiliser: An example of a natural fertiliser is manure. The excreta of live stock and humans is mixed with straw and then the mixture is buried deep into the pits for few months. The mixture decomposes there and manure is obtained.The manure is rich in the nutrients required for the growth of the plants.

Info Bytes!

Laughing gas, used by dentists for anaesthesia, is actually nitrous oxide – a compound also used as a fertilizer!

Artificial fertiliser: Artificial fertilisers are the chemical compounds manufactured in the industries. They contain one or more essential nutrients required for the growth of the plant. Artificial fertilisers can further be classified depending on their chemical composition, i.e., the essential nutrient(s) they contain.

1. **Nitrogenous fertiliser:** These fertilisers replenish the deficiency of nitrogen. Calcium ammonium nitrate, ammonium sulphate, basic calcium nitrate and urea are the examples of nitrogenous fertilisers.
2. **Phosphatic fertiliser:** These fertilisers replenish the deficiency of phosphorus. Triammonium phosphate and superphosphate of lime are the examples of phosphatic fertilisers.
3. **Potash fertiliser:** These fertilisers replenish the deficiency of potassium. Potassium nitrate, potassium sulphate and potassium chloride are the examples of potash fertilisers.

Some Organic Compounds used as Food

Different biological processes that are carried out in living beings require energy. In case of animals, the source of this energy is the food they consume. The food consumed by the animals can be broadly categorised into carbohydrates, proteins and fats based on the chemical composition.

Table 6.6 Different food materials

Types of food	Constituent elements	Examples	Uses
Carbohydrates	Composed of carbon, hydrogen and oxygen.	Glucose ($C_6H_{12}O_6$), sugar ($C_{12}H_{22}O_{11}$), starch ($(C_6H_{10}O_5)_n$). All cereals contain large quantity of carbohydrates etc.	Carbohydrates which we consume break into simpler molecules, i.e., glucose. Glucose molecules are carried to the cells with the help of blood. During respiration, glucose decomposes into carbon dioxide, and water and energy are liberated.
Fats	Mainly composed of carbon, hydrogen and oxygen.	Vegetable oil, animal fat, etc.	Fat provides the maximum amount of energy.
Protein	Mainly composed of carbon, hydrogen, oxygen and nitrogen. Sulphur and phosphorus may also be present in protein.	Salivary amylase, keratin, albumin, etc.	Protein is not only the source of energy but also plays a major role in the development of cells, growth of the new cells and repair of the damaged cells.

The organic compounds which contain only carbon and hydrogen are called **hydrocarbons**.These compounds on combustion give large amount of energy, and hence, are used as fuels. Methane is the simplest hydrocarbon with the formulae CH_4.

Methane is the major component of natural gas. It occurs in nature as underground deposit. The decomposition of farm waste and cow dung in the absence of air gives a mixture of gases called **biogas**. Methane is also the major component of biogas. It is an excellent fuel with a ratio of energy given out by the combustion of methane to its mass being very high compared to the other fuels. Methane liberates carbon dioxide and water vapour on burning. It neither liberates any harmful gas, nor any solid residue. It finds application in households as well as in automobile fuels.

Some Common Solutions in Our Daily Life

Our body needs an adequate amount of fluid to carry the digested food to the cells. In the cells, the digested food gives out energy by the process of respiration. Sometimes the quantity of fluid in our body decreases due to tedious activity or some infection. The loss of fluid can be supplemented by drinking solutions, like, soda water, soft drinks, syrups or solution of glucose. The solution of glucose can be injected directly into the blood if it is urgently required.

Soda Water or Soft Drinks

Soda water is prepared by passing carbon dioxide through water under 30 atm pressure. Excess amount of carbon dioxide gets dissolved in water due to high pressure. If the carbon dioxide is passed through a sugar solution flavoured with desired substances, the solution obtained is called **soft drink**.

Syrups

Highly concentrated sugar solution flavoured with desired substances is called **syrup**. When syrup is diluted with water, a drink rich in energy is obtained.

Glucose Saline

A person suffering from dysentery may get dehydrated, i.e., excessive loss of water from the body may take place. Then a solution of glucose is directly injected into the blood to provide the required water and energy, immediately. The solution of glucose can be taken orally to get instant energy because glucose is the simplest carbohydrate.

Some Important Industrially Useful Materials

Certain mixtures, like, lime, mortar, cement, glass, etc., are manufactured in the industries through a series of processes. These substances not only fulfill our essential requirements but also they find applications even in critical scientific and biomedical researches.

Lime Mortar

It is a construction material prepared by mixing calcined lime and sand. This mixture is converted into thick slurry by adding required quantity of water. It is used for joining bricks and plastering.

Calcined Lime

When lime ($CaCO_3$) is heated to about 1000°C, CO_2 is liberated leaving behind dry lime. This dry lime is called calcined lime.

Cement

Cement is a powdery substance and greenish grey in colour. It forms a hard mass when it is mixed with water, and dried. The major area of application of cement is construction. The early Egyptians used to prepare the building material by mixing lime or clay and gypsum. Romans used to make the building material by mixing volcanic ash and lime. People all over Europe adopted the process developed by Romans for the purpose of construction. Joseph Aspdin, a mason of Leeds, England is the pioneer of the manufacture of cement. In the year, 1824, he observed that a rock-like mass is obtained when water is added to a strongly heated mixture of limestone and clay. This hard mass resembles the Portland rock used by the people of England for the construction of building. Thus, the mixture was named as **Portland cement**.

Manufacture of Cement

The raw materials used for manufacturing Portland cement are limestone and clay. Cement can be produced in two different processes.

1. Dry process
2. Wet process

In the **dry process**, limestone and clay are used in definite proportion to achieve the desired property of the cement. The mixture is pulverised (making fine powder) using pulveriser and then heated to 1500–1600°C to form clinkers (nodules of mixed powder which become very hard after heating). These clinkers are again pulverised to form fine powder and small quantity of gypsum is added, and thus, cement is produced.

In the wet process, water is added to the pulverised mixture and slurry is obtained. Then the slurry is strongly heated to form clinkers.

Uses of Cement

Grouting: Grouting is a technique used in construction activities. Pure cement or cement mixed with sand and water in a definite proportion is applied in the gaps of construction material, like, bricks, tiles, etc., for making the surface smooth and strengthening the structure.

Cement mortar: It is a construction material prepared by mixing cement and sand in the ratio of 1 : 4 by weight. This mixture is converted into thick slurry by adding required quantity of water. It is used for joining bricks and plastering.

Concrete: It is also a construction material prepared by mixing cement, gravel and sand in the ratio of 1 : 2 : 3 by weight and required quantity of water. It is used for casting roofs, pillars, beams, etc.

Reinforced cement concrete (RCC): When cement concrete is reinforced using structural steel, it is called reinforced cement concrete (RCC). RCC structure provides huge strength and is durable. It is used for the construction of bridges, railway sleepers, prefabricated structures, columns, beams, roofs, etc.

Brick

Brick (red brick) is made by using clay. The right proportion of water is added to clay and kneaded properly. The kneaded clay is pressed in the shape of a brick and heated at high temperature (about 1000°C) and this process hardens the brick. Bricks are the structural materials used for construction of walls of a building.

Glass

Early cave people found an igneous rock named Obsidian which is a natural glass produced by volcanic action. They shaped it into tools and spearheads. With the advancement of science and technology, modern techniques have been adopted for the manufacture of a wide variety of glass.

Manufacture of Glass

Glass is made up of silica or sand, limestone and feldspar as major raw materials. Broken pieces of glass, called **cullet** are added to the raw material. Some other ingredients, like, red lead, aluminium oxide, manganese oxide, chromium oxide, etc., are used to impart specific characteristics to glass. The raw materials are mixed in the required proportion and melted in a glass tank furnace or pot furnace. Cullet initiates the melting process at a lower temperature.

Three major techniques are applied on the molten glass obtained in the process of melting for the manufacture of different products of glass.

1. **Blowing of glass:** This technique is used for the manufacture of laboratory glassware, bottles, etc.
2. **Optical glass:** Molten glass is pressed into a circular shape from which different optical glasses are manufactured.
3. **Sheet glass/float glass:** Molten glass obtained from the glass tank furnace is placed on molten bath of tin. The molten glass spreads on the bath of molten tin with uniform thickness from which sheet glass/float glass is drawn.

The different shapes of molten glass obtained from the above three techniques are then subjected to a cooling process called **annealing** at controlled temperature in a long tunnel-type annealing chamber.

General Properties of Glass

Glass is a supercooled liquid. Molten glass obtained from glass-manufacturing furnaces is allowed to cool down slowly. During cooling, viscosity of glass increases manifolds below the range of its freezing temperature and loses its ability to flow. Hence, it appears like a solid. Glass is transparent, highly chemical resistant, a bad conductor of heat and electricity and it can be easily moulded into desired shapes.

Table 6.7 Properties and applications of different types of glasses

Types of glasses	Ingredients and properties	Applications
Water glass	Sodium silicate; soluble in water.	It is used in the soap industry. In the early 20th century, it was used for the preservation of eggs. It is also used for filling up holes and strengthening material.
Soft glass or soda glass or lime glass	Sodium silicate and calcium silicate; cannot withstand high temperature and thermal shock.	It is used for making window panes and cheap articles of glass.
Hard glass or potash–lime glass	Sand, limestone, potassium carbonate; fairly heat resistant.	It is used for making laboratory apparatus.
Optical glass or crown glass	Sand, limestone, potassium carbonate and red lead; highly transparent and possess high density.	It is used in the manufacture of lenses of spectacles and optical instruments, like, lenses of telescope, microscope, etc.
Jena glass or pyrex glass or borosil glass	Sand, limestone, sodium carbonate, aluminium oxide and borax; highly heat resistant and can withstand thermal shock.	It is used for making laboratory apparatus, thermos flasks and baking bowls.
Shatterproof glass or sandwich glass	Sheets of plain glasses are attached with each other with a plastic sheet placed between them as broken pieces of this type of glass do not scatter.	It is used as wind shields of automobiles.

Paints

Paints are nothing but the colouring materials dissolved in the suspension of basic lead carbonate in linseed oil. Plastic emulsion is a kind of paint which is prepared by dissolving coloured plastics in amyl acetate. The durability of plastic emulsion is much more than that of the basic lead carbonate paints.

Medicines

In the olden days, people used to depend on different parts of medicinal plants, like, Tulsi, Vasaka, Neem, etc., or their extracts for the treatment of diseases. Scientists observed and analysed the composition of those substances and developed similar kind of molecules artificially and the direct use of the medicinal plants has reduced gradually. With the advancement of the medical science, scientists developed many new molecules which are more effective and give quicker relief. Incurable diseases could also be cured by administering some of these molecules. These molecules are called **medicines**. Some of the examples of such medicines are penicillin, tetramycine, sulphadiazine, etc. Quinine is a medicine which is extracted from the bark of *Cinchona* plant. It is administered for the treatment of malaria.

Polymers and Plastics

The single molecule present in the long chain is called **monomer** and the chain so formed by repetition of monomers is called **polymer**. One of the examples of such polymers is polyethylene. The monomer of this polymer is the ethylene molecule (C_2H_4). The word 'plastics' originated from the characteristic property of some materials to be moulded into various forms which is called plasticity. **Plastics** are made up of long chains called polymers obtained by the interlinkage of certain specific molecules of the same chemical composition. Plastics have many unique properties, like, light weight, mechanical strength, aesthetic appearance, bad conductor of heat and electricity, etc.

Based on the thermal behaviour, plastics can be divided into two categories: **thermoplastics** and **thermosetting plastics**.

Thermoplastics

This type of plastics can be processed repeatedly by melting and subsequent solidification without undergoing any chemical change. Hence, they can be reused.

Examples: Polyethylene, polyvinyl chloride, polystyrene, nylon, terylene, etc.

Application of thermoplastics: Thermoplastics are used for making utensils, sole of the shoes, fabrics, etc.

Info Bytes!

The first fully synthetic plastic was Bakelite, introduced in 1907. It was used in telephones, jewellery, and even guitar picks!

Thermosetting Plastics

This type of plastic cannot be softened by heating, and thus, cannot be reused.

Examples: Formaldehyde, polyurethane, melamine, bakelite, etc.

Application of thermosetting plastics: Thermosetting plastics are used for making water tanks, water pipes, cabinets of television and radio, unbreakable utensils, etc.

Soaps and Detergents

These are the substances which in combination with water help to remove dirt from the various surfaces such as skin, clothes, metals, etc. Both soaps and detergents work on the same principle as far as their cleansing action is concerned. However, they differ in the composition and hence the basic ingredients.

Soaps and detergents are the two artificially synthesized substances which are indispensable in our daily activity.

Konnect

The word 'soap' is derived from Mount Sapo, a fictitious mountain where Romans did their laundry in the Tiber River.

Soaps

Chemically soaps are the sodium salts of fatty acids. Examples of different fatty acids are olive oil, cotton seed oil, rapeseed oil, coconut oil, etc. When sodium hydroxide solution is treated with vegetable oil, soap is produced.

$$\text{Vegetable oil} + \text{sodium hydroxide} \rightarrow \text{soap} + \text{glycerine}$$

Glycerine is obtained as a by-product which has some different applications.

Various kinds of soaps and their applications are shown in Table 6.8.

Table 6.8 Properties and applications of different types of soaps

Kinds of soaps	Raw materials	Applications
Laundry soap or **washing soap**	Cheapest vegetable oil, contains free alkali.	It is used in the laundry for removing dirt and grease from soiled clothes.
Scouring soap	Finely ground Pumice stone, sand and sodium carbonate are added to the laundry soap as fillers.	They are commonly used for scrubbing floors.
Toilet soap	The best quality of vegetable oil. Does not contain free alkali.	This kind of soap is used for bathing.

(Continued)

Table 6.8 Continued

Kinds of soaps	Raw materials	Applications
Medicated soap	Certain substances which have medicinal value are added to the toilet soap.	Neem soap takes care of the skin.
Soft soap or **liquid soap**	Vegetable oil and potassium hydroxide.	Used for washing hands. It is also used as a shaving soap.
Transparent soap	This kind of soap is obtained by dissolving soap in alcohol. When alcohol is evaporated, transparent soaps are formed.	This soap is also used as a bathing soap.

Detergents

Soap forms a curdy precipitate in hard water and does not lather properly. Hence, soap is ineffective in hard water. **Detergents** are sodium salts of alkyl hydrogen sulphate and can be used effectively in hard water. The cleansing action of the detergent is superior to that of the soap. Example of a detergent is sodium lauryl sulphate.

Cleansing Action of Soap and Detergent

Soaps and detergents remove the oil and greasy material which stick to the clothes. Soaps and detergents both are soluble in water and act as surfactant, i.e., they form a thin film which surrounds the oil and grease spots and help in the removal of those spots along with the dirt. As the removal of dirt by the soaps and detergents involve the formation of emulsion, it is called **emulsification** and these substances are called **emulsifiers**.

EXAMPLE 6.6

Riya had two beakers, one filled with tap water (Beaker X) and the other with distilled water (Beaker Y). She added a few drops of soap solution to each beaker and stirred them vigorously. She noticed that the amount of foam produced in each beaker was different. Can you explain the reason for this observation?.

SOLUTION

The foam or lather formation is affected by the hardness of water. Tap water usually contains dissolved mineral salts, mainly calcium and magnesium, which makes it hard. When soap is added to hard water, it reacts with the mineral salts to form an insoluble precipitate called scum, reducing the lather formation. On the other hand, distilled water is free from these mineral salts, allowing the soap to produce a rich lather. Hence, Beaker Y with distilled water produces more foam compared to Beaker X with tap water..

EXAMPLE 6.7

Sand and clay which are abundantly available in the earth's crust have significant roles in the comfort zone of modern life. Justify.

SOLUTION

Sand is an important component in all types of mortars, such as, lime mortar and cement mortar. Sand is also the component of plain cement concrete and reinforced cement concrete (RCC) which contributes to the infrastructure development in various fields of modern life. Clay plays important role in ceramics, bricks, various building material, sanitary equipment and household articles. Because of their desired properties, they contribute a significant role in the comfort zone of modern life.

EXAMPLE 6.8 Write a short note on the cleansing action of detergent.

SOLUTION

Detergents remove the oil and greasy material which stick to the clothes. Detergents are soluble in water and act as surfactants, that is, they from a thin film which surrounds the oil and grease spots and help in the removal of those spots along with the dirt. As the removal of dirt by soaps and detergents involves the formation of emulsion, it is called emulsification and these substances are called emulsifiers.

EXAMPLE 6.9 Why is bakelite, a thermosetting plastic, used for making electrical switches while polyethylene, a thermoplastic, is not preferred for the same purpose?

SOLUTION

Bakelite is a thermosetting plastic, which means once it is moulded and set, it cannot be remelted or reshaped. This property makes bakelite resistant to heat and electricity. On the other hand, polyethylene is a thermoplastic and can melt upon heating. Electrical switches may be exposed to heat, and using polyethylene could pose a risk of the material melting or deforming. Therefore, bakelite, being heat-resistant and an electrical insulator, is preferred for making electrical switches, while polyethylene is not..

EXAMPLE 6.10 Explain the process of emulsification.

SOLUTION

Emulsification is the process by which two immiscible or unmixable liquids, such as oil and water, are forced to mix together to form a stable, homogeneous dispersion. The resulting mixture is called an emulsion.

POINTS TO REMEMBER

- ✔ Aluminium is the third most abundant element in the earth's crust, whereas hydrogen is the most abundant element in the universe.
- ✔ Helium is the second lightest element and inert in nature, hence, it is used for filling weather observation balloons.
- ✔ Carbohydrates are instant sources of energy, whereas fats are reservoirs of energy.
- ✔ Methane is the simplest hydrocarbon and is present in natural gas or biogas as a major component.
- ✔ Polymers are large molecules formed by the combination of smaller molecules.
- ✔ Cement is a mixture of silicates and aluminates.
- ✔ Setting of cement is due to the hydration of these aluminates and silicates.
- ✔ Glass is a mixture of sodium silicate and calcium silicate. Addition of other components imparts other characteristic properties to glass, used for specific purposes.
- ✔ Glass is a supercooled liquid and appears like a solid due to the increase in viscosity during cooling of molten glass.
- ✔ Detergents are superior to soaps as they do not form insoluble precipitates with hard water.

PRACTICE QUESTIONS CLASSROOM WING

Very Short Answer Type Questions

Directions for questions from 1 to 5:
Fill in the blanks.

1. The technique of manufacturing glass wares used in the laboratory is called ______.
2. Compounds containing elements C, H, O, and N along with P and S that play a major role in the growth, development, and repair of damaged cells are called ______.
3. The major component of natural gas is ______.
4. ______ is used for filling weather observation balloons.
5. Bakelite is an example of ______ plastic.

Directions for questions from 6 to 45:
For each of the questions, four choices have been provided. Select the correct alternative.

6. The metals with the least tensile strength is:
   (a) iron (b) aluminium
   (c) zinc (d) copper
7. Which of the following is not an alloy?
   (a) Brass
   (b) Bronze
   (c) Magnalium
   (d) Magnesium
8. Which of the following elements is used for tinning?
   (a) Iron (b) Tin
   (c) Copper (d) Aluminium
9. The two metals involved in the galvanisation process are:
   (a) iron and copper
   (b) iron and zinc
   (c) zinc and copper
   (d) copper and aluminium
10. Duralumin is used for the manufacture of aircraft frames because duralumin is:
    (a) a bad conductor of heat and electricity.
    (b) more durable and has resistance to corrosion.
    (c) very light and possesses high tensile strength.
    (d) all of the above
11. Which of the following is a noble gas?
    (a) Hydrogen (b) Helium
    (c) Oxygen (d) Nitrogen
12. The elements present in stainless steel are:
    (a) iron, copper and carbon
    (b) iron, copper and nickel
    (c) iron, copper and chromium
    (d) iron, chromium, carbon and nickel
13. Common salt is a mixture of:
    (a) sodium chloride and magnesium chloride
    (b) sodium chloride and iodine
    (c) sodium chloride, iodine and potassium iodide
    (d) sodium chloride, sodium iodide or potassium iodide
14. The chemical composition of limestone is:
    (a) calcium carbonate
    (b) calcium oxide
    (c) calcium hydroxide
    (d) calcium sulphate
15. The chemical name of sand is:
    (a) silicon
    (b) sodium silicate
    (c) silicon dioxide
    (d) calcium silicate
16. Which among the following metals is the most suitable to be used as telecommunication cable?
    (a) Aluminium
    (b) Tin
    (c) Iron
    (d) Copper
17. Which of the following steps is not involved in the preparation of sodium chloride from sea water?
    (a) Evaporation
    (b) Dissolution in water
    (c) Recryztallisation
    (d) Distillation
18. Which of the following properties of silicon is not exploited in the manufacture of non-stick cookware?

(a) High resistance to heat
(b) Poor electrical conductivity
(c) Non-stick nature
(d) High resistance to chemicals

19. Which of the following food items provide the maximum energy?
(a) Vegetable oil (b) Glucose
(c) Cereals (d) Pulses

20. Which of the following materials can be used for plastering?
(a) Cement mortar (b) Concrete
(c) RCC (d) Anyone of the above

21. Which of the following is a difference between thermoplastic and thermosetting plastics?
(a) Thermoplastics can be processed repeatedly.
(b) Thermosetting plastics cannot be softened by heating.
(c) Thermoplastics do not undergo chemical change on heating.
(d) All the above.

22. Which of the following is obtained as a by-product in the manufacture of soap?
(a) Glycerine (b) Sodium hydroxide
(c) Vegetable oil (d) Salt of fatty acid

23. Glass is a/an:
(a) amorphous solid (b) crystalline solid
(c) supercooled liquid (d) solid with a high viscosity

24. Arrange the compounds in sequence of increasing number of oxygen atoms.
(1) Sugar (2) Plaster of Paris
(3) Starch (4) Glucose
(a) 1243 (b) 2413
(c) 2314 (d) 2341

25. Arrange the steps in a sequence for the manufacture of cement in dry process.
(1) Formation of clinker
(2) Pulverisation
(3) Addition of gypsum
(4) Heating to high temperature (1500°C to 1600°C)
(a) 2413 (b) 2143
(c) 2341 (d) 2314

26. The elements present in starch are:
(a) carbon, hydrogen and sulphur
(b) carbon, hydrogen and oxygen
(c) carbon, hydrogen and nitrogen
(d) carbon and hydrogen only

27. Pick out the correct statement(s) among the following.
(a) An alloy is a homogeneous mixture of two or more metals.
(b) An alloy may contain a non-metal in addition to metals.
(c) Alloys possess better physical properties than the metals.
(d) All the above.

28. Arrange the given compounds in the increasing order of carbon atoms present in the following compounds:
(1) Methane (2) Sugar
(3) Glucose (4) Starch
(a) 2 3 4 1 (b) 3 1 2 4
(c) 1 3 2 4 (d) 4 2 1 3

29. Which of the following gases is the most unsuitable for filling up weather-observation balloons?
(a) Helium (b) Neon
(c) Hydrogen (d) Argon

30. Match the following:

Column A	Column B
A. Hydrochloric acid	a. Sprayed over grape vines
B. Hydrated copper sulphate	b. Flooring, statues and monuments
C. Limestone	c. Manufacture of paints
D. Zincite	d. Reduces the acidity of the soil
	e. Bathroom cleaning agent

(a) A → c, B → d, C → b, D → a
(b) A → e, B → a, C → b, D → c
(c) A → b, B → e, C → a, D → c
(d) A → d, B → a, C → b, D → e

31. Which of the following compounds/alloys of silicon is used in grinding wheel and which property of that substance is exploited?

(a) Silicon carbide because it is the hardest substance.

(b) Ferrosilicon because it is resistant to friction.

(c) Sodium silicate because it becomes impervious when heated strongly.

(d) Silicon dioxide because it is resistant to chemicals.

32. Which of the following is a thermosetting plastic?

(a) Polyethylene (b) Nylon

(c) Terelyne (d) Bakelite

33. Arrange the relevant steps in correct sequence for the manufacture of sodium chloride from sea water.

(1) Making of hot saturated solution

(2) Evaporation

(3) Recrystallisation

(4) Collection of sea water

(5) Addition of small quantity of sodium iodide or potassium iodide

(a) 4 5 2 1 (b) 4 5 2 3

(c) 4 5 1 2 3 (d) 4 2 1 3

34. Which of the following noble gases cannot be used for filling up electric bulbs?

(a) Helium (b) Neon

(c) Argon (d) Radon

35. Match the following:

Column A	Column B
A. Cleaning the surface of metal	a. $CaSO_4 . \frac{1}{2} H_2O$
B. Used as an insecticide	b. $ZnCO_3$
C. Construction of Taj Mahal	c. HCl
D. Casting toys, statues, etc.	d. $CuSO_4.5H_2O$
	e. $CaCO_3$

(a) A → e, B → b, C → a, D → c

(b) A → b, B → c, C → a, D → e

(c) A → c, B → d, C → e, D → a

(d) A → d, B → c, C → a, D → b

36. Which of the following substances does not form a curdy precipitate when it is added to hard water?

(a) Potassium salt of fatty acid

(b) Sodium salt of fatty acid

(c) Sodium lauryl sulphate

(d) None of these

37. Which among the following metals is the most suitable to be used as telecommunication cable?

(a) Aluminium (b) Tin

(c) Iron (d) Copper

38. Which of the following can be said to provide instant energy?

(a) A solution of glucose

(b) A cup of tea

(c) Aerated drinks

(d) Milk

39. Which of the following applications of copper require refining of copper instead of alloying?

(a) Making statues

(b) Making household utensils

(c) Making shells of ammunitions

(d) Making electric transmission cables

40. Which of the following fertilisers cannot replenish nitrogen?

(a) Superphosphate of lime (calcium dihydrogen phosphate with gypsum)

(b) Nitre

(c) Ammonium sulphate

(d) Triammonium phosphate

41. Arrange the following steps in a sequence for the manufacture of borosilicate glass.

(1) Addition of ingredients like red lead, aluminium oxide, manganese oxide, chromium oxide, etc.

(2) Addition of broken pieces of glass

(3) Mixing up of sand, limestone, sodium carbonate, aluminium oxide and borax in required proportions

(4) Melting mixture in a glass tank furnace or pot furnace

(5) Annealing process

(6) Blowing of glass

(a) 3 2 1 4 6 5 (b) 3 2 1 6 5 4

(c) 3 4 2 1 6 5 (d) 3 6 5 2 1 4

42. Graphite is used in the manufacture of crucibles where a small quantity of metals can be melted. It is also used as electrodes. Which of the following properties of graphite is not exploited in these two given applications?

(a) Highly resistant to chemicals
(b) Soft nature
(c) High melting point
(d) Good electrical conductivity

43. Which of the following is the most suitable for the construction of a pillar?
(a) Cement mortar (b) Concrete
(c) RCC (d) Pure cement

44. **Assertion (A):** Gold is used for making jewellery coins.
Reason (R): It is relatively a hard metal.
(a) Both (A) and (R) are true and (R) is the correct reason of (A).
(b) Both (A) and (R) are true but (R) is not the correct explanation of (A).
(c) (A) is true but (R) is false.
(d) (A) is false but (R) is true.

45. **Assertion (A):** Fuse wire is made up of an alloy constituted of lead and tin in 1 : 1 ratio by mass.
Reason (R): Both lead and tin have comparatively lower melting points than other metals.
(a) Both (A) and (R) are true and (R) is the correct reason of (A).
(b) Both (A) and (R) are true but (R) is not the correct explanation of (A).
(c) (A) is true but (R) is false.
(d) (A) is false but (R) is true.

Directions for questions from 46 to 48:
Match the entries given in Column A with the appropriate ones in Column B. More than one suitable content of Column B can also be considered correct for an entry in Column A and some content given in Column B may not be the appropriate one for any entry in Column A.

46.

Column A		Column B	
A.	Gold	a.	Sanitary pipes
B.	Copper	b.	Satellite
C.	Lead	c.	Covering tin roofs in cold countries
D.	Zinc	d.	Bell metal
		e.	Iron roofing

47.

Column A		Column B	
A.	Surgical instruments	a.	Duralumin
B.	Speed boats	b.	Bronze
C.	Electrical switches	c.	Stainless steel
D.	Household utensils	d.	Brass
		e.	Alloyed gold

48.

Column A		Column B	
A.	Water glass	a.	Potassium carbonate
B.	Lime glass	b.	Sodium silicate
C.	Crown glass	c.	Borax
D.	Jena glass	d.	Calcium silicate
		e.	Aluminium oxide

Directions for questions from 49 to 68:
Answer the following questions.

49. A medicine, extracted from the bark of a plant, is used in the treatment of malaria. Identify the medicine.

50. Soaps do not form lather with hard water but form curdy precipitates. True or false?

51. Which fertilizer replenishes the deficiency of potassium?

52. Name the process that is employed in extracting sodium chloride from crude salt.

53. Which of the following food items: Vegetable oil, Glucose, Cereals, Pulses; provides the maximum energy?

54. Which of the following: Cement mortar, Concrete, RCC, Pure cement; is the most suitable for the construction of a pillar?

55. Why is magnesium used in fire works?

56. Which non-metal is used for the manufacture of pencil lead?

57. Why is duralumin used for the manufacture of automobiles and speed boats?

58. Which chemical compound is used to reduce the acidity of the soil?

59. Which compound of silicon is used for the preservation of eggs?

60. Name the hardest compound and write one of its uses.

61. Write the formulae of glucose, sugar and starch.

62. Give an example of a solution which gives us instant energy.

63. Write the composition of stainless steel.

64. Name the soap commonly used for scrubbing floors.

65. How is concrete made?

66. What is emulsification?

67. Why is glucose given to patients?

68. What is annealing?

Short Answer Type Questions

69. The characteristic uses of the different types of construction materials are given below. Arrange them in the order of their respective names.

(A) The structural material for the construction of walls of a building.

(B) Mixed with a definite proportion of water, and used in filling the gaps of construction.

(C) Concrete reinforced with structural steel and is used in the con-struction of bridges, prefabricated structures, etc.

(D) Construction material used for joining bricks and plastering.

(E) Construction material used for casting roofs, pillars and beams.

(RCC, cement mortar, cement, brick and concrete)

70. (A) What is blue vitriol? Write its method of preparation and its uses.

(B) (a) Metal A possesses a grey lustre and turns brown on exposure to humid atmosphere for long time. Metal B possesses a white lustre with a light blue tingue and it is neither malleable nor dicticle. Metal C is used in the manufacture of fusible alloy, fuse wires. And also widely used for coating containers used for preservation of food stuff. Identify A, B, C and arrange them in the increasing order of their reactivity.

(b) Why is C preferred over B as a coating on A in order to store food stuff? Give reasons.

71. How is Plaster of Paris manufactured? Mention its applications.

72. How are bricks manufactured?

73. Name two different kinds of plastics and their properties with examples.

74. Distinguish soap from detergent.

75. Write a short note on medicines.

76. Write a short note on compounds of silicon.

77. Mention the physical properties of aluminium.

78. Discuss few applications of graphite.

79. Mention few properties of mercury.

80. Write a short note on marble.

81. (A) Describe briefly the major techniques applied on the molten glass obtained during the manufacture of glass to get the desired variety of glass.

(B) Non-metal A is used in the manufacture of pesticides like DDT and BHC. Another Non-metal B is used in the hydrogenation of oils. A and B react in presence of diffused sunlight to form C which on dissolution in water forms D.

(i) Identity A, B, C and D.

(ii) D is used for pickling metals. Give reasons.

82. Discuss the general properties of glass.

83. Write a short note on hydrochloric acid.

Essay Answer Type Questions

84. What are fertilisers? How are they classified? Explain the classification of fertilisers with an example.

85. Name three organic compounds which are used as food materials. Mention their constituents and uses.

86. (A) How is cement manufactured? Mention the areas of application of cement.

(B) Carbonate of a metal with atomic number 20 on thermal decomposition forms corresponding oxide and a gas.

(i) Identify the metallic carbonate and the products.

(ii) The gas liberated on passing through water under pressure forms a homogenous mixture which helps in the digestion of food. Give reasons.

87. How is glass manufactured? Mention different types of glass, their ingredients, properties and application.

88. What are the different kinds of soap? What are the raw materials used for the manufacture of different kinds of soap? Mention their applications.

89. (i) Name the metal which is used in the manufacture of high voltage electric transmission wire.

(ii) Why is aluminium used in the manufacture of household articles?

(iii) Write the name and the formula of the monomer of polyethylene.

(iv) Among which alloys the percentage of zinc is less (brass/bronze)?

(v) Why is silicone used in the manufacture of non-stick pans?

90. (i) What are hydrocarbons?

(ii) Give the formula of the simplest hydrocarbon.

(iii) What is biogas?

(iv) Give two advantages of biogas.

(v) Name the products obtained on burning methane gas.

91. (i) Name the inert gas which is used for filling weather observation balloons.

(ii) Why is radon used in cancer treatment?

(iii) Why is an alloy of tin and lead used in the manufacture of fuse wire?

(iv) Name the gas which is used in advertising sign boards.

(v) Why is argon used in filling electric bulbs?

92. Mention the appropriate term corresponding to the following sentences.

(i) A solution obtained by passing carbon dioxide through sugar solution flavoured with desired substances.

(ii) A substance formed by highly concentrated sugar solution flavoured with desired substances.

(iii) A hard mass resembles the Portland rock used by the people for the construction of a building.

(iv) The hardest compound of silicon, used in all kinds of grinding wheels.

(v) A complex organic compound used as food, helps in development of cells, growth of the new cells and repair of damaged cells.

PRACTICE QUESTIONS COMPETITION WING

Level 1: Apply your Concepts

Directions for questions from 1 to 15:
State whether the following statements are true or false.

1. Metals combine with other metals to form homogeneous solid mixture called alloys.
2. The process of coating zinc on iron surface is called galvanization.
3. The alloy formed from gold and mercury is called mercury amalgam.
4. Graphite is used as a solid lubricant for machine parts.
5. Iodine in a mixture of potassium iodide and alcohol is called Tincture of iodine.
6. Sodium is a very hard metal.
7. Non-metals are generally non-malleable and non-ductile.
8. Platinum is used as a catalyst.
9. Graphite is a good conductor of heat.
10. Xenon and krypton are used in electric bulbs to slow down the sublimation of tungsten.
11. Blue vitriol is used as a fungicide for grape plants.
12. Deficiency of potassium iodide causes goitre in humans.
13. Carbohydrates are the compounds of carbon, hydrogen and oxygen.
14. Water glass is used for making the lenses of telescopes.
15. Plastics are polymers.

Directions for questions from 16 to 25:
Fill in the blanks.

16. _______ is an example of medicine extracted from the bark of a plant.
17. Duralumin contains _______ percentage of aluminium.
18. Noble gases are chemically _______.
19. _______ are generally non-malleable and non-ductile.
20. _______ is the least reactive metal which is used as a catalyst.
21. Xenon and krypton are used in electric bulbs to slow down the _______ of tungsten.
22. _______ are the organic compounds containing carbon, hydrogen, oxygen and nitrogen.
23. Graphite is a _______ conductor of heat.
24. _______ glass is used as wind shields of automobiles.
25. _______ is used as fuse wire in thermite welding.

Directions for questions from 26 to 45:
For each of the questions, four choices have been provided. Select the correct alternative.

26. **Assertion (A):** Gold threads are used in silk sarees.
    Reason (R): Gold is highly ductile in nature.
    (a) Both (A) and (R) are true and (R) is the correct explanation of (A).
    (b) Both (A) and (R) are true, but (R) is not the correct explanation of (A).
    (c) (A) is true and (R) is false.
    (d) (A) is false and (R) is true.
27. The difference between thermosetting and thermoplastic is that:
    (a) Thermoplastics can be processed repeatedly.
    (b) Thermosetting plastics cannot be softened by heating.
    (c) Thermoplastics do not undergo chemical change on heating.
    (d) All the above
28. Which among the following is a detergent?
    (a) Sodium stearate
    (b) Sodium chloride
    (c) Sodium carbonate
    (d) Sodium lauryl sulphate
29. Mortar is a mixture of:
    (a) cement and gravel
    (b) gravel and sand
    (c) cement, sand and water

(d) cement and water

30. Limestone is used in the manufacture of:

(a) quick lime (b) glass
(c) cement (d) all of these

31. Which of the following compounds is not present in iodized salt?

(a) Sodium iodide
(b) Potassium iodide
(c) Common salt
(d) Lithium iodide

32. Lead is used for making fusible alloy constituted of lead and tin in ______ ratio by mass.

(a) 1 : 2 (b) 2 : 1
(c) 1 : 3 (d) 1 : 1

33. Which among the following types of food can provide maximum amount of energy?

(a) Starch (b) Vegetable oil
(c) Albumin (d) Glucose

34. ______ is used as one of the raw materials for making soft soap.

(a) Sodium carbonate
(b) Alcohol
(c) Potassium hydroxide
(d) Finely ground pumice stone

35. The metallic compounds of which among the following metals is involved in cloud seeding?

(a) Mercury
(b) Aluminium
(c) Copper
(d) Silver

36. Which of the following applications of copper require refining of copper instead of alloying?

(a) Making statues
(b) Making household utensils
(c) Making shells of ammunitions
(d) Making electric transmission cables

37. Graphite is used in the manufacture of crucibles where a small quantity of metals can be melted. It is also used as electrodes. Which of the following properties of graphite is not exploited in these two given applications?

(a) Highly resistance to chemicals
(b) Soft nature
(c) High melting point
(d) Good electrical conductivity

38. Match the statements of Column A with those of Column B.

Column A	Column B
A. Hydrochloric acid	a. Sprayed over grape vines
B. Hydrated copper sulphate	b. Flooring, statues and monuments
C. Limestone	c. Manufacture of paints
D. Zincite	d. Reduces the acidity of the soil
	e. Bathroom cleaning agent

(a) A – e, B – a, C – b, D – c
(b) A – b, B – c, C – a, D – e
(c) A – c, B – d, C – e, D – a
(d) A – d, B – c, C – a, D – b

39. Which of the following can be said to provide instant energy?

(a) A solution of glucose
(b) A cup of tea
(c) Aerated drinks
(d) Milk

40. Assertion (A): Fuse wire is made up of an alloy constituted of lead and tin in 1 : 1 ratio by mass.

Reason (R): Both lead and tin have comparatively low melting points than other metals.

(a) Both (A) and (R) are true and (R) is the correct reason of (A).
(b) Both (A) and (R) are true but (R) is not the correct explanation of (A).
(c) (A) is true but (R) is false.
(d) (A) is false but (R) is true.

41. Which of the following is the most suitable for the construction of a pillar?

(a) Cement mortar (b) Concrete
(c) RCC (d) Pure cement

42. Which of the following is a thermosetting plastic?

(a) Polyethylene (b) Nylon
(c) Terelyne (d) Bakelite

43. Which of the following substances does not form a curdy precipitate when it is added to hard water?

(a) Potassium salt of fatty acid
(b) Sodium salt of fatty acid
(c) Sodium lauryl sulphate
(d) None of the above

44. Assertion (A): Gold is used for making jewellery coins.

Reason (R): It is relatively a hard metal.

(a) Both (A) and (R) are true and (R) is the correct reason of (A).
(b) Both (A) and (R) are true but (R) is not the correct explanation of (A).
(c) (A) is true but (R) is false.
(d) (A) is false but (R) is true.

45. Arrange the following steps in a sequence for the manufacture of glass.

(1) Addition of cullet
(2) Mixing of raw materials in a proper proportion
(3) Addition of colouring pigments
(4) Annealing

(a) 2134 (b) 2341
(c) 3214 (d) 2431

46. Arrange the following steps in a sequence for the manufacture of cement.

(1) Mixture is pulverised using a pulveriser.
(2) Limestone and clay are mixed in a definite proportion.
(3) Mixture is heated to 1500°C to 1600°C to form clinkers.
(4) Clinkers are pulverised to form fine powder and a small quantity of gypsum is added.

(a) 1324 (b) 2134
(c) 2431 (d) 4321

47. Which of the following metals cannot be used in printed circuit boards?

(a) Copper (b) Aluminium
(c) Silver (d) Zinc

48. Graphite is used as a pencil lead because:

(a) it has a high melting point
(b) it is a good conductor of heat and electricity
(c) it is soft in nature
(d) it is highly resistant to chemicals

49. Which of the following gases is the most unsuitable for filling up weather-observation balloons?

(a) Helium
(b) Neon
(c) Hydrogen
(d) Argon

50. Which of the following fertilisers cannot replenish nitrogen?

(a) Superphosphate of lime (calcium dihydrogen phosphate with gypsum)
(b) Nitre
(c) Ammonium sulphate
(d) Triammonium phosphate

51. Assertion (A): Argon and krypton are inert gases used to fill electric bulbs.

Reasons (R): Argon improves the efficiency of a bulb by preventing the oxidation of the filament whereas krypton prevents sublimation.

(a) Both (A) and (R) are true and (R) is the correct explanation of (A).
(b) Both (A) and (R) are true, but (R) is not the correct explanation of (A).
(c) (A) is true and (R) is false.
(d) (A) is false and (R) is true.

52. Assertion (A): Tin is used in the manufacture of fusible alloys.

Reasons (R): Tin is a good conductor of electricity.

(a) Both (A) and (R) are true and (R) is the correct reason of (A).
(b) Both (A) and (R) are true but (R) is not the correct explanation of (A).
(c) (A) is true but (R) is false.
(d) (A) is false but (R) is true.

53. Arrange the following steps in a sequence for the manufacture of borosilicate glass.

(1) Addition of ingredients, like, red lead, aluminium oxide, manganese oxide, chromium oxide, etc.
(2) Addition of broken pieces of glass.
(3) Mixing up of sand, limestone, sodium carbonate, aluminium oxide and borax in required proportions.
(4) Melting mixture in a glass tank furnace or pot furnace.
(5) Annealing process
(6) Blowing of glass

(a) 321465 (b) 321654
(c) 342165 (d) 365214

54. Which among the following metals is the most suitable to be used as telecommunication cable?
(a) Aluminium (b) Tin
(c) Iron (d) Copper

55. Arrange the suitable steps in a correct sequence for the manufacture of sodium chloride from sea water.
(1) Making of hot saturated solution
(2) Evaporation
(3) Recrystallisation
(4) Collection of sea water
(5) Addition of a small quantity of sodium iodide or potassium iodide
(a) 4521 (b) 4523
(c) 45123 (d) 4213

56. Which of the following noble gases cannot be used for filling up electric bulbs?
(a) Helium (b) Neon
(c) Argon (d) Radon

57. Which of the following compounds/alloys of silicon is used in grinding wheel and which property of that substance is exploited?
(a) Silicon carbide because it is the hardest substance
(b) Ferrosilicon because it is resistant to friction
(c) Sodium silicate because it becomes impervious when heated strongly
(d) Silicon dioxide because it is resistant to chemicals

Level 2: Review Your Concepts

58. In an 'aqua regia' quiz competition the quiz master asked one of the teams to name the two hardest substances one of which is naturally occurring and the other one is manmade. As none of the teams could give the answer, he gave a clue that both the substances are used for cutting glass and drilling rocks and contain one common element. Then one of the teams gave the answer. What could be the right answer?

59. Though fat provides the maximum amount of energy, it forms a minor part of our diet while a large part of diet contains carbohydrates?

60. An apartment owner called for a plumber to replace one of the leaking pipe lines. The plumber arrived and found that the galvanised iron pipes are deteriorated and corroded. He advised the apartment owner to replace the galvanised iron pipes with the PVC pipes. Why did the plumber give the above suggestion?

61. A chemistry teacher was teaching polymers in a class. He said that though Bakelite and polyethylene belong to polymer family, only Bakelite is used for making electrical insulators or handles of kitchenware. Why cannot polyethylene be used for the above purpose?

62. In a chemistry laboratory, a research scholar while conducting an experiment, observed at a certain step, that a yellow-coloured gas (X) was released and it has been found to be poisonous. This was later made to react with a highly reactive metal (Y). A new compound (Z) was formed which is used for preservation of fish, meat and pickles. The professor asked him to identify X, Y and Z.

63. Three naturally occurring elements X, Y and Z are good conductors of electricity and are very precious. Z is more reactive than X and Y and on exposure to air for a long time turns black. Z forms an alloy with Y and is used in jewellery and X is used as a catalyst. Identify X, Y and Z.

64. (A) A reddish brown-coloured metal P and a silvery white-coloured metal Q are highly ductile and are good conductors of heat and electricity. P plays a major role in the preparation of brass and bronze, whereas Q is the most abundant element in the earth's crust, after oxygen and silicon, but Q is used as a substitute for P. Give reasons.

(B) Metal 'A' is used in the process of galvanizing iron sheets. 'A' reacts with dilute sulphuric acid forms salt and liberates 'B'. 'B' reacts with 'X' gives 'Y', X is a greenish yellow. pungent smelling and poisonous gas and shows bleaching action. Identify A, B, X and Y. And mention the type of chemical reaction involved in the formation of 'Y'.

65. A gaseous element X is used in the manufacture of bleaching powder. On reaction with hydrogen X forms a substance Y, which after dissolution in water is used to clean metal surfaces. Identify X and Y. Justify the whole process involved.

66. An element X is non-malleable and non-ductile. X is extensively used to protect another element Y from corrosion. Identify X and Y and name the process that is mentioned above. Also, compare the reactivities of X and Y.

67. A salt X of a metal which is used in the galvanising process on heating produces an oxide of that metal Y and a gas Z. Z is used in the preparation of soda water, and Y is used as a base of white paint. Identify X, Y and Z.

68. A non-metallic element X is a good conductor of electricity in one form and is a bad conductor of electricity in another form. Comment on the thermal conductivity of both the forms. Identify the element and mention the above two forms of X.

69. A salt A on heating forms the oxide of the metal B and a gas C. B is used in white washing. When C is passed through water, it forms D. Identify A, B, C and D. Justify the usage of C for the above purpose.

Level 3: Assess Your Concepts

70. Cement replaces lime mortar in the field of construction. Explain.

71. People used to apply a coating of sodium silicate on eggs for the purpose of preservation. Justify.

72. Name the metal which is extensively used in thermometers. Justify the reason for the same.

73. Pyrex or Borosil glass is used for making laboratory apparatus, whereas crown glass is used in the manufacture of optical instruments. Give a reason for the same.

74. A non-metal X is lustrous, insoluble in water but soluble in alcohol, when it reacts with another metallic element Y, it forms a substance Z which are used in cloud seeding or artificial rain. Identify X, Y and Z. What are the advantages of artificial rain? Is there any substances other than Z that can be used for artificial rain? If so, what are they?

75. Metal 'X'is highly malleable, ductile and a good conductor of electricity. Metal Y burns with a white dazzling flame and possesses a silvery white lustre. X and Y are major and minor components in 'Z'. Z is used for the manufacture of aircraft frames. Identify X, Y and Z.

AT

ANSWER KEYS

Crossword

Across

4. Graphite **6.** Chlorine **8.** Gypsum **10.** Blue vitriol
12. Thermoplastic **13.** Concrete **14.** Water glass

Down

1. Detergent **2.** Aluminium **3.** Plaster of Paris **5.** Soap
6. Cement mortar **7.** Dry lime **9.** Glass blowing **11.** Mercury

Classroom Wing

Very Short Answer Type Questions

1. Blowing **2.** Proteins **3.** Methane **4.** Helium **5.** Thermosetting
6. (c) **7.** (d) **8.** (b) **9.** (b) **10.** (c)
11. (b) **12.** (d) **13.** (d) **14.** (a) **15.** (c)
16. (d) **17.** (d) **18.** (b) **19.** (a) **20.** (a)
21. (d) **22.** (a) **23.** (c) **24.** (b) **25.** (a)
26. (b) **27.** (d) **28.** (c) **29.** (d) **30.** (b)
31. (a) **32.** (d) **33.** (d) **34.** (d) **35.** (c)
36. (c) **37.** (d) **38.** (i)-(E), (ii)-(A), (iii)-(B), (iv)-(C) **39.** (d)
40. (a) **41.** (a) **42.** (b) **43.** (c) **44.** (c)
45. (a) **46.** $A \rightarrow b, B \rightarrow d, C \rightarrow a, c, D \rightarrow e$ **47.** $A \rightarrow c, B \rightarrow a, C \rightarrow b, \rightarrow c, d, b$
48. $A \rightarrow b, B \rightarrow b, d, C \rightarrow a, D \rightarrow c, e$

Competition Wing

Level 1: Apply your Concepts

1. True **2.** True **3.** False **4.** True **5.** True
6. False **7.** True **8.** True **9.** False **10.** True
11. True **12.** False **13.** True **14.** False **15.** True
16. Quinine **17.** 95 **18.** Inert **19.** Non-metals **20.** Platinum
21. Sublimation **22.** Proteins **23.** Bad **24.** Sandwitch glass **25.** Magnesium
26. (a) **27.** (d) **28.** (d) **29.** (c) **30.** (d)
31. (d) **32.** (d) **33.** (b) **34.** (c) **35.** (d)
36. (d) **37.** (b) **38.** (a) **39.** (a) **40.** (a)
41. (c) **42.** (d) **43.** (c) **44.** (c) **45.** (a)
46. (b) **47.** (d) **48.** (c) **49.** (d) **50.** (a)
51. (a) **52.** (b) **53.** (a) **54.** (d) **55.** (d)
56. (d) **57.** (a)

Hints and Explanations

CLASSROOM WING

Very Short Answer Type Questions

1. The technique of manufacturing glassware used in the laboratory is called blowing.
Zincite is obtained by heating zinc carbonate.

2. Proteins are compounds that contain elements C, H, O, and N along with P and S that not only act as a source of energy but also play a major role in the growth, development, and repair of damaged cells.

3. Methane
The major component of natural gas is methane.

4. Helium
Helium is used for filling weather observation balloons.

5. Thermosetting
Bakelite is an example of thermosetting plastic.

6. Zinc is non-malleable and non-ductile, hence, it has the least tensile strength.
Hence, the correct option is (c)

7. Magnesium is an element.
Hence, the correct option is (d)

8. The process of coating tin over any article is called tinning.
Hence, the correct option is (b)

9. The process of coating zinc over iron to prevent rusting is called galvanization.
Hence, the correct option is (b)

10. Duralumin is used for the manufacture of aircraft frames because duralumin is very light and possesses high tensile strength.
Hence, the correct option is (c)

11. Helium is inert in nature and hence, helium is a noble gas.
Hence, the correct option is (b)

12. The components of stainless steel alloy are iron, chromium, carbon and nickel.
Hence, the correct option is (d)

13. Common salt is a mixture of sodium chloride, sodium iodide or potassium iodide.
Hence, the correct option is (d)

14. Lime stone is the common name of the compound calcium carbonate.
Hence, the correct option is (a)

15. The chemical name of sand is silicon dioxide.
Hence, the correct option is (c)

16. Electrical conductivity of copper is the maximum.
Hence, the correct option is (d)

17. The process of distillation is not involved in the extraction of sodium chloride from sea water.
Hence, the correct option is (d)

18. Silicon is a bad conductor of electricity and this property is not exploited in the manufacture of non-stick cookware.
Hence, the correct option is (b)

19. Vegetable oil is a fat and it provides the maximum energy.
Hence, the correct option is (a)

20. Cement mortar is used for plastering.
Hence, the correct option is (a)

21. Thermoplastic can be processed repeatedly, can be softened by heating and does not undergo any chemical change on heating.
Hence, the correct option is (d)

22. Glycerine is obtained as a by-product in the manufacture of soap.
Hence, the correct option is (a)

23. Glass is a supercooled liquid.
Hence, the correct option is (c)

24. The correct order is as follows:
(i) plaster of Paris
(ii) glucose
(iii) sugar
(iv) starch
Hence, the correct option is (b)

25. The correct order is as follows:
(i) pulverization
(ii) heating to high temperature (1500°C to 1600°C)
(iii) formation of clinkers
(iv) addition of gypsum

Hence, the correct option is (a)

26. Starch is an organic compound used as a food having the formula $(C_6H_{10}O_5)_n$ and consists of carbon, hydrogen and oxygen.

27. An alloy is a homogeneous mixture of two or more metals or may contain a non-metal in addition to metals. These alloys possess better physical properties than the metals.

28. (a) Methane
(b) Glucose
(c) Sugar
(d) Starch

29. Argon is unsuitable for filling up weather observation balloons because it is heavier than air.

30. A → e: Hydrochloric acid is used as a bath room cleaning agent.
B → a: Hydrated copper sulphate is sprayed over grape vines to protect them from insects.
C → b: Limestone is extensively used for flooring, statues and monuments.
D → c: Zincite is used for the manufacture of paints.

31. Silicon carbide is used in grinding wheels because it is the hardest substance.

32. Bakelite is a thermosetting plastic.

33. (d) Collection of sea water
(b) Evaporation
(a) Making of hot saturated solution
(c) Recrystallisation

34. Radon, being radioactive, cannot be used to fill up electric bulbs.

35. A → c: Hydrochloric acid is used in cleaning the surface of metals.
B → d: Hydrated copper sulphate is used as an insecticide.
C → e: Taj Mahal which is one of the seven wonders is constructed with marble.
D → a: Plaster of Paris is used for casting statues, toys and decorative materials.

36. Sodium lauryl sulphate does not form a curdy precipitate in hard water.

37. Electrical conductivity of copper is the maximum.

38. A solution of glucose, which is the simplest carbohydrate, provides instant energy.

39. Pure copper is required to manufacture electric transmission cables.

40. Superphosphate of lime cannot provide nitrogen.

41. (a) Mixing up of sand limestone, sodium carbonate, aluminium oxide and borax in required proportion.
(b) Addition of broken pieces of glass.
(c) Addition of ingredients, like, red lead, aluminium oxide manganese oxide, chromium oxide, etc.
(d) Melting mixture in a glass tank furnace or pot furnace.
(f) Blowing of glass
(e) Annealing process

42. Graphite is soft but this property is not exploited in the given applications.

43. RCC is very strong because of the presence of structural steel inside it. Hence, it is most suitable for the construction of pillars.

44. Gold is used for making jewellery coins as gold possesses a yellow lustre, is malleable, ductile, soft and highly resistant to chemicals.

45. Fuse wire is made up of an alloy constituted of lead and tin in 1 : 1 ratio by mass as both lead and tin have comparatively low melting points than other metals.

46. A → b Gold metal is used in making space satellite.
B → d Copper metal is used in making bell metal.
C → a, c Lead metal is used in making sanitary pipes and in covering tin roofs in cold countries.
D → e Zinc is used for the manufacture of iron roofing.

47. A → c Surgical instruments are made up of stainless steel.
B → a Speed boats are made up of duralumin.
C → b Electrical switches are made up of bronze alloy.
D → c, d, b Household utensils are made up of stainless steel, bronze and brass.

48. A → b The main ingredient of water glass is sodium silicate.

B → b, d Sodium silicate and calcium silicate are ingredients of lime glass.

C → a Potassium carbonate is one of the ingredients of crown glass.

D → c, e Borax and aluminium oxide are the ingredients of jena glass.

49. Quinine is the medicine extracted from the bark of a plant; cinchona is used in the treatment of disease malaria.

50. Soaps do not form lather with hard water but form curdy precipitates.

51. Deficiency of potassium can be replenished with the fertilizer potassium chloride.

52. Re-crystallization is the process used to extract sodium chloride from crude salt.

53. Vegetable oil is a fat and it provides the maximum energy.

54. RCC is very strong due to the presence of structural steel inside it. Hence, it is most suitable for the construction of pillars.

55. Magnesium burns with a white dazzling flame and hence, is used in fireworks.

56. Graphite is used in the manufacture of pencil lead.

57. Duralumin being very light in weight and impact resistant, is used in the manufacture of automobiles and speed boats.

58. Gypsum is used to reduce the acidity of the soil.

59. Sodium silicate is used for the preservation of eggs.

60. Silicon carbide is the hardest compound. It is used in all kinds of grinding wheels.

61. Glucose ($C_6H_{12}O_6$), sugar ($C_{12}H_{22}O_{11}$) and starch $(C_6H_{10}O_5)_n$.

62. Glucose solution gives instant energy.

63. Stainless steel is an alloy of Fe (83%), Cr (15%), Ni (1%) and C (1%).

64. Scouring soap is used for scrubbing floors.

65. It is prepared by mixing cement gravel and sand in the ratio of 1 : 2 : 3 by weight and required quantity of water.

66. The phenomenon of removel of dirt by the formation of emulsion with soaps and detergent is called emulsification.

67. Glucose provides instant energy to patients.

68. The cooling of molten glass at controlled temperature is called annealing.

Short Answer Type Questions

69. The major source of sodium chloride is sea water. The salt obtained due to the evaporation of sea water is called crude salt because of the presence of sand and clay particles. Crude salt is dissolved in water and thus the soluble component, i.e., sodium chloride is extracted and then recrystallized.

70. (A) Blue vitriol is hydrated copper sulphate. It is prepared by dissolved cupric sulphide or cupric oxide or cupric carbonate in dil sulphuric acid. It finds application as an insecticide. Solution of copper sulphate is sprayed over citrus trees and grape vines to kill the insects.

(B) (a) A → Fe, B → Zn, C → Sn

Increasing order of reactivity is Sn < Fe < Zn

(b) Since tin is much less reactive than zinc, it does not react with the components of food and is used for coating on iron in order to store food.

71. When gypsum is heated over a long period of time, it partially loses its water of crystallization and plaster of Paris ($CaSO_4 \cdot \frac{1}{2} H_2O$) is obtained. It is applied on the body parts to set fractured bones properly. It is also used for casting statues, toys and decorative materials. Modern black board chalks and ceiling panels are also made from plaster of Paris.

72. Bricks are made by using clay. The right proportion of water is added to clay and kneaded properly. The kneaded clay is pressed in the shape of brick and heated at high temperature (about 1000°C) and this process hardens the brick. Bricks are the structural material used for construction of walls of buildings.

73. Based on the thermal behaviour, plastic can be divided into two categories: thermoplastics and thermosetting plastics.

Thermoplastics: This type of plastic can be repeatedly processed by melting and subsequent solidification without undergoing any chemical change. Hence, they can be reused. Examples of thermoplastics are polyethylene, polyvinyl chloride, polystyrene, nylon, terelyene, etc.

Thermosetting plastics: Plastic of this variety cannot be softened by heating and thus they cannot be reused. Examples of thermosetting plastics are urea–formaldehyde, polyurethane, melamine, bakelite, etc.

74. Soaps and detergents are the two artificially synthesized substances which are indispensable in our daily activity.

Soaps: Based on chemical composition, soaps are the sodium salts of fatty acids. Examples of different fatty acids are olive oil, cotton seed oil, rapeseed oil, etc. When sodium hydroxide solution is treated with vegetables oil, soap is produced. Soap forms a precipitate in hard water and does not lather properly. Hence, soap is ineffective in hard water.

Detergents: Detergents are sodium salt of alkyl hydrogen sulphate. Detergents do not form precipitates in hard water and can be used effectively in hard water. The cleansing action of the detergent is superior to that of the soap. Example of a detergent is sodium lauryl sulphate.

75. In the olden days, people used to depend on different parts of medicinal plants like tulasi, vasaka, neem, etc., or their extracts for the treatment of diseases. Scientists observed and analysed the composition of those substances and developed similar kind of molecules artificially and the direct use of the medicinal plants has reduced gradually. With the advancement of the medical science, scientists developed many new molecules which are more effective and give quicker relief. Incurable diseases also could be cured by administering some of these molecules. These molecules are called medicines. Some of the examples of medicines are penicillin, tetracycline, sulphadiazine, etc. Quinine is a medicine which is extracted from the bark of *Cinchona* plant. It is administered for the treatment of malaria.

76. Compounds of silicon

(i) Sand or silicon dioxide is a naturally occuring mineral. Sand, in purified form, is used as the raw material for the glass and cement.

(ii) Sodium silicate is the compound of silicon which is soluble in water and used in the preservation of eggs. Silicone is a polymer manufactured in the industry from silicon. Silicone is highly heat resistant, non-sticky, water repellent and bad conductor of electricity. Hence, it is used in the manufacture of non-stick pans, water-proof clothes, wax polishes, electrical insulators, etc.

(iii) Ferrosilicon is an alloy of iron and silicon which is very hard steel. Silicon carbide, a compound of silicon, is the hardest compound and used in all kinds of grinding wheels.

77. Physical properties of aluminium

(i) It possesses a silvery white lustre.

(ii) It is highly malleable and ductile.

(iii) It is a very good conductor of electricity

(iv) It is very light in weight and corrosion resistant.

(v) It is the most abundant metal in the earth's crust.

(vi) It is relatively soft when compared to other metals.

78. Applications of graphite

(i) Pencil leads are manufactured by mixing graphite with clay.

(ii) Graphite mixed with fine clay is moulded and sintered into crucibles of desired size and shape which are used to melt small quantities of metals.

(iii) It is also used as an excellent lubricant in those parts of the machineries where high heat is generated due to friction.

(iv) Graphite is used in electrolytic cells as electrodes.

(v) Graphite is used in nuclear reactors as a moderator to slow down the neutrons produced due to the splitting of the atoms of uranium or thorium.

79. Properties of mercury

(i) It is silvery-white liquid metal at normal temperature.

(ii) Its melting point is −39°C and boiling point is 357°C.

(iii) It is a very good conductor of electricity and heat.

(iv) It can dissolve almost all metals in it.

80. Marble or limestone is a metamorphic rock formed from the sea shells. Chemically, lime stone is calcium carbonate. Limestone is used as a raw material for the manufacture of cement and glass. Lime, i.e., calcium oxide—a component of mortar—is manufactured from limestone. Mortar is used in the construction of buildings. Lime is also used for white washing. Marble is extensively used in flooring, statues and monuments.

81. (A) The major techniques applied on the molten glass obtained during the manufacture of glass to get the desired variety of glass are the following:

(i) Blowing of glass: This technique is used for the manufacture of laboratory glass ware, bottles, etc.

(ii) Optical glass: Molten glass is pressed into circular shape from which different optical glasses are manufactured.

(iii) Sheet glass: Molten glass obtained from the glass tank furnace is placed on molten bath of tin. The molten glass spreads on the bath of molten tin with uniform thickness from which sheet glass/float glass is drawn.

(B) (i) A is chlorine, B is hydrogen, C is hydrogen chloride and D is hydrochloric acid.

(ii) Hydrochloric acid can rapidly dissolve impurities like inorganic contaminates (oxides, carbonates of metals) present on the surface with minimum loss of base metals. Hence, it is used as a pickling agent.

82. General properties of a glass:

(i) Glass is a supercooled liquid.

(ii) It is transparent, highly resistant to chemicals and bad conductor of heat and electricity. It can be easily moulded into desired shapes.

83. Hydrochloric acid is prepared industrially by heating common salt and concentrated sulphuric acid. It can also be obtained by passing hydrogen chloride gas through water. It is used in the preparation of silver chloride which finds application in photographic printing paper. It is an important laboratory reagent. Industrially, it is used to clean the surface metals. In households, hydrochloric acid is used as a bathroom cleaning agent.

Essay Answer Type Questions

84. Fertilizers are compounds or mixtures of compounds which are added to the soil in order to provide the essential nutrients to the plants.

Fertilizers can be categorized into two types depending on the source from which they are obtained.

(i) natural fertilizer and (ii) artificial fertilizer

Natural fertilizer: Example of a natural fertilizer is manure. The excreta of live stock and humansis mixed with straw and then the mixture is buried deep into the pits for few months. The mixture decomposes there and manure is obtained. The manure is rich in the nutrients required for the growth of the plants.

Artificial fertilizer: Artificial fertilizers are the chemical compounds manufactured in the industries. They contain one or more essential nutrients required for the growth of plants. Artificial fertilizers can further be classified depending on their chemical composition, i.e., the essential nutrient(s) they contain.

(i) **Nitrogenous fertilizers**: These fertilizers replenish the deficiency of nitrogen. Calcium ammonium nitrate, ammonium sulphate, basic calcium nitrate and urea are the examples of nitrogenous fertilizers.

(ii) **Phosphatic fertilizers**: These fertilizers replenish the deficiency of phosphorus. Triammonium phosphate and superphosphate of lime are the examples of phosphatic fertilizers.

(iii) **Potash fertilizers**: These fertilizers replenish the deficiency of potassium. Potassium nitrate, potassium sulphate and potassium chloride are the examples of potash fertilizers.

85.

Types of food	Constituent elements	Examples	Uses
Carbohydrate	Composed of carbon, hydrogen and oxygen.	Glucose ($C_6H_{12}O_6$), sugar ($C_{12}H_{22}O_{11}$) and starch $(C_6H_{10}O_5)_n$. All cereals contain large quantity of carbohydrates.	Carbohy-drates which we consume break into simpler molecules, i.e., glucose. Glucose molecules are carried to the cells with the help of blood. During respiration, glucose decomposes into carbon dioxide and water and energy is liberated.

Types of food	Constituent elements	Examples	Uses
Fats	Mainly composed of carbon, hydrogen and oxygen.	Vegetable oil, animal fat, etc.	Fat provides the maximum amount of energy.
Protein	Mainly composed of carbon, hydrogen, oxygen and nitrogen. Sulphur and phosphorus may also be present in protein.	Salivary amylase, keratin, albumin, etc.	Protein is not only the source of energy but also it plays a major role in the development of cells, growth of the new cells and repair of the damaged cells.

86. (A) **Manufacture of cement**: The raw materials used for manufacture of Portland cement are limestone and clay. Cement can be produced in two different processes:

(i) dry process

(ii) wet process.

In the **dry process**, limestone and clay are used in a definite proportion to achieve the desired property of the cement. The mixture is pulverized (making fine powder) using pulverizer and then heated from 1500°C to 1600°C to form clinkers (nodules of mixed powder which becomes very hard after heating). These clinkers are again pulverized to form fine powder and small quantity of gypsum is added and thus cement is produced.

In the **wet process**, water is added to the pulverized mixture and a slurry is obtained. Then the slurry is strongly heated to form clinkers.

Uses of Cement

Grouting: Grouting is a technique used in construction activities. Pure cement or cement mixed with sand and water in a definite proportion is applied in the gaps of construction material like bricks, tiles, etc., for making the surface smooth and strengthening the structure.

Cement mortar: It is a construction material prepared by mixing cement and sand in the ratio of 1 : 4 by weight. This mixture is converted into thick slurry by adding required quantity of water. It is used for joining bricks and plastering.

Concrete: It is also a construction material prepared by mixing cement, gravel and sand in the ratio of 1:2:3 by weight and required quantity of water. It is used for casting roofs, pillars, beams, etc.

Reinforced cement concrete (RCC): When cement concrete is reinforced using structural steel, it is called reinforced cement concrete. RCC provides huge strength and durability to the structure. It is used for the construction of bridges, railway sleepers, prefabricated structures, columns, beams roofs, etc.

(B) (i) Carbonate is calcium carbonate ($CaCO_3$)

$$\underset{}{CaCO_3} \xrightarrow{\text{heat}} \underset{\text{Calcium oxide}}{CaO} + \underset{\text{Carbon dioxide}}{CO_2}$$

(ii) Soda water is prepared by passing carbon dioxide through water under 30 atm pressure. CO_2 reacts with water to form carbonic acid which is a weak acid and helps in digestion of food since digestion of food takes place in acidic medium.

87. Manufacture of glass: Glass is made up of silica or sand, limestone and feldspar as major raw materials. Broken pieces of glass, called cullet, are added to the raw material. Some other ingredients like red lead, aluminium oxide, manganese oxide, chromium oxide, etc., are used to impart specific characteristics to glass. The raw materials are mixed in the required proportion and melted in a glass tank furnace or pot furnace. Cullet initiates the melting process at a lower temperature.

Three major techniques are applied on the molten glass obtained in the process of melting for the manufacture of different products of the glass.

(i) **Blowing of glass**: This technique is used for the manufacture of laboratory glassware, bottles, etc.

(ii) **Optical glass**: Molten glass is pressed into circular shape from which different optical glasses are manufactured.

(iii) **Sheet glass/float glass**: Molten glass obtained from the glass tank furnace is placed on molten bath of tin. The molten glass spreads on the bath of molten tin with uniform thickness from which sheet glass/float glass is drawn.

The different shapes of molten glass obtained from the above three techniques are then subjected to a cooling process called **annealing** at a controlled temperature in a long tunnel-type annealing chamber.

General properties of glass: Glass is a supercooled liquid. Molten glass obtained from glass-manufacturing furnaces is allowed to cool down slowly. During cooling, viscosity of glass increases manifolds below the range of its freezing temperature and loses its ability to flow. Hence, it appears like a solid. Glass is transparent, highly chemical resistant, a bad conductor of heat and electricity, and it can be easily moulded into desired shapes.

Types of glasses	Ingredients and properties	Applications
Water glass	Sodium silicate, soluble in water.	It is used in the soap industry. In the early 20th century, it was used for the preservation of eggs. It is also used for filling up holes and strengthening material.
Soft glass or soda glass or lime glass	Sodium silicate and calcium silicate, cannot withstand high temperature and thermal shock.	It is used for making window panes, cheap articles of glass.
Hard glass or potash–lime glass	Sand, limestone, potassium carbonate, fairly heat resistant.	It is used for making laboratory apparatus.
Optical glass or crown glass	Sand, limestone, potassium carbonate and red lead, highly transparent and possessed high density.	It is used for the manufacture of lenses of spectacles and optical instruments like lenses of telescope, microscope, etc.
Jena glass or pyrex glass or borosil glass	Sand, limestone, sodium carbonate, aluminium oxide and borax, highly heat resistant and can withstand thermal shock.	It is used for making laboratory apparatus, thermos flasks and baking bowls.
Shatter-proof glass or sandwich glass	Sheets of plain glasses are attached with each other with a plastic sheet placed between them. Broken pieces of this type of glass do not scatter.	It is used as wind shields of automobiles.

88. Kinds of soap

Types of soaps	Ingredients and properties	Applications
Laundry soap or washing soap	Cheapest vegetable oil, contains free alkali.	It is used in the laundry for removing dirt and grease from soiled clothes.
Scouring soap	Finely ground pumice stone, sand and sodium carbonate are added to laundry soap as fillers.	They are commonly used for scrubbing floors.
Toilet soap	The best quality of vegetable oil. Does not contain free alkali.	This kind of soap is used for bathing.
Medicated soap	Certain substances which have medicinal value are added to the toilet soap.	Neem soap takes care of the skin.
Soft soap or liquid soap	Vegetable oil and potassium hydroxide	Used for washing hands. It is also used as a shaving soap.
Transparent soap	This kind of soap is obtained by dissolving soap in alcohol.When alcohol is evaporated, transparent soaps are formed.	This soap is also used as bathing soap.

89. (i) Aluminium metal is used in the manufacture of high voltage electric transmission wire.

(ii) Aluminium is corrosion resistant due to surface oxide formation. Hence, used in the manufacture of household articles.

(iii) Monomer of polyethylene is ethylene molecule having the molecular formula C_2H_4.

(iv) Bronze alloy has less percentage of zinc.

(v) Silicone is highly heat resistant, non-sticky and water repellent.

90. (i) The organic compounds which contain only carbon and hydrogen are called hydrocarbons.

(ii) The formula of simplest hydrocarbon is CH_4.

(iii) The decomposition of farm waste and cow dung in the absence of air gives a mixture of gases called biogas.

(iv) (a) It is pollution free.

(b) It has high ratio of energy given out by combustion as compared to the other fuels.

(v) Carbon dioxide and water vapour are the products formed on burning methane gas.

91. (i) Helium

(ii) Radon is a radioactive element.

(iii) Tin and lead have lower melting points than other metals.

(iv) Neon

(v) Argon is filled in electric bulbs to improve the efficiency of bulb by preventing oxidation of tungsten filament.

92. (i) Soft drinks

(ii) Syrups

(iii) Portland cement

(iv) Silicon carbide

(v) Proteins

Competition Wing

Level 1: Apply Your Concepts

1. Metals combine with other metals to form homogeneous solid mixture called alloys.

2. The process of coating zinc on iron surface is called galvanization.

3. The alloy formed from gold and mercury is called gold amalgam.

4. Graphite is used as a solid lubricant for machine parts.

5. Iodine in a mixture of potassium iodide and alcohol is called tincture of iodine.

6. Sodium is a very soft metal.

7. Non-metals are generally non-malleable and non-ductile

8. Platinum used as a catalyst for most of the reactions that take place in gaseous state.

9. Graphite is a good conductor of electricity but bad conductor of heat.

10. Xenon and kryptons are used to slow down the sublimation of tungsten in a bulb.

11. Blue vitriol is used as a fungicide for fruit trees in the form of Bordeaux mixture.

12. Deficiency of iodine causes goitre in human beings.

13. Carbohydrates generally contain carbon, hydrogen and oxygen.

14. Optical glass is used for making the lenses of telescopes.

15. Plastics are polymers.

16. Quinine is an example of medicine extracted from the bark of a plant.

17. Duralumin contains 95% of aluminium.

18. Noble gases are chemically inert.

19. Non-metals are generally non-malleable and non-ductile.

20. Platinum is the least reactive metal which is used as a catalyst.

21. Xenon and krypton are used in electric bulbs to slow down the sublimation of tungsten.

22. Proteins are the organic compounds containing carbon, hydrogen, oxygen and nitrogen.

23. Graphite is a bad conductor of heat.

24. Sandwich glass is used as wind shields of automobiles.

25. Magnesium is used as fuse wires in thermite welding.

26. In silk sarees, gold threads could be used as gold is highly ductile by nature.

    Hence, the correct option is (a).

27. Thermoplastic can be processed repeatedly, can be softened by heating and do not undergo any chemical change on heating.

28. Example of detergent is sodium lauryl sulphate.

29. Mortar is a mixture composed of cement, sand and water.

30. Lime stone is one of the raw materials used for the manufacture of quicklime, glass and cement.

31. The common salt containing sodium iodide and potassium iodide is called iodised salt. Lithium iodide is not present in the iodised salt.

32. Lead is used for making fusible alloy constituted lead and tin in 1 : 1 ratio by mass.

33. Fats provide maximum amount of energy and vegetable oil is an example of fat.

34. Potassium hydroxide is used as one of the raw materials for making soft soap.

35. Silver nitrite or silver iodide is used in cloud seeding for artificial rain.

36. Pure copper is required to manufacture electric transmission cables.

37. Graphite is soft but this property is not exploited in the given applications.

38. (i) → (E):

    Hydrochloric acid is used as a bathroom cleaning agent.

    (ii) → (A):

    Hydrated copper sulphate is sprayed over grape vines to protect them from insects.

(iii) → (B):
Limestone is extensively used for flooring, statues and monuments.

(iv) → (C):

Zincite is used for the manufacture of paints.

39. A solution of glucose, which is the simplest carbohydrate, provides instant energy.

40. Fuse wire is made up of an alloy constituted of lead and tin in 1 : 1 ratio by mass as both lead and tin have comparatively low melting points than other metals.

41. RCC is very strong because of the presence of structural steel inside it. Hence, it is most suitable for the construction of pillars.

42. Bakelite is a thermosetting plastic

43. Sodium lauryl sulphate does not form a curdy precipitate in hard water.

44. Gold is used for making jewellery coins as gold possesses a yellow lusture, is malleable, ductile, soft and highly resistant to chemicals.

45. (i) mixing of raw materials in proper proportion
(ii) addition of cullet
(iii) addition of colour pigments
(iv) annealing

46. (i) Limestone and clay are mixed in a definite proportion.
(ii) Mixture is pulverised using a pulveriser.
(iii) Mixture is heated to 1500°C to 1600°C to form clinkers.
(iv) Clinkers are pulverised to form fine powder and a small quantity of gypsum is added.

47. Zinc is brittle, and hence, cannot be used in printed circuit boards.

48. Graphite is used as pencil lead because it is soft and leaves an impression on the paper.

49. Argon is unsuitable for filling up weather observation balloons because it is heavier than air.

50. Superphosphate of lime cannot provide nitrogen.

51. A – e Hydrochloric acid is used as a bathroom cleaning agent.

B – a Hydrated copper sulphate is sprayed over grape vines to protect them from insects.

C – b Limestone is extensively used in flooring, statues and monuments.

D – c Zincite is used for the manufacture of paints.

52. Tin is used in the manufacture of fusible alloy as it has very low melting point.

53. Both (A) and (R) are correct but (R) is not the exact explanation of (A).
Hence, the correct option is (a).

54. Electrical conductivity of copper is the maximum.

55. (i) collection of sea water
(ii) evaporation
(iii) making of hot saturated solution
(iv) recrystallisation

56. Radon, being radioactive, cannot be used to fill up electric bulbs.

57. Silicon carbide is used in grinding wheels because it is the hardest substance.

Level 2: Review Your Concepts

58. Diamond and silicon carbide are the two hardest substances known. Diamond occurs naturally (one is diamond and the other is silicon carbide) as it is obtained by the reaction between carbon and silicon. The common element present in diamond and silicon carbide is carbon.

59. Both fats and carbohydrates are energy giving food nutrients and both contain carbon, hydrogen and oxygen, but the molecular structure of fat is more complex than that of carbohydrates. Carbohydrates break up to glucose which are simple molecules and which on combustion in presence of oxygen breaks down to form carbon dioxide and water and releases energy. Combustion of fat takes a long period of time, and hence, carbohydrates are preferable to fats. Fats are considered as reservoirs of energy while carbohydrates serve as an instant source of energy.

60. PVC pipes are polyvinyl chloride pipes which are thermoplastic in nature and more durable as they are completely rust free and less expensive than galvanised iron pipes. Though galvanisation prevents rusting, since the pipelines are in continuous contact with water, the coating may get worn off over a period of time and it may be corroded.

61. Polythene and Bakelite are the polymers and have a lot of applications in daily life. Since polythene is a thermoplastic (which melts on heating), therefore, cannot be used for making electrical insulators or handles. Bakelite can be used for these purposes as it is a thermosetting polymer (once set into hard mass cannot be remelted).

62. A greenish yellow poisonous gas X is chlorine. On reaction with the metal sodium (highly reactive metal) chlorine gas forms sodium chloride which is used for preservation of fish, meats and pickles. So, Z is sodium chloride, X is chlorine gas and Y is sodium metal.

63. Three precious elements that occur in nature are silver, gold and platinum. Silver is more reactive than gold and platinum. On exposure to air for longer time, silver turns black due to the formation of silver sulphide. Platinum is used as a catalyst. Alloy of gold with silver is used in jewellery. So, X is platinum, Y is gold and Z is silver.

64. (A) Brass and bronze mainly contain copper which is a reddish brown-coloured metal. The most abundant element in the earth's crust after oxygen and silicon is aluminium which is silvery white-coloured metal. So, P is copper and Q is aluminium. Both copper and aluminium are good conductors of heat and electricity. Since copper is a costly metal, aluminium is used as a substitute for copper.

(B) A → Zinc (Zn)

X → Chlorine

$$Zn + H_2SO_4 \rightarrow \underset{\text{Zinc sulphate}}{ZnSO_4} + \underset{\text{(B) Hydrogen}}{H_2}$$

$$\underset{(B)}{H_2} + \underset{(X)}{Cl_2} \rightarrow \underset{\text{(Y) Hydrogen Chloride}}{2HCl}$$

Formation of HCl, from hydrogen and chlorine is an element-element combination reaction.

65. The element chlorine is used in the manufacture of bleaching power. It reacts with hydrogen to form hydrogen chloride which dissolves in water to give hydrochloric acid. It is used to clean the metal surfaces. So, X is chlorine and Y is hydrochloride which on dissolution in water gives hydrochloric acid. Metal surfaces have coating of metal oxides and hydrochloric acid can react with the metal oxides and removes the coating.

66. Element X is zinc which is non-malleable and non-ductile. Y is iron. The process of protecting iron by zinc is called galvanisation. The element X(Zn) is more reactive than Y (Fe).

67. Since Z is used in making soda water, it is carbon dioxide. The metal carbonate is zinc carbonate because zinc carbonate on heating produces zinc oxide and carbon dioxide. Zinc oxide is used as paint. So, X is zinc carbonate, Y is zinc oxide and Z is carbon dioxide.

68. Carbon occurs as graphite and diamond in a free state. Graphite is a good conductor of electricity and diamond is a bad conductor of electricity. So, the element X is carbon and the two forms of X are graphite and diamond. Diamond is a good thermal conductor, whereas graphite is a poor thermal conductor.

69. RCC - (C): Concrete reinforced with structural steel used in the construction of bridges, and prefabri-cated structures.

Cement mortar - (D): Construction material used for joining bricks and plastering.

Cement - (B): Used in filling the gaps of constriction.

Brick - (A): The structural material used for the constriction of walls of buildings.

Concrete - (E): Construction material used for casting roofs, pillars and beams.

∴ Order is CDBAE.

Level 3: Assess Your Concepts

70. Both cement mortar and lime mortar are used for construction since they get hardened on exposure to air. But cement is a stronger binding material than lime and due to complex chemical reactions it forms a harder mass over a period of time. Moreover, on combining with gravel, it forms concrete which is much harder. Its strength is further enhanced when used in combination with steel in the form of RCC. Therefore, cement replaces lime mortar as a better construction material.

71. Sodium or potassium silicate is used as a protective covering for eggs. When egg is dipped in a solution of sodium silicate in water, a layer of sodium silicate forms on the surface of the egg which is very impervious to water, air and heat. As a result, bacterial growth is prevented in the egg so that it can be preserved for relatively longer periods of time.

72. Mercury is generally used in clinical thermometers as it expands on heating and has high density and does not stick to container.

73. Pyrex or Borosil glass consists of borax which reduces the expandability of glass and provides heat resistance, whereas presence of red lead in crown glass increases the density of glass to a great extent making it useful for optical instruments.

74. A lustrous non-metal which is soluble in alcohol is iodine. It reacts with the metallic element silver to form silver iodide which is used in cloud seeding or artificial rain. So, X is iodine, Y is silver, Z is silver iodide. Artificial rain is very much useful in agriculture at the time of drought or water scarcity. Silver nitrate and dry ice (solid carbon dioxide) can also be used for artificial rain.

75. X → Aluminum

Y → Magnesium

Z → Duralumin

PHOTO CREDITS

CHAPTER 1

Page 1.3—Mohammed Ali. Pearson India Education Services Pvt. Ltd; **Page 1.6**—Designua. Shutterstock

CHAPTER 2

Page 2.5—Oxford Designers & Illustrators Ltd. Pearson Education Ltd; **Page 2.6**—Pearson Education Ltd

CHAPTER 3

Page 3.15—Oxford Designers & Illustrators Ltd. Pearson Education Ltd

CHAPTER 4

Page 4.4—Designua. Shutterstock; **Page 4.14**—Mohd Suhail. Pearson India Education Services Pvt. Ltd; **Page 4.18**—Oxford Designers & Illustrators Ltd. Pearson Education Ltd; **Page 4.24**—HL Studios. Pearson Education Ltd; **Page 4.25**—Pearson Education Ltd

CHAPTER 5

Page 5.6—Artisticco. Shutterstock; **Page 5.12**—Oxford Designers & Illustrators Ltd. Pearson Education Ltd; **Page 5.13**—Rainer Lesniewski. Shutterstock

CHAPTER 6

Page 6.5—Julia Reschke. Shutterstock; **Page 6.5**—Joseph Belanger. 123rf.com; **Page 6.5**—Fablok. Shutterstock; **Page 6.5**—Kompaniets Taras. Shutterstock; **Page 6.5**—Albert Russ. Shutterstock; **Page 6.5**—jarous. 123rf.com; **Page 6.6**—vvoe. Shutterstock; **Page 6.6**—nebuto. 123rf.com; **Page 6.6**—Fablok. Shutterstock; **Page 6.6**—MarcelClemens. Shutterstock